Dear Sol: - Glenn Frank is always
interesting and refreshing. In this book
he fully maintains his reputation.

Sincerely, James

1/12 - 34

# THUNDER AND DAWN

THE MACMILLAN COMPANY
NEW YORK · BOSTON · CHICAGO · DALLAS
ATLANTA · SAN FRANCISCO

MACMILLAN & CO., Limited
LONDON · BOMBAY · CALCUTTA
MELBOURNE

THE MACMILLAN COMPANY
OF CANADA, Limited
TORONTO

GLENN FRANK

# THUNDER AND DAWN

The Outlook for Western Civilization
with Special Reference to the
United States

*I could smile when I see the hopeful exultation of many at the new reach of worldly science and vigor of worldly effort, as if we were again at the beginning of days. There is thunder on the horizon as well as dawn.* —*JOHN RUSKIN.*

THE MACMILLAN COMPANY
NEW YORK      MDCCCCXXXIII

PRINTED IN THE UNITED STATES OF AMERICA
NORWOOD PRESS LINOTYPE, INC.
NORWOOD, MASS., U.S.A.

## TO MARY

WHOSE LOVELINESS AND LIVELINESS
WOULD BRIGHTEN EVEN
THE DARKEST AGE

# Contents

PROLOGUE: WESTERN MAN FACES THE FUTURE . . PAGE 1

CHAPTER
I. THE CRISIS OF THE WESTERN SPIRIT . . . 19
II. THE PROPHETS OF DOOM SPEAK . . . 43
III. THE LITERATURE AND LEADERSHIP OF HOPE . 127
IV. RALLYING CRIES OF WESTERN ADVANCE . . 158
V. EDUCATING FOR SOCIAL MASTERY . . . 205
VI. THE SOCIAL DYNAMISM OF RELIGION . . . 226
VII. RACIALISM AND THE NAZARENE . . . . 248
VIII. THE CHURCH AND WAR . . . . . 266
IX. THE WEST GOES AMERICAN . . . . 278
X. MYSTIC AND MUCKRAKER VIEW THE MACHINE 292
XI. HUMANISM THROUGH TECHNOLOGY . . . 319
XII. THE TREASON OF STATESMANSHIP . . . 366
INDEX . . . . . . . . . . 401

# Clues to the Argument

|  |  | PAGE |
|---|---|---|
| PROLOGUE: WESTERN MAN FACES THE FUTURE | . . | 1 |
| 1. Towards a Strategy of Survival | . . . | 1 |
| 2. A New Renaissance | . . . . | 11 |
| 3. A New Reformation | . . . . | 12 |
| 4. A New Industrial Revolution | . . . | 12 |
| 5. Towards Scientific Humanism | . . | 17 |

CHAPTER

| I. THE CRISIS OF THE WESTERN SPIRIT | . . | 19 |
|---|---|---|
| 1. Pre-war Materialism | . . . . | 20 |
| a. The Idols of Imperialism | . . | 21 |
| b. The Idols of Industrialism | . . | 21 |
| c. The Idols of Hedonism | . . . | 21 |
| 2. War-time Idealism | . . . . | 25 |
| 3. Post-war Cynicism | . . . . | 28 |
| 4. Panic-born Planning | . . . . | 39 |

| II. THE PROPHETS OF DOOM SPEAK | . . | 43 |
|---|---|---|
| 1. The Biological Fear | . . . . | 46 |
| 2. The Psychological Fear | . . . . | 56 |
| 3. The Political Fear | . . . . | 66 |
| a. The Challenge of Science | . . | 69 |
| b. The Challenge of Distance | . . | 71 |
| c. The Challenge of Technology | . . | 74 |
| d. The Challenge of Nomadism | . . | 80 |
| e. The Challenge of the Majority | . . | 84 |
| f. The Challenge of Party | . . | 87 |
| g. The Challenge of Leadership | . . | 93 |
| h. The Challenge of Revolution | . . | 97 |
| 4. The Economic Fear | . . . . | 105 |
| a. Capitalism | . . . . . | 105 |
| b. Fascism | . . . . . | 105 |
| c. Communism | . . . . . | 105 |

CHAPTER                                                            PAGE

5. The Administrative Fear     .    .    .    106
6. The Moral Fear  .    .    .    .    .    110
    a. A Rebel Generation     .    .    .    111
        (1) Its New Liberty .    .    .    111
        (2) Its New Levity  .    .    .    112
        (3) Its New Looseness     .    .    112
    b. The Soils of Rebellion  .    .    .    113
        (1) The New Politics     .    .    114
        (2) The New Economics     .    .    114
        (3) The New Theology     .    .    119
        (4) The New Biology     .    .    120
        (5) The New Philosophy .    .    121
        (6) The New Psychology .    .    123
        (7) The New Physics     .    .    123
    c. The Climate of Opinion Changes  .    .    126

III. THE LITERATURE AND LEADERSHIP OF HOPE  .    127
  1. The Literature of Hope .    .    .    .    128
    a. Raw Materials of Renewal     .    .    129
    b. Four False Dawns .    .    .    133
    c. Towards Social Realism     .    .    133
    d. The New Credulity     .    .    136
  2. The Leadership of Hope .    .    .    138
    a. The New Encyclopedists     .    .    140
        (1) A Social Inventory     .    .    141
        (2) An Evangelism of Science .    .    141
        (3) The Scholar's Neutrality  .    .    142
        (4) A Too Pure Science     .    .    143
        (5) Towards Tentative Dogmas  .    145
    b. A Ringmaster of Specialists  .    .    150
        (1) Group Action  .    .    .    152
        (2) Personal Leadership .    .    154

IV. RALLYING CRIES OF WESTERN ADVANCE  .    158
  1. Cultural Nationalism     .    .    .    164
  2. Economic Internationalism     .    .    167
  3. Rationalized Politics     .    .    .    174
  4. Mass-conscious Industrialism  .    .    .    177
  5. Socialized Religion .    .    .    .    184
  6. Biological Enrichment .    .    .    190
  7. Realistic Pacifism .    .    .    .    .    194

# Clues to the Argument xi

CHAPTER  PAGE

V. EDUCATING FOR SOCIAL MASTERY . . . 205
 1. Society without Direction . . . . 206
 2. Schools without Focus . . . . . 207
 3. The Specialist Comes to Power . . . 207
 4. The Educator Abdicates . . . . . 210
 5. The Partialist Is Born . . . . . 214
 6. The Great Conflict . . . . . 215
  a. The Claims of Scholarship . . . 215
  b. The Claims of Education . . . 215
 7. Training for Scholarship . . . . . 217
 8. Education for Leadership . . . . 219

VI. THE SOCIAL DYNAMISM OF RELIGION . . . 226
 1. Social Motive Power . . . . . 226
 2. Education Is Not Enough . . . . 232
 3. The Cynicism of Reason . . . . . 236
 4. Quixotism and Progress . . . . . 236
 5. Science and the Religious Impulse . . . 241
 6. The Next Reformation . . . . . 245

VII. RACIALISM AND THE NAZARENE . . . . 248
 1. The Ku Klux Mind . . . . . 249
 2. The Trans-racialism of Jesus . . . . 250
 3. Race and Scientific Fact . . . . . 253
 4. Race and Social Procedure . . . . 253
 5. The *Weltanschauung* of Jesus . . . . 261
  a. The Primacy of Moral Values . . 261
  b. Reverence for Personality . . 262
  c. The Centrality of the Individual . . 262
 6. Towards Biological Statesmanship . . . 263

VIII. THE CHURCH AND WAR . . . . . 266
 1. Courage in Chains . . . . . 267
 2. Three Ways the Church May Go . . . 271
  a. The Way of Aloofness . . . 271
  b. The Way of Compromise . . 272
  c. The Way of Renunciation . . 273
 3. The Duty of the Churchman . . . . 275

CHAPTER                                                          PAGE
   4.  The Duty of the Statesman  .    .    .    . 275
   5.  Towards a Logic of Contradiction  .    .    . 276

IX. THE WEST GOES AMERICAN      .    .    .    . 278
   1.  The Technologic Leap of America  .    .    . 279
   2.  The Technologic Lag of Europe    .    .    . 279
   3.  We Symbolize the Machine Age    .    .    . 283
   4.  Rebels Who Resent Us  .    .    .    .    . 284
   5.  Mastering the Inevitable.    .    .    .    . 291

X.  MYSTIC AND MUCKRAKER VIEW THE MACHINE 292
   1.  The Temper of the Rebels    .    .    .    . 295
   2.  The Grounds of Their Rebellion  .    .    . 297
     a.  The Machine Is Uncontrollable  .    . 298
     b.  The Machine Puts Man to Rout  .    . 299
     c.  The Machine Rapes Nature  .    .    . 300
     d.  The Machine Destroys Beauty    .    . 301
     e.  The Machine Deletes Local Color .    . 302
     f.  The Machine Limits Men's Movements . 304
     g.  The Machine Ruins Craftsmanship.    . 305
     h.  The Machine Produces for Sale  .    . 306
     i.  The Machine Robs Men of Work  .    . 307
     j.  The Machine Breeds Class Conflict    . 308
     k.  The Machine Degrades Taste    .    . 309
     l.  The Machine Encourages Waste  .    . 310
     m.  The Machine Makes Bad Citizens .    . 311
     n.  The Machine Wars on Self-Reliance    . 311
     o.  The Machine Concentrates Wealth    . 313
     p.  The Machine Cancels Its Advantages  . 314
   3.  What the Rebels Forget .    .    .    .    . 317

XI. HUMANISM THROUGH TECHNOLOGY  .    .    . 319
   1.  Ford and Gandhi Talk It Over    .    .    . 321
   2.  A Social Magna Charta .    .    .    .    . 324
   3.  Engineers and Reformers    .    .    .    . 326
   4.  Industrialism and Liberalism  .    .    .    . 332
   5.  As The Machine Economy Matures.    .    . 332
     a.  It Will Decentralize Industry .    .    . 333
     b.  It Will Distribute Wealth Widely .    . 339
     c.  It Will Bring Leisure to Men .    .    . 339

CHAPTER                          PAGE

      d.  It Will Stabilize Agriculture .   .   .  343
      e.  It Will Compensate for Routine   .   .  345
      f.  It Will Revive Small Industries   .   .  350
      g.  It Will Evolve a New Beauty .   .   .  353
   6.  A Tool of Emancipation .     .     .   .  365

XII.  THE TREASON OF STATESMANSHIP   .   .  366
   1.  Western Man Betrays the Machine .   .   .  366
   2.  The Anatomy of Depression .   .   .   .  367
   3.  The Economic Impasse of the West .   .   .  369
      a.  It Involves All Nations   .   .   .  369
      b.  It Involves Finance     .   .   .  370
      c.  It Involves Industry     .   .   .  370
      d.  It Involves Agriculture .   .   .  371
      e.  It Involves Manufactured Goods   .   .  372
      f.  It Involves Raw Materials   .   .  372
   4.  We Were Ready for Utopia   .   .   .  374
   5.  The House of Cards Fell .   .   .   .  375
   6.  The Spreading Roots of Disaster   .   .  375
   7.  The Tap-root of Depression   .   .   .  376
   8.  Deserting the New Credo of Business   .   .  378
   9.  Surplus and Hunger     .   .   .  379
  10.  Two Roads to Recovery .   .   .   .  380
      a.  Slow Down Production .   .   .  380
      b.  Speed Up Consumption .   .   .  380
  11.  A Coward's Policy .   .   .   .   .  380
  12.  Taking the Soap Box Indoors .   .   .  381
  13.  A Wider Distribution of Wealth   .   .  382
  14.  Why Buying Power Was Frozen   .   .  384
  15.  An Anti-toxin for Radicalism   .   .   .  386
  16.  Wages as a Market Investment   .   .  386
  17.  Poverty and Profits     .   .   .  387
  18.  Three Roads of Destiny .   .   .   .  388
      a.  Statesmanlike Business .   .   .  388
      b.  Drastic Taxation .   .   .   .  388
      c.  Social Revolution .   .   .   .  388
  19.  If We Are Content to Improvise   .   .  389

THUNDER AND DAWN

# Western Man Faces the Future

THIS is a sort of book that no single human being on earth is really equipped to write. And yet it is a book that some one must attempt to write. As I set down its opening words, the Western world is beset by economic depression, political distraction, and social dishevelment that puzzle its masses and palsy its leaders. We know that no malign plague has been sent by the gods to work this triple disruption of Western life. We shall find its cause, we suspect, in ourselves. Our leaders have failed us, we have failed our leaders, or both have blundered in the enterprise of social management. Of an unsettlement so general we must undertake to achieve a general understanding that brings together and burrows under the explanations of the experts.

Despite the complex and technical character of the enterprise, which calls for a series of specialized scholarly equipments that no single student can fully command, this book sets shamelessly out to consider comprehensively the probable causes and possible cures of this general sickness that has fallen upon Western society. Even if such generalized diagnosis and prescription fail to satisfy, in every detail, the passion of the experts for precision, it is an enterprise that some one must boldly attempt to execute. There is behind it a profound social urgency. The critical posture of affairs governmental, financial, and economic throughout the Western world compels Western man to turn his mind to the strategy of survival. This study is, therefore, concerned with the immediate critical situation in which the Western social order finds itself, but it owes its origin to an earlier impulse.

In the dark and disillusioning days directly following the war, my wife and I spent a crisp November week-end at the country house of a distinguished American banker whose intellectual interests run far beyond a Shylockian concentration on his ducats and his daughters. There were a score or more of house guests. The diverse personnel of the party suggested the breadth of the host's interests. The members of this party stand out clearly in my memory as I recall the incident that has kept this book in incubation for a round dozen of years.

There was a journalist with a Platonic passion for ideas and a Wellsian range of information and interest; an ambassador who had been appointed on account of his mind rather than his money; a scientist who had explored with open eyes, avid mind, and an acute sense of social values the living sciences of biology, psychology, and anthropology; a business man who saw his business as an organic part of the social process of his time, not as a mere matter of buying low and selling high; a politician who, although adept in all the routines of his craft, was altogether cynical of the crass improvising that marked the politics of the period, and spoke of statesmanship as the process in which knowledge meets power and becomes socially effective; a financier who considered banking more than money-lending, and thought it the business of the banker to be a kind of impresario of the productive energies of his time, a statesmanlike coördinator of the team-work of his fellow men; an educator who was seeking to strip education of its sterile pedantries and convert it into the research magnificent, the enterprise of making students at home in the modern world, enabling them to work in harmony with the creative forces of their generation, not at cross-purposes to them. These and like spirits insured the week-end against boredom.

Late Sunday afternoon the members of the party came in from the wine-like stimulation of walks over the hills and rides along the autumn-painted Palisades of the Hudson. After dinner we drifted into the library for coffee and cigars. It was a spacious room, symbolizing the spacious mind of its owner. From floor to ceiling the walls were covered with thousands of volumes that well-nigh ran the gamut of classic and contemporary thought. A notable Joshua Reynolds was over the mantel. The whole room was in subtle conspiracy against that "ordeal by tattle" which was Oscar Wilde's notion of a British week-end in the country. Hosts and house alike ministered to the almost lost art of stimulating conversation.

A brisk fire licked its way gracefully here and there behind the screen, now and then breaking into the conversation with the staccato crackle of resin as it dripped explosively from the burning logs. The air and the night outside were clear and moonlit. An almost desert quiet had dropped down over the countryside. Only as we looked through the long windows at the end of the library and caught sight of the brilliantly lighted boats plying up and down the Hudson were we reminded that we were still citizens of a world of traffic and travail.

After a while, the host lighted a fresh cigar and, as I have often seen him do, took a meditative turn round the room, stopped a moment to look at the moonlit Hudson, and came back to the company before the fire, obviously ready to cast a provocative fly into the stream of conversation. After a lapse of a dozen years, I think I can recapture, in essence if not in exactness, what he said. I shall not undertake to reproduce the verbal cross-fire of interrupting observations to which we subjected him.

"Here we are," he began, "a group of decently representative Americans. We have read a good deal. We think we have thought a little. And all of us, I am sure, want to understand the forces that are making and unmaking and remaking the world in which we are living. We should like to know how the balance sheet of our social order looks. And we should like to know what we may count on in days to come. I doubt that our fathers were ever heckled by as many questions as beset us.

"Is it a healthy time we are living in, or is the age out of joint?

"Where are we headed?

"What is happening to us biologically, psychologically, economically, politically, spiritually?

"Are the unfit outbreeding the fit?

"Is the fund of genius in our people rising or falling?

"Are we forgetting the individual in that fanatic mob-mindedness the war taught us to practice with a new and terrible effectiveness?

"Is democracy developing or degenerating?

"Is the quality of our political leadership growing richer or poorer as our civilization grows older?

"Is the old political order up to the job of administering the new social order?

"Is our educational system training men for life and leadership in the midst of the complexity and change that mark our time, or is it too steeped in the traditions of its scholastic past to do other than give men a bookish culture that may even blind them to the brute facts of the bloodless revolutions that are going on under their very eyes? Is our society too complicated to control?

"Will organized religion hamper or help intelligent social advance?

"Will the machine, geared to mass-production, bring us prosperity and leisure that will prove permanent and available to the masses, or will its promise peter out, and the machine sink us in a sea of surplus production that we shall not be statesmanlike enough to use to the social advantage of ourselves and of the world?

"Will science, in the long run, save us, or will civilization commit suicide with the new wealth and the new weapons that science gives it?

"Is Western civilization, in general, and American

civilization, in particular, likely to go into decline during the next quarter century, or is our star in the ascendant?

"These questions are far less academic and far more practical than they may sound. We do not have to be high-brow students of the rise and fall of civilizations to appreciate their urgency. Even Babbitt, who may never have heard of Oswald Spengler or Flinders Petrie, must before long realize that he has to know something about the general health of the civilization in which he is doing business if he is to plan at all intelligently for the next ten years of his firm's operations. What happens to Western civilization during the next twenty-five years will create the atmosphere that our lives and our enterprises must breathe If it is to be an exhilarating atmosphere, in which it will be easy to evolve and to execute significant undertakings, we should know it. If it is to be a stifling atmosphere, in which it will be difficult to think and to act in large and generous ways, we should know it. And we should know it now.

"A strange palsy seems to have fallen upon leadership pretty well throughout the Western world. I suspect that it is partly due to the fact that, for most men, the future is shrouded with a baffling uncertainty. And a leadership that is uncertain about to-morrow is likely to be a bit unnerved about to-day. Life would be a lot easier if we were all infallible prophets. But we are not. And we have seen so many of our confident guesses strike the rocks that we have begun to doubt our genius as seers, and the temptation to improvise for the moment is powerful.

"Some of us have tried to find a clue to our probable future by reading the current books as they have come from the press. But still we are at sea. One day we read a book that leaves us with the feeling that our civilization is doomed, that the war was the death-rattle in its throat. The next day we read a book that tells us we are on the eve of a radiant new era. Which are we to believe? How can we tell the true prophets from the charlatans? If you can decide, you have me bested. But I am growing garrulous. I did not intend to lecture you at such length. I only wanted to put a proposition that I thought might give us a good bone to gnaw for the rest of the evening.

"This is the proposition: Our civilization is admittedly a pretty muddled affair. And we are pretty muddled. We do not know the kind of world in which we shall have to live out the rest of our lives. And this ignorance is a heavy handicap as we sit down to plan the future of our lives and our enterprises. Books are not sufficient as guides. There are so many of them. Their counsels are contradictory. And we cannot cross-examine them when they cloud their meaning in phrases that are technical or obscure. There is one way I think we might get a fairly accurate sense of where we are headed. Let me put it to you as a question.

"Suppose we could bring together for a month or two in some quiet place—say Jekyll Island—the clearest minds in all the basic fields of thought and action in which the future of our civilization will be determined. The best biologist. The best psychologist. The best anthropologist. The best economist. The best business man. The best labor leader. The best physicist. The best chemist. The best philosophic mind in the field of religion. The best analyst of the rôle of education in the building and maintenance of a civilization that shall be at once stable and progressive. The best student of statecraft. And so on. Suppose we could spend a month or two talking things over with these priests and prophets of modern knowledge. Might we not get, as we could get in no other way, a pretty accurate picture of what we may expect during the next quarter century?

"Theoretically, of course, we can read the books these men are writing. But remember that most of us are busy men. We are lucky if we get to read one such book a week. There are millions of Americans, and literate Americans at that, who do not read even one such book a year. And we are regrettably amateur. We lack the background that would enable us to see the inter-relations of this run of fifty-two books that we might, if lucky, read in a year. When the experts disagree, or seem to us to disagree, in their books, we have no way of knowing what they might say to each other in a face to face defense of their respective contentions. Lots of their seeming differences might be ironed out in the give-and-take of discussion. And if we could only eavesdrop them in their talk, I have a notion that we might find a way out of the muddle we are in.

"Now I happen to have plenty of money. Suppose I should offer to finance such a party of experts and take them as our house guests to some such place as Jekyll Island for a month or two. Whom would you invite to the party?"

We talked far into the morning about the possible personnel of this hypothetical house party. The party never actually took place, but, in the years since, I have tried to carry it out on the installment plan. I have sedulously shadowed, in their books and in their persons, the sort of expert minds that we decided, that crisp November weekend on the Hudson, we should like to take with us to Jekyll Island for our projected clinic in Western civilization. And out of these lay explorations among the experts I have arrived at certain tentative conclusions respecting the future of our Western social order which I record in this book.

The studies that comprise this volume have thus grown out of an attempt to assess realistically the elements of health and the elements of disease in the political, social, and economic orders of Western life. But in a certain sense they are the personal record of my own fight against fatalism as I found myself, at the end of the war, facing the possibility of having to live out the rest of my life in the chill and shadow of a disarticulate and despiritualized world. They are leaves from the diary of an attempt to find some valid grounds for courage despite the highly problematic future of Western civilization which, as the

Spenglerian school of social analysts believes, sees its biological virility waning, its social fabric disintegrating, its economic machine running down, its political genius paralyzed, its spirit soiled by hatred and harried by fear, its noblest traditions repudiated, and, in significant instances, the development of centuries abruptly broken off.

A normal interest in the intelligent opinion of my time and the habit of following rather closely the generalizations that intermittently emerge from the various sciences have made me a fairly careful reader of the literature of social analysis that has been so lushly produced during the last dozen years. Much of it has been darkly predictive of dire developments. Month by month I have read grimly detailed forecasts of a new dark age in which civilized values will disappear and the race be plunged back into the precarious existence of its primitive ancestors without their primitive strength with which to meet its challenge. A man several years past his majority can read all this with a measure of confidence that, even if the direst of these predictions prove true, there will remain, for his lifetime at least, scattered oases of civilization to which he might turn as to cities of refuge. But I have had an uneasy fear that, if this heralding of decline should prove true, my son may, once he fully understands its implications, damn me for having given him life so late that he will be obliged to enter what should be the morning glow of his career in the bleak twilight of 1950.

A personal concern has thus fused with a professional interest in prompting me to ask whether there may not be some untapped reservoirs of power, some fresh sources of social health, to which the peoples of the West might turn in their extremity. This volume is a sort of log-book of the quest for an answer to this question, and it records at least a tentative victory over the post-war cynicism that drenched so much of the world in despair. It is not, however, in the common usage of the term, an optimistic book. It is written in full realization of the singular service that prophets of doom render by their ruthless social diagnoses. It enters no blanket denial of the prediction that Western civilization is doomed, nor does it venture any confident guess that the West is assured of a stable and satisfactory future. Its sole purpose is to consider the raw materials of social renewal that are to-day lying about us in confusion and challenge, waiting only for adequate leadership to bring them together and to touch them into life. It does not presume to predict what *will* happen. It attempts only to suggest what *may* happen if we use, wisely and promptly, the forces of health that are at hand.

It is an attempt to explain, in terms of the current scene, three ideas that have come to color my whole outlook upon the future of Western civilization, three ideas that will, I believe, condition the personal future and fortune of every man now living, three ideas with which I find myself forced to reckon in any attempt to arrive at a personal and social philosophy of life that will be both intellectually and spiritually satisfying. These three ideas are: (1) the idea of a New Renaissance; (2) the idea of a New Reformation; and (3) the idea of a New Industrial Revolution.

I label these three ideas in this fashion because the three historic movements of the Renaissance, the Reformation, and the Industrial Revolution seem to me to afford singularly fruitful starting points for realistic thinking about the plight and problems of contemporary civilization. But thinking from these three starting points will go awry if we unduly simplify these three movements. To the uncritical layman, the Renaissance was a cultural movement, the Reformation a religious movement, and the Industrial Revolution an economic movement. In strict truth, of course, no such rigid distinctions are justified. Historic movements are not as segregate in life as in the text-books. Each of these movements in turn affected profoundly the whole of men's lives.

Humanity could not indulge in a great cultural adventure like the Renaissance without altering its thought and action

in the fields of religion and economics. When men think
differently, they pray differently and work differently.
When the *Zeitgeist* is preparing a vast revolt and readjustment in the social life of a people, it frequently heralds the
fact by an analogous revolt and readjustment in the intellectual and cultural life of the people. A cultural movement affects more than its avowed followers. It subtly
colors the common life.

Humanity could not indulge in a great religious adventure like the Reformation without altering its moods and
its motives in parliament and workshop. Men have often
created their gods in the image of their governments and
their social orders, but their gods have in turn reacted upon
their governments and their social orders. Even a decadent
religion can affect profoundly the total life of a people. A
vital religion may dominate the social tendencies of a time.

Humanity could not indulge in a great economic adventure like the Industrial Revolution without altering its intellectual and spiritual outlook. The tone and temper of
men's lives are determined in the workshop no less than in
seminar and cathedral. The current status of religion in
the West is due, in no small measure, to the effect that the
scientific and technological forces of the industrial system
have had upon the Western mind. And certainly the culture
of our time has been colored, if not controlled, by the forces
peculiar to a machine age.

The scholar, the priest, and the captain of industry are
not specialists dealing with distinct thirds of men's lives.
Each, whether he realizes it or not, is dealing with the
whole of men's lives. Men are not minds on Saturday,
spirits on Sunday, and machines on Monday. They are
human beings all week, and anything that affects any part
of their lives affects the whole of their lives.

In the long odyssey of the human spirit, the Renaissance,
the Reformation, and the Industrial Revolution were not
three discrete movements. They were three correlate parts
of one coherent drama. They were cries in the night, fitful

tossings of the human spirit as it dreamed of a finer adjustment to its environment and a more fruitful use of its resources. The culture, the religion, and the industry with which they dealt are not different departments of life. They are but different doorways into life, different paths men take in the pursuit of living values. It is a seamless vestment that the human venture wears. It is only in the interest of clarity that I discuss the current implications of the Renaissance, the Reformation, and the Industrial Revolution as if they were three severely separate aspects of our social evolution.

I am convinced that the renewal, the stabilization, and the enrichment of Western civilization, in general, and of American civilization, in particular, can be accomplished only as we correct and complete these three historic movements in terms of our newer knowledge and later experience. If contemporary statesmanship, official and unofficial, is to lead the West out of its current confusion, it must, I think, inspire and direct a New Renaissance, a New Reformation, and a New Industrial Revolution, three basic movements that might, I believe, by the grace of creative and courageous leadership, be got well under way within the lifetime of my generation. Let me set down a few advance hints of what I mean by these three movements.

By a New Renaissance I mean a secular movement of social renewal that shall rescue culture from the pedant and the poseur, redeem it from its dilettante implications, rid it of its drawing-room inanities, and make it a magisterial force in the affairs of the age; a movement that shall give short shrift to that debilitated classicism which hangs like a discarnate ghost over so much of contemporary education and put in its place the dynamic classicism of the ancient Greeks which was not, with them, a drab discipline of the class-room, but a guide to behavior in a novel world, a way of thinking and living, the way of reasoned experimentation, ruthless self-examination, and realistic valuation; a movement that shall consciously direct men's minds, through press and school and church, towards the comprehension and control of a civilization born of science and the machine; a movement that shall establish social control of the impact of modern knowledge upon modern life; a rational adventure that shall at last make science the servant of life and culminate in the flood-tide of a valid humanism that shall water the parched roots of Western culture.

By a New Reformation I mean a clearing of the clogged conduits of religious institutionalism which are now checking the flow of spiritual initiative; the lighting of a bonfire of theological vanities; a resurgence of religious vitality that shall need no credentials save its own inherent effectiveness; a supplementing of the skeptical caution of the age of science with the spiritual courage of the ages of faith; a healing of the innumerable dualisms into which we have divided life, a remarriage of the material and the spiritual, a recovery of the lost unity of human affairs; a movement that shall tap deeper levels of psychic energy than we have lately utilized and assuage the unconfessed hungers of an age that has grown lean on its alternate diets of sentimental metaphysics and sterile negations.

By a New Industrial Revolution I mean a movement with somewhat richer content than the current use of this phrase carries; a movement, under statesmanlike industrial leadership, in the negative phase of which Western industrialism shall effect a self-correction of the over-centralization, the new fatigue and nagging monotony of work, the fitful insecurity of employment, the alternate swings between panic and plenty, the ugly utilitarianism, and other anti-social results that came in the wake of the old Industrial Revolution; a movement in the positive phase of which Western industrialism shall effect a self-development of the machine economy that shall emancipate mankind from drudgery, make widely accessible a stabilized prosperity, bring beauty of fabric and form back from the exile into which the machine for a time sent it, and guarantee to the

many as well as to the few adequate leisure for the cultivation of values that lie beyond economics.

This New Industrial Revolution, which I premise as one
of the three basic developments essential to the security
and soundness of the Western future, will not, in my judgment, be realized through any dictatorship, whether proletarian or plutocratic or personal. It will be realized, if
at all, through an evolution of the existing machine economy of the West, an evolution consciously controlled and
accelerated by an industrial statesmanship and a political
statesmanship in sympathetic and active collaboration.

Enlightened self-interest and intelligently controlled
technical advance may be trusted to establish at least certain phases of this New Industrial Revolution, despite the
fact that unenlightened self-interest and uncontrolled technical advance have, for the moment, brought Western industrialism to an impasse. But, if this Revolution is to be
fully and richly realized, it is imperative that business men,
bankers, and industrialists generally be alertly aware of
the forces that are effecting rapid changes in the form and
function of machine industry, that they understand the
social implications of these changes, and that they be animated by a determination to bring to the direction of this
New Industrial Revolution a higher quality of social foresight and economic statesmanship than the men who in-
augurated the machine age were able to muster.

This foresight and this statesmanship exist in the brains
of a select few of the business leaders of the West. I think
I could select a dozen American business, financial, and
industrial leaders who, acting as a directorate of economic
America, could formulate for American industry as a whole
a clear and coherent chart of policies that would rectify
and regularize our economic life and make machine industry the dependable servant of a secure and socially valid
civilization. But such business leaders are a slender
pioneering minority. The New Industrial Revolution, in
the wider meaning I have given it, will not be realized until

we make epidemic this economic statesmanship that is now exceptional. And for the popularization in business councils of the points of view and policies of these more statesmanlike business minds, political leadership must, I think, assume some responsibility. Governmental intervention in business processes is often inept, but governmental inspiration of business policies may now and then be imperative. After all, political leadership is charged with the guardianship of the common good. And in nothing is the common good so much at stake just now as in the active promotion of policies that shall bring the New Industrial Revolution to fruition.

Western man has been responsibly scientific in the design and development of his separate economic enterprises, but he has been recklessly empiric in the matter of the general economic order—or disorder—into which his separate enterprises must fit and under which they must function. The current situation calls for the elaboration of a sound philosophy of machine civilization. Western man is now the victim of a widespread ineffectiveness and insecurity of economic enterprise, not because his separate enterprises are technically ill-conceived, but because the Western economic order as a whole lacks a workable philosophy of the social function of industrialism and the inter-relationships of its separate parts. This needed philosophy of a socially creative industrialism will not be formulated by frightened publicists who permit the disheartening rhythm with which depressions have periodically visited the industrialized West to blind them to the potentialities of the machine economy once it is brought under statesmanlike control. Nor will this philosophy ever come from the smart-aleck school of criticism which washes its hands of the West because every factory worker does not rise to the stature of a Hindu sage and every bricklayer become a Buddha. The raw materials for such a philosophy are being thrown up out of the scattered deliberations and decisions of the more incisive and socially sensitive minds in business, industry, and finance. But there is need for the responsible social philosopher who, standing on the sidelines of industry, will coördinate these dawning insights of the industrial world and relate them to a conscious evolution of machine civilization towards humanistic ends, coherently conceived and clearly stated.

If the John Ruskins and the William Morrises could warn us against the social perils of the machine age at its birth, their successors in social analysis might do something to interpret the social possibilities of the machine age as it emerges from its adolescence. The indictment of machine civilization drawn by the Ruskins, the Tolstois, and the Gandhis is the picture that is etched most deeply on the popular mind. Unless it can be replaced by a more veracious insight into the human use to which we can, if we will, bend our machine economy, a day may steal upon us unawares when a clever demagogue, taking advantage of a period of economic depression and leaderless confusion, will be able to recruit a revolt against Western industrialism just when the opportunity is ripest for creative statesmanship to convert it into a tool for human emancipation and social enrichment.

The elaboration of a philosophy of machine civilization is an ambitious enterprise I have not presumed to undertake in this book. With respect to the New Industrial Revolution, I have done no more than call attention to the need for a wisely developed and widely disseminated philosophy of industrial purpose and procedure, recount the indictment that has been drawn by the rebels against the machine age, analyze the more obvious tendencies of machine industry, suggest their probable effect upon the future of our social order, and subject to critical review the inadequate economic leadership that has, in the last two decades, betrayed the machines and withheld from Western man the personal emancipation and social security the machines have themselves made possible.

In the projection of a New Renaissance and a New

Reformation, we are dealing with the more intangible processes of intellect and the imponderable propulsions of spirit. I have attempted to uncover the probable sources of power and to chart the course of such movements of rebirth and revitalization in the conviction that Western man can escape a new dark age only through some fresh advance of the human spirit that shall give to the peoples of the West effective sovereignty over their new instruments and bring a new dynamic into the lives alike of individuals and of institutions. The initiation of the renewal of Western civilization must, as I see it, lie very largely in the realm of the spirit. This does not mean our following some emotional prophet who would have us withdraw from the world of tangled economics and treacherous politics in a vain attempt to live above the battle. The genius of Western man has ever lain in vigor of personality, vitality of action, and a courageous grappling with his material environment. He cannot afford to trade this courage and this realism for a counterfeit Asiaticism that all-too-frequently means paralysis of character rather than profundity of spirit. But the next cycle of Western enrichment must, I am convinced, be ushered in by a vast spiritual awakening that has its roots deep-set in reality, a spiritual awakening that might, indeed, differ so widely from the historic revivals and reformations, and be so inextricably entangled in political, economic, and educational ventures that traditional religionists might fail to sense its significance.

Are such movements *probable?* I do not know. I shall not so much as hazard a guess. Are such movements *possible?* I think they are. Within the next ten years, we could, I believe, light the fires of renaissance and set the redemptive processes of reformation going if we had the wisdom to recognize, the genius to coördinate, and the will to utilize the raw materials of renewal that are obviously at hand—those new ideas, new idealisms, and new spiritual values that have been thrown up out of the sciences, philosophies, and practical experimentations of the modern mind.

Contemporary opinion, in many quarters, is so steeped in disillusionment that a book asserting even this limited confidence that a new dark age is preventible can hardly hope to escape the charge of Utopianism. This book is, frankly and without apology, Utopian. But Utopian with a difference! Books dealing with the future of civilization —from Augustine's *City of God,* on through More's *Utopia,* Bacon's *New Atlantis,* Campanella's *City of the Sun,* Harrington's *Oceana,* Bellamy's *Looking Backward,* and Hertzka's *Freeland,* down to Wells's *Modern Utopia* —have usually given us the picture of a finished product, the detailed organization chart of the author's private Utopia. This book, on the contrary, is not the picture of a finished product. It offers only the suggestion of a process. It presents no sketch of The City of God. It deals rather with The Politics of God, those religio-secular processes of creation and renewal by which Western man may make and keep his civilization a going concern.

I have sought to consider the issues of contemporary Western society from the point of view of a scientific humanism as distinguished from a sentimental humanitarianism. I appropriate the term scientific humanism, as descriptive of my approach to the dilemmas of my time, with some reluctance, for it has been made ludicrous by some of the latter-day acolytes who huddle about its altars. In the philosophy of some of these, scientific humanism is compounded of a scientific spirit that narrows the range of human values and a human spirit that reaches but little beyond a negative Stoicism of resignation. I use the term scientific humanism as meaning the use of our good sense to achieve the good life for ourselves and for our fellows, the intelligent relating alike of the seasoned wisdom of the centuries and the ideologies and instruments of the modern age to the dignity and desires of healthy human beings. A humanism of this sort, at once spiritual in purpose and scientific in procedure, seems to me to offer the most likely escape from the perilously partial leaderships of men who do not know how to be intelligent without being hard and of men who do not know how to be spiritual without being soft.

I do not offer these ventures in opinion as a corpus of nicely articulated social doctrines to which I wish to make fixed and final commitment. They are but the tentative approaches and tentative judgments of one American who has been trying to make himself at home in the modern world, seeking to orientate himself among the new forces that are making this at once a time of threatening insecurity and exciting promise. I have made no excursions to the far frontiers of knowledge for fresh intellectual plunder. Such forays into unmapped regions are first the business of the specialists. I have kept my inquiry centered on one question: What are some of the next steps towards the renewal and undergirding of Western civilization that might be taken on the basis of our present knowledge?

I send these studies out in the hope that, though their conclusions are tentative and their appeal restrained, they may here and there recruit men and women who will, in the years immediately ahead, consciously help to prepare the way for the Erasmus of a new and more spiritual Renaissance, for the Luther of a new and more realistic Reformation, and for an economic statesmanship that shall dominate and direct a new Industrial Revolution in which our machine economy shall become tool instead of traitor to the human spirit.

*En avant!*

# I

## The Crisis of the Western Spirit

MY study window opens this morning upon a summer
scene of utter calm and loveliness. Green lawns, great
oaks with their faintly sedative rustle of leaves, a quiet lake
a few rods away, and a sky of topaz and white! It is difficult to realize that this summer sky looks down upon a
strangely distraught people. A sky filled with the bat-
talions of storm would better reflect the social scene in
these middle months of 1931.

Since the closing weeks of 1929, the United States has
been in the grip of a profound and paralyzing economic
depression that has expressed itself in a marked retardation of business and industrial enterprise, a wide disturbance of mass confidence in current leadership, and a vast
social unsettlement in which hungry men have looked on
while food surpluses burst the walls of warehouses.
Throughout these months of maladjustment, the average
American has been impatient with discussions that seemed
not to drive directly at the crucial issue of economic recovery. This all-too-human impatience with anything save
the immediate and the near at hand tends to induce a
shallow and suicidal simplification of the malaise from
which the American polity currently suffers. In our for-
givably anxious concern with the more obvious factors of
depression, we must not cast our consideration in terms too
narrowly national or in terms exclusively economic. The
plight of the United States is an organic part of the plight
of the Western world. And the plight of the West is due
to a sickness that goes deeper than economic dislocations.

For more than the lifetime of most of us, the chill winds

of materialism have been blowing across Western civilization. Its spiritual fires have been banked, if not burned out. As the shadow of war fell athwart the world in 1914, the West faced a crisis of the spirit. It was not the war that produced the crisis of the spirit. It was the crisis of the spirit that produced the war. The Western world just now shows signs of emergence from the third phase of this spiritual crisis, the causes and the character of which it is necessary to understand if we are to deal at all intelligently with the dilemmas that are distracting Western civilization, in general, and American civilization, in particular. A fourth and healing phase of this crisis hovers among the possibilities of the next decade.

Since a diagnosis of the distempers of the Western spirit runs throughout this book, I want just now to do no more than place historically the varied phases of this spiritual crisis and suggest the moods these phases have in turn generated in the casual as well as the critical minds of the time.

At the risk of over-simplification, I list the four phases of this crisis in terms of four distinct periods in the life of the modern West. The first phase culminated in a new materialism that dominated the pre-war period. The second phase culminated in a new idealism that was the dynamic of the war period. The third phase culminated in a new cynicism that chilled and arrested the post-war period. The fourth phase, as yet in gestation, promises to culminate in a new faith in the possibility of planned progress that shall rescue the Western peoples from the epidemic of insecurity now sweeping over them and stabilize their now shaky social orders. The current mood of the Western mind can best be understood, I think, against the background of these four periods and the objectives towards which they have respectively driven or drifted.

The new materialism of the pre-war period is now so starkly evident that no labored rehearsal is needed to recall it. The creeping paralysis of a neo-paganism had long been coming over Western civilization, a neo-paganism that displayed all of the faults and few of the virtues of that ancient paganism which, in its best moments, represented a healthy love of life and laughter and a realistic recognition of the legitimate rôle that power may play in the progress of a people. It is not this healthy paganism of earlier centuries, but the perversions of it, into which the Greek and Roman worlds ultimately fell, that I have in mind when I use pagan as an adjective of accusation.

Pagan ideals of power and profit and pleasure had spread their nets anew for the capture of the pre-war soul of the West. Power was the goal of the state. Profit was the goal of the economic order. Pleasure was the goal of the people. Pre-war politics was dominated by a passion for power at any price. Pre-war business was dominated by a passion for profit at any price. Pre-war society was dominated by a passion for pleasure at any price. These three passions had pretty thoroughly paganized the Western nations, and had produced the perilous trinity of a perverted imperialism, a perverted industrialism, and a perverted hedonism, which, in the anti-social forms they assumed, cast over Western civilization the shadow of a bleak and barren materialism. The civilization that preceded and precipitated the war was at best a thinly veneered barbarism that was slowly sapping the spiritual integrity of the Western nations.

In this spiritual audit of the pre-war West, it should in justice be noted that Western civilization has been powerfully predisposed towards a materialistic outlook by the decisive rôle that material factors have played in its unique development. Many factors in the material environment of the Oriental peoples predispose them to the subjective life and its concern with spiritual values, even if their absorption in spiritual considerations is sometimes but an unconscious excuse for evading a courageous conquest of their material environment. The main factors in the material environment of the Occidental peoples, on the contrary,

predispose them to the objective life and its concern with
material values.

The Western peoples have lived in a temperate and
varied climate that has been a tonic to their minds and a
spur to an activist life of enterprise and inventiveness. The
Western world has been well stocked with natural resources for its industrial development. Where these resources have not been adequate in volume and variety
within the borders of the separate nations of the West,
the effective development of transportation and trade has,
potentially at least, put the resources of all at the disposal
of each, and has enabled the Western nations to tap the
resources of the rest of the world as well. The Western
peoples have not suffered from the economic handicap of
over-population. Roughly and relatively considered, the
population of the Western world has been sparse. With
climate playing into their hands, with raw materials within
ready reach, and with a decently reasonable population
growth, the peoples of the West have been able to live at
a relatively high level of material well-being.

There is in all this no final reason why the Western
peoples should fall victim to a shallow materialism of mood
and motive. The richer the material environment, the more
radiant may be the life lived in it, if the human spirit but
brings matter into subjection to its purposes. But in the
pre-war West, busy with the building of its vast industrial
structure, the human spirit went renegade to its responsibility. The material environment and the physical instruments of the Western world had become sovereign instead
of servant. And the false gods of a neo-paganism found
their altars crowded with pathetically credulous communicants.

In this reluctant indictment of the pre-war civilization
of the West, little, if any, discrimination can justly be made
between the allied, the enemy, and the neutral peoples of
the West. We were all guilty of the sin of surrender to

pagan ideals. We practiced paganism while we professed
Christianity. Western civilization was thus a vast corporate hypocrisy. And this meant that it had no inner peace.
For a generation before 1914, the peoples of the West
stirred uneasily in their dreams, and, when they were not
too deeply drugged with self-delusion, shivered with a
sense of impending disaster.

The ultimate verdict of history may well be that Germany caused the war, but for a deeper and less exclusively
German reason than the politicians and propagandists of
the war period asserted. The historian will not find this
deeper reason by meticulous research among the blue books
and red books and gray books and orange books in which
the diplomacy of the neo-paganism stole the livery of political decency, anaesthetized the conscience of mankind, and
sought to bolster up the tottering self-respect of the West.
An objective analysis of the diplomatic and military documents of the war and immediately pre-war periods drives
one, I think, to the resistless conclusion that the war-time
allocation of war guilt deserves a drastic revision. But
the question of war guilt, in the narrow sense of who
started the war, is quite beside the point I am concerned
with here. Post-mortem investigation is important only
as it issues in prophetic insight. From the point of view
of the Western future, it is more important to determine
what caused the war than to decide who started the war.
And the historian will discover the real cause of the war,
not by assiduous burrowings in the records of foreign
offices, but by a searching analysis of the spiritual status
of all the Western nations in the pre-war period. And
what the historian will find at the end of this adventure
in spiritual pathology is, I think, clearly predictable.

The historian will find that before the war the pagan
program of self-interest and material satisfaction, prosecuted under the protecting aegis of brute force, despite
the velvet-gloved suavity it sometimes assumed, was com-

ing to dominate all of Western civilization. This program happened to come to a head in Germany first. The neo-paganism of politics and economics which the rest of the Western nations piously denounced and persistently practiced, Germany openly adopted as the creed of her secular religion of nationalism. Germany, contrary to war-time legend, was the least Machiavellian of the Western nations, at least in her relation to the neo-paganism of the period. In terms of astute political strategy, Germany was guilty of an inept candor. As Benedetto Croce observed, her statesmen, her publicists, and her political historians laid bare her *arcana imperii* and made her political action uniquely transparent and self-conscious. Where the rest of the Western nations were furtively and unconfessedly neo-pagan, Germany was frankly and unconcealedly neo-pagan.

When Germany had at last caused the neo-paganism of the West to walk nakedly to the center of the stage, all that was left of the more humanate concepts of the state joined with self-interest and the subtle hypocrisies of the war mind in a mélange of motives that drove the rest of Western civilization into common action against the neo-paganism that had grown so candid and challenging in Central Europe. If Germany caused the war, it was not by any last-minute caprice of a mad Kaiser or his militarist councillors, as the over-simple and the under-informed hastened to assume, but simply because Germany outran the rest of the Western world in a paganization that was everywhere in process.

If Germany was the blind Samson who pushed down the pre-war temple of Western civilization, candor compels the confession that the temple was tottering even before broad Germanic shoulders were brought against its pillars. If Germany caused the war, it was not because she alone had sinned, but because she sinned more perfectly than the rest of us. Had the war happened fifty years later, any one of the major nations of the West might have been its initiator, for the neo-paganism that was in flower in Germany was at least in bud in the other Western nations.

*It is August, 1914!*

The new materialism of the pre-war period has borne its bitter fruit, and the first phase of the spiritual crisis of the West is ending. War breaks with incredible suddenness over Europe, and the Western world enters the second phase of its crisis of the spirit, a phase that is to see the emergence of a new idealism, here fostered by the forces of wistful sincerity, there frustrated by the forces of wilful self-seeking.

The war shocked the West into a sense of its spiritual bankruptcy. The peoples of the West were literally scared into a new idealism. It was, we must admit, a somewhat hastily improvised idealism. It bore many of the marks of a deathbed repentance. And it proved to be a transient idealism, but it was not, in my judgment, an insincere idealism. The trickster and the trader haunted the corridors of the foreign offices, and there was, I know, much tongue-in-cheek preachment of civilized ideals that were secretly shelved, but, for the inarticulate millions throughout the West, war and world politics seemed, for the moment, to have become the supreme spiritual adventure of mankind. These mute millions really believed that out of the womb of war a new world might be born.

The Machiavellism of some leaders aside, for the Western masses, the motivating stakes of the war were certain basic principles, upon the vindication of which they felt the integrity of Western civilization hinged—the principle of right as the basis of all human association, the validity of the moral law for public as well as for private affairs, the guaranty of the weak against the lawless aggression of the strong, and a lasting peace in which a non-militant democracy might develop. The masses held these concepts naïvely and with little critical sense of their meaning in terms of the day-to-day direction of the Western social order. They were abstract but flaming phrases that roused and recruited for war the emotional energies of the West. That the forces of self-seeking played upon this mass mood of naïve idealism, and used these high phrases as a smoke screen to hide the very politics of plunder they indicted, is now obvious. But, by and large, these were the principles that set the tone of civilian morale, invoked an unprecedented outpouring of industrial and military energy, and ran through the state papers and diplomatic conversations of the time with the insistent recurrence of a *motif*.

The uncritical millions of the West, in mood at least, stopped for a time the precipitate plunge towards paganism, that had marked the pre-war period, and sought to effect a rebirth of the spiritual forces of their civilization. Every warring nation had its profiteering and patrioteering traitors, for whom the war was a chance to indulge their respective lusts of piracy and prejudice, but, for the common millions throughout the West, the war was a time of sincere, if superficial, moral expansion, one of those spacious hours of human history when even little men seem to take on something of the largeness of the time. The horizons of men's interests were pushed out. The studied frivolities of dinner-table conversation gave way to serious discussion of the spiritual conflict that was going on above the battle of arms. Men who had before read but little save the sporting page began poring over the foreign despatches and devouring long articles on world affairs. Men who a few months before had been living narrow and self-centered lives went about like new converts with a passion for disinterested public service. Men gave and fought for peoples they had never seen, for peoples whose names they could not pronounce. Business men who before had brought daybook and ledger minds to their factories began studying the human problems of industry, and erstwhile conservatives began to speak tolerantly of industrial democracy as an inevitable corollary of political democracy.

Later retrogressions of interest in the humanization alike of industrial and of international relations have blurred our sense of the singular exaltation of spirit that marked the war period. Men felt not so much that they were at war as that they were on a crusade. A millennial content had crept into the vision of victory that stirred and sustained the millions in their grim enterprise of war. They were out to beat the enemy to his knees. And they would brook no interference with their battling. But, beyond that, they were on the hunt for a new world, in the conquest of which the defeat of the enemy was an incidental, even if imperative, factor. In the midst of the mud and murder of their battle-fields, they dreamed of a more secure and socially valid civilization. Men moved in an atmosphere of spiritual adventure. It was a time of political Pentecost! The peoples of the West seemed actually eager to face fresh problems with fresh minds.

To the cynical, all this seems, in retrospect, to have been but emotional frenzy, a spirituality that was only tongue deep, a kind of parade-ground piety. That this exaltation was temporary we know. That it was subject to manipulation by the forces of social treason we know. I simply record the fact that, for the moment, this was the lordly and liberal mood of the inarticulate millions. And this mass mood is all that I mean when I speak of the new idealism of the war period.

*It is November, 1918!*

After four fateful years, in which its social order came near to suicide, a war-weary West is celebrating an armistice in a rare riot of satisfaction with what seems to it a work well done. The post-war period is on! The second phase of the spiritual crisis of the West is not ended, but, unsuspected by the naïve millions, it is drawing to a close. The new idealism that gave this phase its force and fervor has a few more months to run before its devotees awaken disillusioned from their dreams of spiritual renewal and social reconstruction to follow the war. But even now, as grizzled men and boys grown old before their time embrace each other in the streets of London and Paris in the mad delirium of relief from the stresses and strains of war, the third phase of the crisis of the spirit looms on the horizon, a phase that is to see an epidemic cynicism take hold of the hearts of men throughout the West. The energizing faith of the war period is about to be superseded by the enervating fatalism of the post-war period.

The new cynicism of the post-war period has reflected alike the distraction of the leaders and the disillusionment of the led throughout the contemporary West. The statesmanship of the West struggles distractedly to function in the midst of dilemmas it lacks either the wit or the will to resolve. And the Western masses, by and large, surrender to one or the other of the equally sterile moods of resignation or revolt. The post-war West goes skeptic to many of its pre-war gospels and deserts the altars of some of its most ardently worshipped war-time gods. I name five of these deserted altars: (1) confidence in war as an instrument of national policy and an inspiration to social reconstruction; (2) the willingness to act in common for the achievement of common ends; (3) the compulsion to think out and to work for a consciously planned social future; (4) a sense of dedication to something more sweeping than individual rights or national interests; and (5) faith in the doctrine of progress. All these that marked, in varying degrees, the mood of the pre-war and war-time West are now either flouted or forgotten. Isolate individuals, alike among the leaders and among the led, still cling to the gods and to the gospels these reflect, but, in the main, they are disbelieved and deserted. Let me describe these disbeliefs and desertions in turn.

The Western masses surrendered reluctantly their confidence in war as an instrument of national policy and an inspiration to social reconstruction. For four years they were in the grip of the will-to-believe that the most ruthless war of history would result in the regeneration of Western civilization. Despite its naïveté, and despite the sordid aftermath of the war, there was beauty and sincerity in this

transient idealism. And it lasted well into the peace conference period. The diplomatic conversations between
Washington and Berlin and the Allied capitals that hurtled
over our heads in the closing days of the war were, in A.
G. Gardiner's phrase, like the dialogue of gods. Even
seasoned cynics were, here and there, thrown off their
guard. Many who were not by nature millennial minded
thought that maybe the day of a new deal had dawned.
This godlike talk would surely be followed by godlike
action! There was an almost pathetic popular confidence
in these Olympian conversations. The new idealism of the
war period held stubbornly to its hopes. The military
victory of the Allied forces was to mean a spiritual victory
over the neo-paganism of the pre-war West!

But it soon became clear that the luminous words of the
pre-armistice diplomacy has struck a Stygian darkness they
could not penetrate. The high audacities of a new internationalism were checkmated by the high ambitions of a
resurgent nationalism. It became obvious, even to the man
in the street, that the neo-pagan spirit that brought the
West to war was not to be exorcised by the holy water of
brilliant state papers.

The ancient parable of *The Sower* was reënacted with
the world for a field. Behold, sowers went forth to sow, at
Paris, seed-bearers of a new world order. And when they
sowed, some seeds fell by the wayside, and the fowls,
ravening vultures of a narrow nationalism, came and de-
voured them. And others fell upon rocky places, where
they had not much earth, where statesmanship displayed
a stony indifference to principles that looked beyond
nationalism, and straightway they sprang up, because they
had no deepness of earth, only the transient repentance of
war time, and when the sun had risen, when statesmen met
to translate announced war aims into policies of peace,
they were scorched, and because they had no root they
withered away. And others fell among the thorns, and the
thorns grew up and choked them, the seed-principles of a

new world order were choked by a thorny mass of detailed problems, in the handling of which piecemeal compromises obscured the avowed ideal. And others fell upon good ground, and yielded fruit, some a hundredfold, some sixty, and some thirty. Only here does the parallel grow dubious.

Versailles failed to supplement Verdun. The statesman betrayed the soldier. Destructive force was not followed by constructive policy. Armageddon ended in a gigantic play with irrelevancies and a petty skirmish for nationalistic interests. Where courageous reconstruction had been expected, a log-rolling restoration emerged, a reëstablishment of the old order of things under new names, a pouring of old wine into new and misleadingly labeled bottles, with the new wine of freshly awakened aspirations left to flow where it might.

The theretofore credulous millions of the West were disillusioned. They had entered the war in the spirit of an active international mission. They had fought hard. They had achieved victory. But the new world they had thought they were fighting for had eluded their grasp. World politics had lost its soul.

In the United States, what should have been a coalition consideration of ways and means of discharging America's moral responsibility in world affairs—to say nothing of protecting by far-sighted foreign policy those legitimate self-interests to-day so seriously threatened by European insecurity—degenerated into nothing better than a disgraceful orgy of President-baiting, a chapter in American history that our grandchildren will wish might be expunged from the record. With much of the attack on the Treaty of Versailles realistically minded men were and are in agreement. It was not a document that fulfilled the promise of Mr. Wilson's prophetic pronouncements and the pre-conference agreement to them by Allied statesmen. And the presidential promotion of the treaty might well have been less intransigeant! The justice of opposition to important aspects of the treaty cannot be defensibly questioned. But the American opposition failed utterly to formulate any substitute policy that made any moral appeal to the mind of the nation. It was an adventure in sterile negation. World politics was dragged to the level of ward politics.

The spiritual bankruptcy of American statesmanship that followed the war made strange bedfellows. High-minded and sincere critics of the treaty found themselves madly applauded by all or most of the anti-social reactionaries, recklessly irresponsible radicals, blatherskites, and jingoes in the country. American liberalism linked arms with American reaction, and, with a world half in ruins and socially leaderless, was content to play the rôle of critical negation. When the historian balances the books of the post-war period, American liberals will have to share the blame for the fact that the Western world is still in the toils of the old order, with its cunning calculations for a balance of power that will tip in profitable directions at desired times, its trouble-making doctrines of economic exclusion, and its fatalistic clash of races. For American liberals were in their arm-chairs when they should have been in the arena!

In post-war elections, the Western masses, here and there, followed sheep-like the leadership of men who had helped to make the peace a sterile and shoddy thing. But mankind is not logical. Individual inertia and group tradition will sometimes dictate a ballot that belies the profoundest belief of the balloter. And politics rarely plumbs the depths of men's spirits. Had it been possible to take a non-political referendum of the hearts of men throughout the West in the months immediately following the peace conference, it would have shown, I am sure, a deep and widespread disillusionment with war as an instrument of national policy.

But even this disillusionment did not wholly destroy the idealistic hope that the Western millions had worn as an amulet through the dark days of war. The leaders had failed to legislate the clear demands of the led. There was a collapse of statecraft throughout the West. This the masses knew, even if some but sensed it dimly. They no longer looked for a new world order at the hands of the diplomats and legislators then at the helm in world affairs. But they still cherished the hope that, in their several nations, the idealism of war days would carry over into civilian affairs and effect a far-reaching social reconstruction. What happened to this lingering hope is now history.

During the war, men in the trenches and in the lone trails of the night sky practiced heroism as men back home were practicing professions. It was said that these and their civilian associates in war service would return to civil life as the insistent sponsors of a new and better social order. But this new order failed to arrive! Pledges and principles that had invested the war with social significance for the fighting masses were on the scrap heap before the post-war period was many moons old. The war had been fought, as the millions saw it, in defence of democracy. But, before long, those sections of the Allied world that had not frankly surrendered to dictatorship were furtively skeptical of democracy as they looked wistfully over their shoulders at the swift efficiencies of the cinema Napoleons who had arisen in neighboring states. It was said that the fires of war had burned up our denominational differences. Tales were told of Protestant pastors and Jewish rabbis holding the cross before the eyes of dying Catholics, and of Catholic priests comforting Jews and Methodists in their last hours. But, in a short while, we were suffering the suppressed civil war of Ku Kluxism.

The few moral disciplines we had built up before the war were, in many cases, scrapped without apology. The repressed libertinism of the race was released by the war. Not only the men who fought in the trenches, but the men and women behind the lines who were vicariously vicious as they knit socks or sold liberty bonds, despite the loftiness of their intent, had been schooled by war in a cruelty

of temper it had been the business of generations to subli-
mate if not eradicate. For four years the men and women
of Western civilization had lived, despite their idealization
of their aims, by a philosophy of getting what they wanted
by fighting, and here, there, and yonder they carried this
philosophy over into the civil affairs of the post-war period.
Men who before the war had been sensitive and shrinking
at the thought of brutality brought firing-squad minds to
the issues of peace. Social revolutions, labor wars, and the
madness of Ku Kluxism were among the certificates that
showed how apt the race had been to learn its lesson of
conquest by cruelty.

The war brought a transient discipline to mankind, but
in sinister paradox it also bred a revolt against discipline.
Men will submit to rigid discipline if the adventure is
dramatic enough, as in war, but peace, save when it brings
a stirring challenge to spiritual adventure, seems drab and
purposeless to the many after a war. And the sterile peace
that followed the World War bred, for a time, a world-
wide revolt against hard work, against loyalty to homes
that seemed humdrum after the lawless liaisons of war
time, against all the controls and traditions and disciplines
that had been slowly built up by generations of civilized effort. And so, as they watched their war-time hopes one by
one go glimmering, the Western masses were at last driven
to doubt the efficacy of war, not only as an instrument of
national policy, but as an inspiration to spiritual renewal
and social reconstruction.

Organic unity of aim and action is indispensable to a
civilization that aspires to authentic greatness. The civilization of the pre-war West was a high carnival of competition which meant an underlying disunity. The war
brought a quick integration to the West. Its peoples displayed an unprecedented willingness to act in common for
the achievement of common ends. They merged their
separate patriotisms in a *union sacrée* for the prosecution
of the war. And it was part of the new idealism of the war

period to hope that this unity of aim and action would survive the war and bring fresh guaranties of peace and progress to the peoples of the West. Once again the uncritical millions were doomed to disillusionment. The smoke had hardly cleared from the battle-fields before the solid front of war days had become a Donnybrook Fair of snarling friends. Allied integration fell into anarchic individualism of policy and procedure. And, in the several nations, the concentration of war was followed by the chaos of peace.

The disunity of the West that followed the war meant more than the dismantling of the machinery of unity that had been improvised for war purposes. It meant a sweeping disunity of the Western mind as well. The post-war West became a West at wit's end. And this disintegration is still evident in all fields of Western thought and action. In philosophy, in religion, in science, in politics, the contemporary West is the victim of a paralyzing indecision as it stands in the midst of clashing concepts, conflicting tendencies, and competitive forces.

The old dualisms have ceased to satisfy. Western man is haunted by the dream of new unities. But Western philosophy has, save in the minds of isolate seers, slumped into a socially impotent agnosticism of outlook. Old dogmas have lost their savor. Western man hungers for a religion in which the living experience of modern men shall take precedence over the lifeless exegesis of ancient formulas. But Western religion is more a rudderless excursion than a realistic experimentation. Western man finds himself now wooed by the virtues and now wracked by the vices alike of democracy and of dictatorship. Both have techniques that the current phase of Western development demands. Each is shot through with unlovely qualities. Neither seems quite to meet the needs of the human spirit. Western man waits for a synthesis of the best in both. But Western politics, lacking coherence of aim and courage of action, is powerless to reconcile these contra-

dictory forces. It now leashes and now liberates the will
of its masses. It tries authority for a time, and then toys
with liberty for a season. It makes the individual its major
concern for a while, and then suddenly subjects him to the
terrible tyranny of the majority. It swings alternately
from one to the other of these opposites, when the future
of the West depends upon their creative correlation. The
politics of the West is a politics of drift.

The common action for common ends that gave
momentary might to their war efforts did not rest, as many
uncritically assumed, upon any permanently achieved unity
of the Western peoples. It was a defensive huddle! The
peoples of the West must meet their dilemmas—now made
so vivid and urgent by the economic depression, the political
distraction, and the social dishevelment in evidence the
world around—with the handicap of a widespread intellectual, spiritual, and social disintegration.

The war laid upon men throughout the West the compulsion to think out and to work for a consciously planned
future. The demands of war dramatically exposed the
frailties of the social order of the pre-war West. It soon
became clear, even to the sluggish, that Western man had
been unpardonably casual about the development of his
civilization. Through the pre-war period, and indeed over
the centuries, he had been an improviser, doing his political
and social thinking under the spell of the immediate. He
had not learned to take long views. He had brushed aside
as academic the suggestion that he should anticipate and
discount crises. He had never acquired the habit of preparing well in advance for even the most predictable demands of the future. He had been amazingly forehanded
in the administration of his private enterprises, but he had
seemed to think that great civilizations are conceived in fits
of absence of mind. The war convinced him of the fallacy
of this *laissez-faire* attitude towards the development of
his social order. The democracies of the West had learned
in a costly school what it means to become warring nations

unprepared for war. The end of the war must not find them peaceful nations unprepared for peace!

It was part of the new idealism of the war period to hope that this intensive interest in a planned future would carry over into the post-war period. And for a time it seemed as if it might. Even while war was most loudly hammering at their doors, the governments of the West created elaborate reconstruction commissions, and charged them with the duty of charting the future and drawing blueprints of policy for post-war days. These governmental commissions were widely supplemented by voluntary associations that brought sustained research to the probable issues of the post-war period. The bibliography of the literature of social reconstruction, written during the war, runs into thousands of books, pamphlets, and reports. Western man was in the prow of the boat with the spray of the future beating against his face. His mood, for the moment, was the mood that men must have if they are to create great civilizations.

But once again a war-time hope was to disappear in a post-war disillusionment. Once the war was definitively ended, the Western nations went largely recreant to their war-time resolutions of social reconstruction. Save in Germany, in Russia, in Italy, and occasional areas where lesser Lenins and minor Mussolinis strutted for a day, there was everywhere throughout the West a scurrying back to the ancient shelters instead of the building of new ones. Interest in social evolution was superseded by a concern for social equilibrium. The political catch-words of the early post-war period reflect this recantation. England was offered a policy of "tranquillity" by Bonar Law. America was offered a policy of "normalcy" by Warren Harding. The goal of post-war politics, pretty generally throughout the West, was restoration rather than reconstruction. In one of his flashes of sagacious phrase-making, Lloyd George rightly remarked that tranquillity is not a policy but a yawn. Social equilibrium is an obvious essential in any sound economy, but equilibrium is a by-product, not the exclusive concern, of a creative politics. But the post-war politics of tranquillity and normalcy played primarily for equilibrium. And so, those early post-war years, relatively considered, were barren of socially creative action. The intensive interest in a planned future that arose during the war disappeared, to remain for a decade or more but the private thesis of lay critics of the political and economic scene.

While the war was on, men were moved by a sense of dedication to something more sweeping than individual rights or national interests. It was part of the new idealism of the war period to hope that this broadening of outlook would survive the war and bring to birth a new social statesmanship. But, once the war was over, Western man suffered a marked emotional let-down. The human spirit relaxed. The star of social Utopianism, that had shone above the battle, went into eclipse, and the gates to Vanity Fair opened. A carnival mood settled paradoxically down over a Europe that was beset by paralyzing fears, quivering insecurity, and contagious unrest. A Western world, with a staggering amount of unfinished business on hand, took a day off. Job turned jester despite his boils. And something of this forcedly gay irresponsibility held over during the decade that followed the end of the war, expressing itself in a devil-may-care cynicism respecting the possibility of any consciously controlled social development.

In itself, lightness of spirit is not, of course, inimical to a very genuine sense of social responsibility. And there is always a little of the saving salt of cynicism in the realistic mind to keep it from credulity. It was well for Western man to lose the super-seriousness he brought to his social outlook during the war. It was an artificially stimulated seriousness, a mood that, in peace time, gives us the pathological seriousness of the professional reformer. A saving lightness of spirit helps nations as well as men to achieve poise and to avoid an undue emphasis of one aspect of life at the expense of other and equally significant aspects. "The mother of debauchery," as Nietzsche said, "is not joy, but joylessness." In its moments of highest achievement, the race has invariably been high-hearted.

There is a laughter of understanding as well as a laughter of escape. But much of the cynical indifference the post-war decade displayed towards a reasonable Utopianism of social purpose seemed little more than a moral laziness that enabled Western man to go to hell gaily. The amusements and arts of the post-war West show markedly the influence of the escapists. And this is no insignificant factor in the current life of the West. If the Western peoples, in a mood of social indifference, increasingly turn to diversion as a dope fiend turns to dope, to forget their troubles, gaiety of spirit will flit across the night of their disorder like a firefly, ornamenting but not illuminating the darkness.

Important as the four disillusionments I have just described are, in accounting for the mood that fell upon men throughout the West, at the root of the new cynicism of the post-war period lay a lost faith in the doctrine of progress that had long been the animating and all-dominant thought of the Western mind. In the pre-war period, Western man brought a blind belief to the doctrine that civilization had moved, was moving, and would continue to move in a desirable direction. He had his apprehensions as he saw the mustering of forces that seemed clearly making for war. But wars, phases of economic depression, and other recurrent set-backs were considered but eddies in the stream of history. The main current moved resistlessly on! In short, Western man believed in the doctrine of progress. It may be that he surrendered all the more easily to the neo-pagan materialism and hedonism because he thought that, for all his philandering with false gods, the net historic result of Western development would be progress. But the war dealt a death-blow to popular faith in this doctrine of progress. Post-war literature is filled with references to the *myth* of automatic progress.

The post-war West is inclined to suspect that the pre-war idea of progress was an *idolum saeculi,* the easy error of a generation that was all too eager to believe in a beautiful destiny.

Disillusioned with war as an instrument of national policy, realizing that the inspiration towards spiritual renewal that came to men during the war had proved transient and untrustworthy, witnessing an almost over-night collapse of the coöperation that the Western nations practiced under pressure, seeing a wholesale truancy from war-time resolves to build a planned civilization, and feel-ing the chill of cynicism fall over the social purposefulness that was regnant in men's minds while the war was on, many of the more sensitive spirits of the Western nations went darkly pessimistic.

Three phases of the crisis of the Western spirit are thus rounded. The new materialism was temporarily disavowed by a new idealism that was succeeded by a new cynicism. The disunity, the headlessness, the cynical distrust of the possibility of planned progress, and the widespread social irresponsibility that followed the war still haunt and harass the Western world. The third phase of the crisis of the Western spirit is by no means behind us, but hints of a fourth and favorable phase begin to streak the sky. This fourth phase, if it proves more than a false dawn, will see the period of depression, through which the Western world is now passing, culminate in a new statesmanship.

It may be the lot of the Americans to determine whether this fourth phase shall materialize in something more than frightened resolutions made in the midst of depression and forgotten at the first upward thrust of the economic curve. In the United States, the general malaise of the Western spirit, that has marked the third phase of its crisis, was for a time offset by the false tonic of an unprecedented economic optimism. For the better part of the decade that ended with the Black October of 1929, we drank the heady wine of high profits. We went in for planless expansion and paranoiac speculation. We babbled lyrically of a New Era in which, so the man in the street was led to believe, depression would prove impossible and prosperity inevitable. We romanticized our economics. But, as always, reality took its revenge on the romancers. We were caught in the debris of a diastrous market débâcle, and a stubborn plague of frozen confidence and faltering business followed. This sudden collapse sobered us. We had long taken our economic order for granted, but it had failed us just when we were expecting most from it. And so, at least the more realistic minds among us began burrowing about its foundations to see if they were secure and to examine its superstructure to see if it was faulty.

The fact that most impresses us, as we proceed with this critique of our ill fortune, is the striking contrast between the planlessness that has marked the social development of our economic order and the meticulous planning that has been brought to the technical development of the separate enterprises that function under it. Neither in national policy nor in national action have we yet recognized the fact that we have passed definitely out of the simple pastoral era, in which *laissez-faire* was at once possible and productive, into a complex technologic era, in which *laissez-faire* is suicidal and some measure of central planning imperative. The depression, signalized by the 1929 market crash, has driven a realization of this home to many Americans who were still trying to wrest nutriment from the dead rinds of a defunct individualism. A plea for a planned economy has, in consequence, become a common note in the national clash of ideas.

Part of this fresh interest in social planning is but a fear-born reaction to the incidence of drastic economic depression, a clutching at the idea of control as we see a system we thought tightly reined go runaway. In a sense, therefore, this new passion for planning bears a family resemblance to the reconstruction resolves that men made during the war. There is, however, a difference. The

movement for planned reconstruction, reflected in the
lay literature and official commissions of the war period,
was largely inspired by idealistic considerations and
fostered, in the main, by intellectuals serving in the
peripheral agencies of government. The current interest
in national planning, on the contrary, is supported by intensely practical considerations. The self-interest of the
industrialist joins the impersonal thinking of the social
statesman in realizing the peril involved in a catch-as-catch-
can administration of the national economy in a technologic
age. In the light of the economic impasse in which the
Western world now finds itself, conservative captains of
American industry begin to question the sense and soundness of a *laissez-faire* capitalism. They have been accustomed to plan carefully their separate enterprises. But
events have proved that this is not enough. Even the most
perfectly planned parts of our economic life have suffered
stagnation because the whole of the economic order has
been essentially planless. And so, at last, even the most in-
transigent apostle of capitalism begins to plead for
planned production and planned distribution, with whole
industries, whole nations, if not, indeed, the whole world as
the fields to be covered by the planning.

Concurrent with this enforced interest of the industrialists, the lay philosophers of economics and politics are
elaborating a new literature on the need and the nature of
national planning for the American future. The lush output of leader-articles by the Charles A. Beards, the Stuart
Chases, the George Soules, and other scholar-publicists
indicate the emergence of this fresh literature of national
foresight. This literature of planning may be saved the fate
of the social reconstruction literature, written in war time,
by the fact that the self-interest of the business system is
now urgently and consciously at stake in seeing the aims of
a philosophy of planning realized through means made
workable in a self-governing democracy.

There are, I realize, a disheartening number of practical

difficulties in the way of national planning in a democracy with its innate suspicion of centralized authority. Particularly does the political tradition of checks and balances render American government lumbering and laggard where, in this era of imperative readjustment, promptness and precision are the essence of effective statesmanship. I do not minimize the hurdles on the road to a planned social order made consistent with the new circumstances of the age of science and technology. At the moment, I do no more than suggest that, from the current coming together of the self-interest of the industrialist and the social vision of the philosophers of economics and politics, there is a chance that we may recapture, in a less emotionalized and more dependable form, the mood of conscious civilization-building that moved men for a fleeting hour while the war was on. If we do, we may lead the Western world out of the chill of its post-war cynicism into a creative adventure in social creation and social control. Whether this fourth phase of the crisis of the Western spirit will be realized is still on the lap of the gods.

Without falling into an abortive messianism of uncritical hope, there is a noticeable recovery from the post-war cynicism among the men of letters and arts throughout the Western world, a noticeable awakening of a sense of social concern, an awakening that is not confined to Russia where the arts are conscript to the cause of the revolution. This emergent mood marks an important shift from the mood in which Western man, coming out of the war and surveying its tragic aftermath, surrendered himself quite fully to speculation upon the probable downfall of Western civilization. Out of that post-war analysis and introspection came a voluminous literature of despair. I want now to describe and to analyze this literature, because it presents the searching diagnoses of the maladies of the Western social order that must be clearly before us if our plans for the future are to be rooted in reality.

## II

# The Prophets of Doom Speak

THE decade following the war was prolific in social prophecy. The resulting literature of forecast has been largely written by the prophets of doom, by men who are skeptical of the capacity of the West to liquidate the grave confusion into which an inadequate leadership has plunged its civilization. This literature has been written from varying levels of disillusionment, ranging from the philosophical assessment of the situation by George Santayana to the persistent gloom of Dean Inge.

In his *Character and Opinion in the United States,* Mr. Santayana ventures the prophecy that "Civilization is perhaps approaching one of those long winters that overtake it from time to time. A flood of barbarism from below may soon level all the fair works of our Christian ancestors, as another flood two thousand years ago levelled those of the ancients. Romantic Christendom—picturesque, passionate, unhappy episode—may be coming to an end." But even so black a future is, for Mr. Santayana, touched with light, even if it be a distant light, reaching us in fitful and fragile rays. "Such a catastrophe," he bravely asserts, with the calm of the philosopher who can afford to wait, "would be no reason for despair. Nothing lasts forever; but the elasticity of life is wonderful, and even if the world lost its memory it could not lose its youth. Under the deluge, and watered by it, seeds of all sorts would survive against the time to come, even if what might eventually spring from them, under the new circumstances, should wear a strange aspect." Mr. Santayana feels the warning

43

frost of a spiritual winter that may freeze the fountains of Western energy and enterprise, but he does not doubt that another springtime lies ahead in the human cycle.

Dean Inge is a more nearly unqualified prophet of doom. He reflects the post-war mood in his disillusionment with the doctrine of progress. "Human nature has not been changed by civilization," he contends in his *Outspoken Essays.* "It is not certain that there has been much change in our intellectual and moral endowments since pithecanthropus dropped the first half of his name. . . . Apart from the accumulation of knowledge and experience, which are external and precarious acquisitions, there is no proof that we have changed much since the first stone age." And he reflects the post-war mood even more vividly in his special observations on the Western outlook. Again, in his *Outspoken Essays,* he says, "I have, I suppose, made it clear that I do not consider myself specially fortunate in having been born in 1860, and that I look forward with great anxiety to the journey through life which my children will have to make. . . . We must cut down our hopes for our nation, for Europe, and for humanity at large, to a very modest and humble aspiration. . . . We are witnessing the suicide of a social order, and our descendants will marvel at our madness. . . . The possibility of another dark age is not remote." When the feel of frost, that touches without terrorizing the sensitive spirit of a Santayana, strikes the somber mind of a Dean Inge, he suspects that it is the herald, not of a transient winter, but of the irrevocable cooling of the social planet.

This sampling of the post-war literature of despair suggests the range of its moods from casual depression to confirmed disillusionment. Its net effect is to say that Western life, individual and institutional, is moving into the twilight of a new dark age, or that, at best, Western man is facing a long winter of the spirit. If this literature of despair consisted entirely of generalized predictions, even by such distinguished philosophers and publicists as Mr.

Santayana and Dean Inge, it might be dismissed as a kind of intellectual fatigue-poison generated by post-war weariness. For the prophetic spirit is not immune to the enervating atmosphere of an age in which the general spirit has surrendered to events. There is always danger that the prophet will get tired and abdicate just when he is most needed to bring a rigorous sanity to the social analysis of his time. There have been eras in history when humanity grew tired, when men's emotions went quickly gray, and when realistic prophets disappeared. A man who had spent his life pleading for intelligent social control might understandably give up the ghost, and surrender to a superficial despair, after a war that seemed to send all his hopes of an ordered world aglimmering.

The current literature of despair, however, can hardly be dismissed as the gloomy rationalizations of tired prophets. It is not a mass of facile generalizations floating in the speculative ether far above the brute facts it pretends to interpret. Its more solid sections are devastatingly detailed. The major part of it has been written, not by journalistic generalizers, but by men of specialized scholarship. The prophets of doom include men who have subjected the living sciences of biology and psychology to intensive experimental study, archaeologists and anthropologists who have deciphered with infinite care the record in stone and bone of human tendencies over the centuries, economists and administrators who have wrestled at firsthand with the forces and trends of the machine economy of the West, students of statecraft who have prosecuted their researches behind the scenes of Western politics, historians who have sought to be social diagnosticians of the eras they chronicled, in short, men who have tried to think from fact to theory rather than from theory to fact. It is a chorus of responsible specialists that chants the litany of Western doom.

I have followed with a fair faithfulness this literature of despair. In the midst of the distracting demands of an executive post, I have had neither the freedom of time nor the freedom of mind to subject it to exhaustive analysis, but I have read it with something more than a casual effort to clarify my own mind respecting the current trend of Western affairs. And I think it is accurate to say that this literature of despair, in so far as it has been written by responsible scholars and not by professional sensationalists, has been inspired by six distinct fears that have arisen in six distinct fields of research and experience: (1) the biological fear; (2) the psychological fear; (3) the political fear; (4) the economic fear; (5) the administrative fear; and (6) the moral fear. These fears are not as severely separate as I seem to make them. They do not lie edge to edge as flagstones; they blend as colors. Disarrangement or degeneration in one field registers its effects in other fields. We cannot divorce biology and economics, let us say, in realistic social analysis. But scholars render their social verdicts in terms of their special fields, and it is simplest so to discuss them.

I want now to chart the grounds of these six fears, and to summarize the considerations that have given rise to them. I do not want to be understood as suggesting that the following summaries of judgment reflect the conclusions of the whole fraternity of scholars in the fields of investigation and interpretation here considered. Here and there, later research has modified, if not reversed, some of the darker conclusions I shall here record. I am dealing here exclusively with the assumptions and outlook of the scholars who have produced the literature of despair.

### The Biological Fear!

As the biologist looks from his laboratory window upon the Western scene, he is, if I may somewhat over-simplify his outlook, disturbed (1) by the social implications of the current trend in the biological quality of the Western peoples, (2) by the economic implications of the rate at which the world population is increasing, and (3) by the political implications of the tension between the white races of the Occident and the colored races of the Orient.

Here, again, the sharp distinction I seem to draw between the social, economic, and political implications of the biological process is not to be taken too literally. These implications overlap and interlock. And interwoven with them are cultural and spiritual implications I do not specify. The biological quality of the Western peoples, the tempo of world population growth, and the race tension between the white and colored worlds are separate phases of a single problem that roots in the biological process. Their subtle interdependence need not be obscured by their separate consideration. So let me define, in turn, the three phases of this problem in terms of which the biologist considers the Western outlook.

As he considers the question of human quality, the biologist sees the Western nations tending to reproduce their populations from their less and least fit human stocks rather than from their better and best human stocks. The best families incline to have the smallest families, while the worst families are likely to have the largest families. Birth control is practiced by the fit and passed up by the unfit. Family limitation among the kind of folk the West needs most! Prodigal fecundity among the kind of folk the West needs least! The fittest are unfertile, while the unfittest are fertile. This cannot but mean a dangerous dilution of the quality of the Western peoples. The West must, unless this trend is reversed, resign itself to biological bankruptcy. So runs the reasoning of the biologist.

The biologist does not want the West to go back to barbarism and let natural selection weed out its weaklings. His concern that the West shall halt the increasing survival of its less fit has not brutalized the biologist's attitude towards the social unfortunate, as some maudlin commentators contend. The biologist does not suggest that the Western nations leave their unfit to hang themselves by the noose of their own ignorance or indigence. But he insists that they set in motion forces of enlightenment and use every legitimate device that shall tend to prevent the unfit and the unfortunate from outbreeding the fit and the fortunate. And this, he thinks, will prove, in the long run, merciful to the unfit, for by the sheer mathematics of the case the present differential birth-rates of the fit and the unfit will bring the West to a time when there will not be enough fit to take care of the unfit.

The biologist is convinced that the social stability of Western civilization requires the consistent rearing of larger families by the more desirable classes and smaller families by the less desirable classes. And the biological concept of desirable and undesirable is not a snob concept. The biologically desirable are those whom heredity has endowed with sound bodies and sound minds. The biologically desirable may be rich or poor, lettered or unlettered, elites or exiles by drawing-room standards, but they are built of sound stuff. And the occasional flame of genius that burns in a blighted body does not invalidate this general biological criterion. The biologist is not counselling race suicide. He is the protagonist of race improvement. He is contending only that, in the higher ethics of science, we have no moral right to bring into the world children biologically too weak to stand the strain that the complex and swiftly changing life of the modern West imposes upon its peoples. To breed such offspring is to send them with chained feet into the race of life. And this, as the biologist sees it, means cruelty to the children as well as catastrophe to the civilization into which they are born.

The biologist is keenly aware of the retarding hurdles that stand across the road to rational race improvement. The sentimental democrat will continue to whip himself into a fever of protest against any biological hierarchy of fit and less fit and least fit as a negation of the doctrine of equality. He will cry out, and the uncritical will listen, that science is setting up a new Calvinism that tears hope from the hearts of men by its ruthless predestinations. The traditional religionist will continue to execrate the counsels of biology, denouncing as hateful immorality what the biologist offers as a higher morality. Demagogic politics and dogmatic religion will fight the forces of race improvement at every turn. Refusing to underestimate these and allied forces of ignorance, inertia, and self-indulgence which dispute the advance of scientific social policy, the biologist is not sure that the peoples of the West will either sense or practice the necessary biological discrimination in time to prevent the biological bankruptcy towards which the present differential birth-rates of the fit and the unfit are heading Western civilization.

Even with the conscious control of reproduction making marked headway during the quarter century ahead, everything will depend upon the relative degrees of control developed among the more desirable and the less desirable classes. The problem is that of changing the present dangerous disparity between the birth-rates of the fit and the unfit. To correct this disparity, either the more desirable classes must radically lessen their control of reproduction or the less desirable classes must radically increase their control of reproduction. The conscious control of reproduction might make rapid headway quantitatively, but if the ratio of control among the unfit to control among the fit should remain approximately what it is now, the biological outlook of the West would not be materially changed. The effect would be simply a reduction in population bulk. The future of the Western peoples qualitatively depends upon a definite checking of the out-breeding of the fit by the unfit.

The biologist who seeks to see his problem entire must take into account the quantity of population as well as the quality of population. In considering the rate of world population growth, the biologist has had his fear somewhat mitigated by recent research, but, in his earlier contributions to the post-war literature of despair, he was obviously disturbed lest the increase in population should outstrip the increase in the means of subsistence. This is the fear that, in 1798, dictated Malthus's *Essay on the Principle of Population as It Affects the Future Improvement of Society*. The Malthus essay was written in revolt against the contentions of Rousseau, Condorcet, Godwin, and their colleagues in the doctrine of the indefinite perfectibility of man and his exclusive dependence for progress upon political institutions and social arrangements. Its argument was based upon the thesis that the achievement of a stable and significant civilization will always be blocked by the tendency of population to increase faster than the means of subsistence increase unless reproduction is subjected to rational control. This contention persisted in all the revisions that Malthus made down to 1816 when the text assumed the final form in which we now know it.

From the historical and philosophical points of view, the work of Malthus was, as I have suggested, a reaction against the easy optimism of the Rousseau school which, with its superficial grasp of the factors that condition human life, and with its facile formulas for social regeneration, informed the theory and instigated the action of the French Revolution. The Malthus contention was not new. In varying stages of formulation, it can be traced in the writings of Plato, Montesquieu, Robert Wallace, Benjamin Franklin, David Hume, Adam Smith, Richard Price, Arthur Young, and other lay and expert students of the population problem. But Malthus surrounded the contention with a wealth of data and gave it an impressiveness of statement that has kept it, down to our own time, an important influence in the study of population growth and its implications for the social and economic future of man.

The modern biologist has approached the problem of population with a richer equipment of information and investigational technique than Malthus was able to muster. An enormous amount of quantitative data, directly and indirectly bearing upon the population problem, has been made available during the last decade. The progressive perfection of the instrumentality of statistics has transformed the study of population problems. Since Malthus, transportation developments have enabled man to slip the tether of locality and race about the world in quest of food which formerly he had to find, if he found it at all, near at home. The chemist has evolved ways and means of supplementing with synthetic foods the more normal forms of the means of subsistence. Increasing impetus has been given to the propaganda for the conscious control of human reproduction. Although Malthus used the method of inductive reasoning from objective data that the modern scientist uses, the modern scientist considers the population problem from a broader fact base, with a perfected technique of investigation, and in terms of a radically changed world.

Calling upon the correlate sciences to help him in his examination of the population problem, the biologist supplements his own research with the results his colleagues have found in the fields of food chemistry, soil analysis and activation, crop production, agricultural economics, plant breeding, animal genetics, oceanography, and still other fields that impinge less obviously upon the biological province. In the light of an unprecedented amplitude of data, the biologist attacks crisply the questions: Will the baby supply outstrip the bread supply? Will population increase faster than the means of subsistence? Is Malthus still valid or is he a discredited soothsayer? Must man ultimately placard the planet with *Standing Room Only* signs?

The answers the biologists have given to these questions involve a wilderness of technical details I shall not attempt to invade here. The biological fraternity does not emerge from its studies with a solid front of judgment. Some late studies of the European population curve in terms of the age and sex composition of certain regions indicate the possibility of an increasingly sharp decline in the rate of population growth in these areas. The studies of Robert

R. Kuczynski, for instance, point towards a stationary, if not declining, population in Northern and Western Europe if the fecundity per woman of child-bearing age is not increased. The studies of Louis I. Dublin, long a critic of the statistical procedures and social predictions of the more Malthusian students of the population problem, point towards an approximately stationary American population by about 1950 or early in the latter half of the century. These and other contemporary population studies have thrown new doubt upon the dark prophecy of a world doomed to suffocation from over-crowding as a result of its rabbit-like rapidity of reproduction.

Whether later biological research, further changes in the social and economic factors affecting the birth-rate and the death-rate, technical developments in the field of food production, and more elaborate statistical studies of population growth will strike a body-blow at the old Malthusian fear cannot yet be said with certainty. There may be temporary post-war factors entering into the picture that a Kuczynski paints. It is difficult to make, with any feeling of assurance, statistically detailed prediction of the effect that reproduction control is likely to register in the curve of world population growth during the next quarter century. The current situation in areas that show a marked decline in the rate of population growth may be but an eddy in the main Malthusian current, although it must be admitted that these declines suggest a fundamental shift in tendency. The flattening or falling of the population curve at any given time may be but the later phase of a cycle of population growth, with imminent industrializations and culture factors in the offing that may induce another growth cycle that will leave the Malthusian fear valid for a longer run of generations.

Whatever change or confirmation further population studies may bring to biological judgment on population questions, the biologist, until recently, has looked to a Western future in which population would tend to increase faster than the means of subsistence. Before these later studies, to which I have referred, came to raise disturbing questions, he had not come upon any strictly biological factor that would lead him to think otherwise. And an examination of the extra-biological factors left him still Malthusian in his outlook. Neither in the possible increase in food production from the land nor in synthetic foods from the laboratory had the biologist seen an adequate offset to the tendency of the normal increase in population to outstrip the normal increase in the means of subsistence. He had foreseen the world politics of the next hundred years coming down to a race between the baby supply and the bread supply. Since the war, the American farmer has had to wrestle with crop surpluses rather than with food shortages, but to the biologist this had seemed a temporary result of economic mismanagement and maladjustment rather than a permanent adjournment of the age-old race between population and the means of subsistence.

A third phase of the biological fear arises from a consideration of the tension between the white races of the Occident and the colored races of the Orient. This aspect of the biological fear has been expressed less by responsible biologists than by certain camp followers of science who have stolen the patter of the laboratory to lend an air of importance to their sensational journalism. These observers are disturbed by what seems to them the weakening hold of the white races upon world supremacy. They consider the current political control of nine-tenths of the world by the white races as a delusive control. They decline to take the political map of the world too seriously. They think the racial map is more significant for the Western future. Without stopping to consider the soundness of their observations or to record the devastating criticism that has been directed against their statistical picture of the tempo of growth in the white and colored worlds, let me list what they say they see as they look at the racial map.

They see a world that is racially four-tenths white and

six-tenths colored. They see 31,000,000 square miles of
the world's surface given to the colored races as against
22,000,000 square miles given to the white races. They
see the white races outnumbered by the colored races by
about two to one. They see four-fifths of the whites concentrated in Europe which is less than one-fifth of the white
world's territorial area. They see the remaining one-fifth
of the whites scattered far and wide and undertaking to
protect the remaining four-fifths of the white world's
territorial area against the pressure of colored races that
outnumber this white one-fifth by about eleven to one.

As they bring collateral considerations to bear upon
their racial map reading, they see the white races weak
from the blood-letting of the World War. They see the
white world at loggerheads, less capable than ever of
common action against a common peril. They see the toler-
ation of economic conditions that tend to slow down the
marriage-rate and birth-rate of the directive classes of the
white world. And they see white solidarity further
menaced by a malevolent propaganda of social revolution.

When they turn from an examination of the status of
the white races to a survey of the mind and mood of the
colored races, they see a vast fund of bitterness that has
been built up against the white races for their having
preëmpted so much of the world's surface that the colored
races need and that the white races are not using to full
possibility. They see a sullen anger against the discrim-
inatory laws that the white races have levelled against the
colored peoples. They see the colored races looking with
an ominous glee upon the weakened and bickering state
of the white races as offering to the colored races their
opportunity to strike, sooner or later, for elbow-room and
equality. They see an Asian unity in which even the current Japanese-Chinese disunity will disappear.

All this that they see, or think they see, suggests to them
two fearful possibilities: (1) a vast race war in which the
existing dissensions of the colored world will merge in a

solid front against white world supremacy, or (2) a more
subtle but equally fateful infiltration of colored folk into
white lands. Let me sketch these two possibilities as they
lie in the minds of the observers I am here seeking to interpret.

The thinking of those who foresee an ultimate color
war runs somewhat as follows: Before the World War, five
despotic military empires existed—Germany, Austria,
Turkey, Russia, and Japan. At the end of the war, four
of these lay shattered. The Japanese Empire survived.
The next great issue in world politics will be the mastery of
the Pacific. Japan wants it. And the disintegration of the
old European order leaves her in an advantageous position
in the struggle for it. When this issue is joined, Japan may
not be contending single-handed for Pacific dominance.
Japan may be but the clenched fist of the long arm of Asia.
The Asian unity of their fears will then appear.

The thinking of those who foresee a subtle sapping of
the biological integrity of the white world by colored infiltration runs somewhat as follows: The white races are
biologically superior to the colored races. They must be
kept biologically segregate. The gates of the white world
must be locked against colored incomers. And behind exclusion walls that are unscalable, the white races must
breed themselves back to racial purity. This may mean
another world war, but such a war, say these frightened
readers of the racial map, is preferable to the slow suicide
of white civilization that seems inevitable to these white
knights errant unless the white and colored races are
severely segregated.

Out of the biological field, then, this triple-faced fear
has arisen: (1) the fear that the quality of the Western
peoples may go bankrupt through a disproportionate
survival of the unfit; (2) the fear that the increase in world
population may outrun the increase in the means of subsistence; and (3) the fear that the white races of the West
may go quickly down in a colossal clash of color or slowly

succumb to a subtle assault upon the biological integrity of the white world through colored infiltration into white lands.

*The Psychological Fear!*

The minds of the uncritical many have been harassed by elaborate fears of the moral and social incidence of the mechanistic and behavioristic theories that have flowered from the soil of psychological research and speculation. It is not these emotional panics of the traditionalist, when he hears of new hypotheses, that I have in mind when I speak of the psychological fear that animates an important section of the post-war literature of despair. I speak here of the single fear that the West is rapidly developing a crowd-civilization that increasingly standardizes thought and action in terms of crowd-moods and crowd-movements, the fear that the institution is submerging the individual to whom, after all, we must look for the initiation of sound social policy.

The psychologist sees the Western mind walking all too willingly into a strait-jacket. He sees the saving insurgency of the individual disappearing in a subtle surrender to the crowd-mind. He sees emerging a Western social order in which there will be no room for the rebel. And, since living conservatives owe most of the comforts and concepts that lift and light their lives to dead rebels, the psychologist throws a towering interrogation point against the Western future.

This fear of the submergence of the individual in the crowd is most keenly realized in time of war. When war falls upon a people, the individual is nothing, the crowd everything. It is rightly assumed that wars cannot be won by debating clubs that exalt dialectics above defence. War demands a swift and sure crowd-integration. When war looms, the crowd-mind grasps the scepter. The crowd ultimately dominates presidents and premiers, even when the statesmen in question are wedded by temperament and social philosophy to the processes of peace. Legislators, with a few flaming exceptions, bow to presidents and premiers. Editors surrender the hard-won freedom of the press, as if it were but a fair-weather right, and become rubber stamps of the military. Professors take leaves of absence from their scholarly judgments as well as from their chairs, and uncritically press-agent the war aims of their governments, quite regardless of whether the aims are dictated by cupidity or by conscience. Clergymen put their gospel in cold storage and hunt with the pack. The peace-time guardians of mind and morals sway drunkenly with the wine of war-time hysteria and join the witch burners. The thought of the nation is cut to a pattern. We give up thought as well as sugar for the duration of the war. When war comes, intelligence and morals are alike adjourned, and the mob-mind is supreme. And while war lasts, save for the abstentions of the saintly and the rebellions of the revolutionary, the judgment of the herd goes unchallenged.

The psychologist does not argue that this war-time submergence of the individual is unnecessary. One of the reasons he hates war is that he suspects that this exaltation of the mob-mind is necessary if modern men are to be led to fight modern wars with fervor and faith in their avowed objectives. The war-mind is doubly interesting to the psychologist because he sees in its selling of the individual into slavery to the crowd but a dramatization in the extreme of a process of impersonalization that goes on in peace time, even if a bit more subtly, throughout the West. And it is the peace-time conquests of the crowd-mind that most disturb the psychologist as he tries to read the Western future.

The psychologist sees Western man wrestling with one of the most difficult dilemmas of modern life. The personal freedom and hearty individualism of the frontier grow less and less possible in the complexity of a maturing society. The simplicity of our pioneer past meant less

elaborate enterprises, but it made possible a free-lance
life that men can hardly live, save by heroic renunciation,
in the highly organized and highly urbanized social order
of the modern West. Social simplicity makes for independence. Social complexity forces interdependence. The
modern West functions increasingly through orders and
organizations and associations that express the crowd-
principle in their purposes and in their procedures. Western man finds himself more and more under crowd-com-
pulsions. The weak man joins the crowd to hide his
incapacity. But even the strong man, with more than
ordinary capacity and character, is almost irresistibly
driven to join the crowd to gain effective leverage in the
affairs of his time. The weak man, happy to escape his
erstwhile sense of impotence, struts in the borrowed
feathers of group-prestige. The strong man, eager to
augment his sense of strength, sets calmly out to utilize
the power of the group as a supplemental aid to achievement.

It is here that the great paradox of a crowd-ruled civilization appears. As a stock-holder in the massed power of
the crowd, Western man is at once a man of greater
strength and less self-respect. Certainly he has less self-
reliance. He cannot live aloof from organization, unless
he is willing to be a kind of St. Francis of the boulevards,
stripped of most of the comfort and prestige to which the
conventional aspire, but, once in the crowd, he finds the
crowd-mind towering and tyrannizing over him.

Under these circumstances, he is all too likely to become
a sleek conformist, a cynical slacker, or a sullen revolutionist. Finding the road to professional power reserved, in
the main, for the regulars, whatever dreams of originality
of mind or motive he may have had he locks away with the
trinkets and toys of his immaturity, and proceeds to play
the game by the crowd-established rules. Finding political
independence an adventure in loneliness and ostracism, he
turns in disgust from any active concern in the social de-

velopment of his time. Finding business and industry increasingly vast and impersonalized machines, he listens sympathetically to undiscriminatingly wholesale denunciations of modern industrialism, and joins the army of the chronic malcontents. The cowardice of the conformist! The cynicism of the slacker! The sullenness of the revolutionist! The West can ill afford to entrust its future to men animated by these moods. And yet the increasing crowd-mindedness of the contemporary West is daily driving millions of men into just these moods. The psychologist cannot feel confident of the future of a civilization that does not throw adequate protection around the free minds of its first-class men. The free minds of first-class men can build a great and glowing civilization. The crowd-mind cannot.

The free mind of the first-class man knows no loyalty higher than loyalty to the truth which it seeks to see clearly and without bias in the dry light of facts. The free mind of the first-class man resists enslavement to passion and to prejudice, brings to the bar of disinterested judgment the pleas of all parties and of all powers, and ceaselessly searches out the motives that coin the catchwords of all classes, all cliques, and all clans. The free mind of the first-class man turns a deaf ear alike to democracy when it grows sentimental and to plutocracy when it grows selfish. The free mind of the first-class man is independent alike of tyrannical majorities and of tirading minorities when the truth happens to abide in neither. The free mind of the first-class man inspires its motives with sincerity and informs its methods with science. The free mind of the first-class man serves the crowd without flattering it and believes in it without bowing to its idolatries.

Of course freedom will not generate these virtues in the minds of blockheads and bounders, but these are the virtues that mark the free mind of the first-class man. The West must, the psychologist thinks, protect its first-class men from the now subtle and now swaggering tyranny of the crowd-mind. Unless a civilization deliberately nourishes intellectual independence and guarantees to its first-class men the utmost feasible autonomy of opinion and action, it must rest content with the sterility of a standardized social order. And a great civilization will know its first-class men when it sees them, whether they happen to be at the moment riding in the engines of prestige and power or trudging disinherited down the tracks. The West must, as the psychologist sees it, recover its lost sense of the central significance of the individual. For crowd-dominance means death to a creative civilization.

The crowd-mind is at every point a treacherous guide. More than twenty years ago, in his *Social Psychology*, which I wrestled with as an undergraduate, Edward Alsworth Ross charged the crowd-mind with instability, credulity, irrationality, simplicity, and immorality. Research in the field of social psychology has reversed some of the conceptions that were current and convincing twenty years ago, but the two decades of Western experience that have since gone by have not invalidated this five-fold indictment of the crowd.

The crowd-mind *is* unstable. It falls an easy victim to emotional epidemics. It is whipped about by every wind of doctrine. It is easily bamboozled by the designing. The crowd-mind *is* credulous. The demagogue can impose upon it dogmas that would never pass muster before the mind of the straight-thinking individual. It rarely prods about the foundations of an idea it is asked to accept. It is not given to cross-examining programs it is asked to support. The crowd-mind *is* irrational. It feels rather than thinks. It does not reason from cause to effect when faced by a situation upon which it must pass judgment. The crowd-mind *is* simple. It thinks in catch-words. It is baffled by complexities. It over-simplifies both the diseases and the remedies of its time. And it is impatient of men who tell it that social issues are never as simple as the slogans that grow up around them. The crowd-mind *is* immoral. It lacks a sense of moral responsibility for its conclusions. The crowd will indulge in judgments and actions against which the majority of its members, if acting independently, would revolt as basically indefensible.

The psychologist recognizes to the full the impracticability of an anarchic individualism in a necessarily interdependent society, but he insists nevertheless that the current crowdizing of the Western mind is driving even strong men into an uncritical boot-licking of the powers that be which cannot but mean a drying up of the wellsprings of social creativeness. For it is only through the free minds of first-class men that we can keep a stream of creative thought playing upon the social issues in the solution of which the secret of the Western future lies locked. A bridge can safely vibrate only within its vibration limit. If you bring to bear upon it an intensity of vibration beyond this vibration limit, the structure will totter. And if this over-intensity of vibration is kept up long enough, the structure may be literally shaken to pieces. Regiments of soldiers crossing a bridge do not march in step lest the incessant rhythm of their tramping produce an intensity of vibration that might bring the bridge to collapse. The psychologist sees Western civilization as a bridge we have built from anarchy to order, and he suspects that the movement of our minds across this civilization may be not unlike the movement of soldiers across a bridge. If we permit the crowd to regiment our minds into the rhythmic regularity of the goose-step, we may bring this bridge of civilization to collapse.

The psychologist finds his study-table swamped with a mounting mass of evidence that the crowd-mind grows annually more proficient in goose-stepping the individual. As he turns his field-glass on the Western future, he sees the probability of an increasing release rather than an increasing restraint of the crowd-mind. Three considerations make him skeptical that Western man will preserve that creative individualism which is essential to his social future.

In the first place, the psychologist sees the modern West making it possible for the crowd-mind to function without crowd-contact. The West has elaborated astounding instruments of communication. Radio! The talking film! Television! The newspaper that even the pennies of the poor may buy! And allied agencies for the quick transference of ideas and emotions! These have created a new kind of mob that endangers the Western future more than the old kind of mob ever endangered the Western past. The new mob need not meet in one place to have its emotions recruited by some Robespierre of the rostrum. The soap-box joins the town crier in the limbo of the obsolete. The members of the new mob sit severally before a syndicated talking screen here and there and yonder. They may listen in at the radios of a million homes and halls. They may read the head-lines of revolution or reaction which are alike designed to create a crowd-mind. And before long television may bring to the uncritical millions, with a sense of personal contact that even the talking film cannot convey, the rabble-rousings alike of the red radicals and of the red reactionaries, assuming that the radicals will ever gain much access to such nation-wide agencies of communication. These and like devices have enabled the mob to dispense with dramatic assemblies. With these new instruments of facile communication, and with the lately developed techniques of propaganda, the new mob-master may sell his ideas quickly to millions who would never take the trouble to attend a mass meeting. The old mobs were local affairs and, at worst, did no more than wound a few participants and bystanders. The new mob without a meeting place may stab the mind of a whole people before the people is aware of the attack. The psychologist sees these tools of communication and techniques of propaganda making for a fuller and fuller release of the crowd-mind. That the radio, for instance, demands a less flamboyant mode of speech than marked the old mob-master does not seem to the psychologist to alter the case. Men who have a vested interest in the maintenance of crowd-mindedness will, he thinks, master the new technique and bend it to their purposes.

In the second place, the psychologist sees the modern West progressively stripping the individual of his protective coverings. With the perfection of television, reducing the transmission of the face as well as the phrases of the speaker to the commonplaceness of an ordinary telephone conversation, the psychologist sees the end of isolation for men, for communities, and for nations. The man in the far frontier cabin will be at the ringside of the world's events. In time to come, it is said, the backwoodsman will be able to attend the coronation of a king on the other side of the world more easily than he now attends a county fair ten miles away. This is generally hailed as a hopeful emancipation of man from his erstwhile slavery to distance. The boundaries of his interests will, it is said, be pushed out. His mind will be fertilized by ideas and impressions from a thousand hitherto sealed sources. The psychologist is not so sure that all this will mean the expansion of the individual. It may mean his extinction.

When television makes even the walls of our homes transparent, may we not become a race of self-conscious poseurs? What will happen to our sincerity when we have to keep our company manners at all hours of the day and night? Will all the West become a stage on which we shall all be actors, without even an off-stage hiding place between acts? May not the temptation to play constantly for the regard of the crowd prove more powerful than ever? I put the theoretical possibilities of television extravagantly, not in sober prediction of television developments, but to enforce a point. Television may at least be taken as a dramatic symbol of the new nakedness of modern life. The house of the modern Westerner is no longer his castle. His birth, his marriage, his income-tax return, his

death must all be registered. More and more his enterprise must run in lanes fixed and fenced by legislation.
Every year still other inspectors are set on his trail to
keep track of what he thinks and what he drinks. Modern
journalism is less and less a respecter of the privacy of the
individual. Many of these invasions of the old individualism are in the interest of sounder social control, but this
does not, as the psychologist sees it, do away with the fact
that these increasing invasions of privacy are giving the
crowd freer and freer access to the opinions and actions
of the individual. And the more the crowd knows about
the individual, the more powerfully tempted the individual is to conform to the passions and policies of the
crowd.

In the third place, the psychologist sees Western education doing less than it might to manacle the mind of
the mob. He knows that the only sure safeguard against
the new mob lies in a drastically reformed education. If
the millions of young men and young women passing
through our schools are to be saved from servility to the
crowd-mind, they must be trained in the use of their judgments. But any discipline of judgment that is to be socially fruitful is impossible unless schools stimulate in
their students an eagerness and expertness in cross-
examining the beliefs they have brought to the school-
room and the bases of the social order that surrounds the
school-room. The schools must make this cross-examina-
tion of the social environment and inherited beliefs of their
students the binding thread of the educational process.
This is far from an easy enterprise. It means turning
schools into breeding-grounds of doubts. And this hardly
adds to the comfort and popularity of teachers and
administrators. The disconcerting raiser of doubts is
the only man who can save the West from the crowd-
minded rule of the mob, but the psychologist sees the
schools of the West more inclined to staff themselves with
belief-peddlers than with doubt-raisers. The schools of

the West are readier to support a press-agent than to sub-
sidize a Socrates. The psychologist sees the majority of
our sons and daughters coming out of our schools regrettably incurious about the fundamental policies that underlie the civilization whose insecurity to-day threatens their
future. And he thinks he sees why this is.

The schools of the West are controlled by adults who
are dominated, in the main, by points of view that came
out of the education of another generation when Western
civilization did not face many of the issues that now beset
and baffle it. Unless the schools of the West can be made
more adventurous than the adults who create, conduct,
and control them, the psychologist sees little hope of establishing an effective restraint of the crowd-mind. And he is
more than a bit skeptical that adults, who do not themselves go beyond an uncritical acquiescence in the *status
quo,* will either invent or tolerate schools that make for
a continuously critical reassessment of their ideas, their
ideals, and their institutions. Although it is sun-clear to
the psychologist that reactionaries have even more at
stake than radicals in the creation of schools that cultivate
a responsibly critical attitude towards the folkways of the
time. For it has invariably been the social orders that
have smothered criticism and sought to manufacture men's
opinions from above that have fallen with the most ruinous results. The standardizations of the crowd-mind may,
for a time, prove powerful safeguards of vested interests,
but, in the end, they always prove fragile reeds upon which
to lean.

The psychologist knows, of course, that the current concern with adult education looks to the creation of a more
flexible adult mind to the end that the schools of the West
may stop compounding the conservatisms of succeeding
generations and become in fact, as they are in theory, the
nurseries of an intellectual individualism that is at once
disciplined and free. But the psychologist has not allowed
himself to be hustled into a premature optimism regard-

ing the adult education movement as a restraint on the crowd-mindedness of the modern West. He fears that the bustling organizers, with their passion to create a world-wide movement over-night, may do little more than lift over into the field of adult education all too many of the futilities and formalisms that to-day hamstring so much of the conventional schooling of the West.

Here, then, are the three phases of the psychological fear that animates some of the more somber sections of the post-war literature of despair: (1) the fear that a growing crowd-mindedness may seal the sources of free and creative thought on the more crucial issues of Western life; (2) the fear that improved instruments of communication and perfected techniques of propaganda may give greater and greater ascendancy to the forces of crowd-mindedness; and (3) the fear that Western education may not live up to its responsibility for producing not only expertness of mind for the technical tasks of the world's work, but that emancipation of mind which alone can restrain these forces of crowd-mindedness that paralyze social inventiveness and produce a social order that is standardized and sterile.

### The Political Fear!

As he seeks to forecast the future of the self-governing peoples of the West, the student of statecraft is disturbed by the stubborn reluctance of Western democracies to re-adjust the forms and functions of their governments to meet the changed and changing needs of the Western social order. He suspects that we Westerners are, in the main, political illiterates. Despite our noisy devotion to the dogmas of popular government, we are not politically minded. We may display a short-lived interest in dramatic issues and give a fleeting loyalty to picturesque political personalities, we may for a season follow the bright oriflamme of some brave reform movement, as bored wives embrace a current cult, but we lack a sustained interest in

the undramatic enterprise of a continuously wise and adaptable administration of our common life. With most of us,
it takes a case of clumsy treason or high-pressure stimulation of a campaign to focus our interest on government.
We are politically lazy. The way of least resistance is the
main boulevard of Western politics.

The student of statecraft is disturbed by the extent to
which Western civilization, in general, and American civilization, in particular, fosters a political fundamentalism
that would withdraw from effective criticism all of the
ideas and institutions of the *status quo*. From his wide-
sweeping studies of political history, the student of statecraft knows that a democracy must maintain a relentlessly
critical reassessment of its theory and practice if it is to
keep continuously fit to handle its ever-changing agenda of
problems and make itself, as nearly as possible, invulner-
able to the materialists who seek to rob it and the muddlers
who seek to run it. He knows that when the constitutions
and institutions of government are withdrawn from criticism and made sacrosanct the stage is set for corruption
and catastrophe. And, particularly in the United States,
the student of statecraft finds this essential enterprise of
political criticism, which should be most ardently prosecuted in the inner councils of practical politics, pretty generally blocked and bowed out by Bourbons who are either
unable or unwilling to see the difference between social
discontent with government and scientific discontent with
government.

Social discontent with government may be but a blind
and inarticulate rage against a leadership that has blundered in its job. Social discontent is dangerous because it
acts in a mood of anger. And men do not make great
civilizations while they are mad. Social discontent brews
when things go bad. It is a child of storm. Scientific discontent, on the other hand, functions in fair weather as well
as foul. It does not wait for catastrophe to stir it to critical study. It undertakes to detect and do away with the

obsolete before it becomes obvious to the uncritical many. It is the child of reason rather than the offspring of rage. Scientific discontent with government is preventive statesmanship. Its practitioners know that the time to stop a revolution is a hundred years before it starts. Its objective is to keep the tools of government adjusted to the tasks of government. Its most difficult problem is the cultivation in men of a willingness to change the tools when the tasks change. Scientific discontent immunizes a people against social discontent, not by inoculating men with subservience or simpering optimism, but by keeping the policies of the political order intelligently adapted to the problems of the social order. The student of statecraft is worried over the Western future as he sees men and women, whose scientific discontent means simply their determination to make government intelligently adaptable to changing conditions, hounded and harassed by a political Bourbonism that lumps such men and women together with the hooligans of demagogic insurrection. For the West is obviously entering an era in which governments insensitive to the needs of a changing social order will not survive!

The student of statecraft knows that democracy is by no means the regnant religion it once was. He knows the acid criticism that has lately corroded the democratic dogma. He knows the dramatic secessions from democracy that have marked the post-war politics of the West. But he does not take the surface news too seriously. He sees dictatorships as intermittent reactions against democracy when it runs amuck. But he finds democracy running increasingly amuck throughout the West. Convinced that he is right in his two seemingly incompatible assumptions that, save for occasional backslidings into dictatorship, Western man will long cling with an uncritical tenacity to democracy, in shadow if not in substance, and that democracy, as currently conceived and carried out in the Western nations, has many rusted links in its armor, the student of statecraft believes that the paramount political problem of the West is not the renunciation but the revision of democracy.

In such Western nations as the United States, the student of statecraft sees democracy entering a new phase. Political America has reached the end of the quantitative extension of democracy. We are now a ballot-blessed people entire. Political America must now undertake the qualitative development of democracy. It is upon the threshold of this new phase of the democratic experiment that a great fear chills the heart of the student of statecraft. Will democracy rise to the demands of this phase of qualitative development? Some think not. And these doubting Thomases of political science are detailed in the defence of their doubts. They see democracy in the United States, for instance, facing eight specific challenges which, in its failure to be ruthlessly self-critical, it shows little sign of meeting decisively and creatively: (1) the challenge of science; (2) the challenge of distance; (3) the challenge of technology; (4) the challenge of nomadism; (5) the challenge of the majority; (6) the challenge of party; (7) the challenge of leadership; and (8) the challenge of revolution. Let me define and discuss, in turn, these eight Sphinx-riddles that the political prophets of doom doubt democracy will answer with the requisite promptness and adequacy.

The challenge of science to democracy is this: The life of the modern West has been largely created by science. That is to say, the machine economy of the West, the whole material set-up of Western life, and Western man's attitude towards his non-political interests have been more profoundly affected by science than by any other force. But the public affairs of the West are, ordinarily and in large measure, controlled by democracy. At some risk of over-simplification, it may be said that the modern West has been created by the spirit of science but is being controlled by the spirit of democracy. And the future of the West will depend upon the working relationship that Western man establishes between these two spirits. The future will be bright if they collaborate. The future will be black if they conflict. The student of statecraft is more fearful of conflict than he is hopeful of collaboration.

The student of statecraft is doubtful that science and democracy will coöperate in the creation of a viable and valid social order because their motives and their methods have seemed at such wide variance. In his moments of deepest disillusionment with the current politics of the West, here is the picture that the competing forces of science and democracy have presented to the student of statecraft: Science thinks in terms of the laboratory. Democracy thinks in terms of the legislature. Science is on the hunt for verities. Democracy is on the hunt for votes. Science rests its case on experimentation. Democracy rests its case on exhortation. Science works from facts to policy. Democracy works from policy to facts. Science tests its conclusions by their precision. Democracy tests its conclusions by their popularity. Science trusts the expert. Democracy distrusts the expert. Science is in the business of creating power. Democracy is in the business of controlling power. Science is interested in the advance of intelligence. Democracy is interested in the accumulation of influence. Science is emancipated from catch-words and labels. Democracy is enslaved by catch-words and labels. Science bases its social philosophy on the biological inequality of men. Democracy bases its social philosophy on the political equality of men. Science exalts the exceptional man. Democracy exalts the average man. And so on to the end of a long list of actual or apparent antagonisms between the spirit of science and the spirit of democracy!

The student of statecraft fears that these two titanic forces of science and democracy may cancel each other and leave the Western future robbed of the possible contributions of both. He is aware that many of the existing antagonisms between science and democracy are due neither

to anything inherent in science nor to anything inherent
in democracy but to a perversion of politics. He does not
consider it impossible, but thinks it improbable, that Western man will bridge this chasm between science and democracy by creating a new politics that will be simply his technique for bringing the world's knowledge to the service
of the world's life. He is something less than hopeful
that the laboratory will supplant the log-roller in Western
politics. He suspects that the knowledge of the scientist
will continue to languish for lack of political power, and
the power of the politician continue to run amuck for
lack of scientific knowledge.

The challenge of distance to democracy is this: Can
democracy, however admirably adapted to the administration of a small society, effectively direct the affairs of a
society vast in numbers and widespread in territory? Many
of the national populations of the West run into millions
multiplied, and the outstanding Western nations govern
extensive territories. What happens to civilization, in
general, and to democracy, in particular, when nations
extend their boundaries beyond a certain point? Was H. G.
Wells right when he suggested that democracy dies five
miles from the parish pump?

The greatest civilizations and the most effective democracies have flowered from small areas. The majesty of
ancient Greece was born in a tiny territory. The Greece
of ancient greatness is dead, but, being dead, her intrinsic
quality still lives to water the parched roots of the world's
culture and the world's conscience, whereas the more bulky
civilizations of antiquity have died of dropsy and left a
doubtful heritage. The smaller the society the more effectively democracy has worked. The larger the society
the less effectively democracy has worked.

The student of statecraft thinks that we Americans have
yet to realize the profound influence that the sheer extent
of American territory is exerting on American thought
and American politics. One effect is obvious. Save in mo-

ments of great crisis, the wide sweep of our territory makes
it almost impossible for political leadership to get us to
think nationally and to achieve national unity of purpose
or policy. The sprawled-outness of the United States in-
clines us to think regionally instead of nationally. There
is an Eastern mindedness. There is a Southern mindedness.
There is a Middle Western mindedness. There is a North
Western mindedness. And so on. If we doubt the reality
of these regional minds, we need but to watch the national
committeemen of the Republican and Democratic parties
as they wrestle with these rebellious localisms which
strain at the leash of party regularity. These regional
minds are still pretty docile when the pinch comes in a
national election. To date, their bark has been worse than
their bite. Traditional loyalties die hard. Established political parties can usually count ancestry and inertia among
their most dependable allies. But the existence of these
regional minds is a fact with which the student of statecraft must reckon as he tries to forecast the American
future.

We do think nationally about certain things and under
certain circumstances. We are masters of an advertising technique that can make a breakfast food, a tooth
paste, or a garter a household word throughout America.
And we do, once in a blue moon, pull ourselves together
and think all at once about political policy, provided the
policy is dramatically linked with the crowning or cruci-
fixion of some nationally known leader, so that we can
register our verdict with a simple hiss or hurrah. But, save
in times of crisis, it is very difficult for political leadership
to focus the attention of this entire people on a statesmanlike political program.

The problem of making government effective over
swarming populations and sweeping territories has always
troubled political philosophers. Before the latter part
of the eighteenth century few could be found who considered republicanism or democracy workable save in states

that were small in population and restricted in territory. The student of statecraft has thrown overboard many of the political notions of Machiavelli, Montesquieu, Rousseau, and their like, but he suspects that they were right in their contention that republicanism and its democratic variants are subject to serious limitations of scale. The ancients recognized this difficulty. Xenophon speaks in amazement of the sure-handed control Cyrus exercised over his subjects "though some of them dwelt at a distance which it would take days and months to traverse, and among them were men who had never set eyes on him, and for the matter of that could never hope to do so." The only way in which this Greek commentator could reconcile the dominance of Cyrus with the distance of his subjects was on the grounds that "Cyrus was able so to penetrate that vast extent of country by the sheer terror of his personality that the inhabitants were prostrate before him." Even if Xenophon's explanation were not half in his fancy, we could hardly dismiss the challenge that distance flings to contemporary democracy with a prayer for statesmen with a Cyrus-like death-ray in their eye. We must meet the issue of distance more realistically.

Political leadership may some day fashion the now peril-laden processes of propaganda into a social tool of national value. But we must remember that there is danger as well as promise in any methods and machinery we may devise for spreading ideas quickly over vast masses of people. Our very success with them might mean only an increasing standardization of American thought. And the student of statecraft suspects that a nation's thought would better be scrappy than standardized. It is still an open question whether we can nationalize some 123,000,-000 minds without numbing them. The radio, the talking film, television, and unsuspected journalistic developments may in time overcome the paralyzing effect of distance on the struggle for national mindedness. But the student of statecraft shares with the psychologist the fear that these new instruments of communication may be so mishandled that they will but muster a new mob mindedness.

The challenge of technology to democracy is this: In nations like the United States, democracy devised its techniques of government and determined the bases of its systems of representation in terms of an agricultural civilization in which the problems of government were simple and the interests of its citizens similar. In the generations since, physical science and industrial technology have radically changed the stage-setting of politics. The current social and economic order is not at all like the social and economic order the existing techniques of government and systems of representation were designed to serve. In this evolution from an agricultural civilization to a technical civilization, there has been a marked political lag. The tools of government have not been kept adjusted to the tasks of government. And the result is that, pretty generally throughout the West and dramatically in the United States, an old political order is attempting in fumbling fashion to administer a new social order.

The student of statecraft knows that when, as in the United States, political leadership isolates government from the other and deeper forces of the time, and fails to correlate it with them, government will be at best blundering and at worst corrupt and disintegrative. It is this that he has seen happening throughout the West. It is illuminating to follow, somewhat in detail, the student of statecraft as he analyzes, in terms of American political life, the challenge that a technical civilization is putting to democratic representative government.

The agricultural era of American civilization gives the student of statecraft his starting point. The first fact that strikes him full in the face is the fact that all of the main patterns of American politics were formed when we were a small nation, populating a relatively narrow band of territory along the Atlantic seaboard. The social order was predominantly agricultural. Large-scale business and industry had not entered the picture. Physical science and industrial technology were still imprisoned in the brains of the lonely investigator and the erratic inventor. Science and technology had not then recruited their army of researchers or reached the point of wholesale practical application. Even well into the technologic era, whatever sizeable enterprises existed were essentially family affairs, in the matter of ownership, and, in the matter of management, were usually captained by the blustering, buccaneering, improvising, pioneer type of business man who played his hunches in blissful disdain of the scientific and technological forces that have since produced the machine economy of the West.

The problems of government were simple in this initial phase of American civilization. The functions of government were simply conceived. The government of the United States was originally charged with the limited function of protecting American citizens in their rights and in their liberties. It was not so much designed to do things for its citizens as to safeguard them in a freedom to conduct their lives and their enterprises in their own way, subject only to the irreducible minimum of restrictions necessary to safeguard the general interests of the community at large. The correlate political documents of the time indicate that the constitutional promise to "promote the general welfare" was considered by the makers of the Constitution as largely a by-product of the promise to protect American citizens in their exercise of the utmost feasible freedom. These simple problems in protection could be met by men of ordinary intelligence and ordinary executive capacity. Government was not then obliged to wrestle with the complicated social and economic tasks that have since been committed to it.

The interests of citizens were similar in this initial phase of American civilization. The interests of the rank and file of Americans were the interests of small-scale agriculturalists. And the interests of the professional men of the time

were the interests of men who served small-scale agriculturalists. When men entered the Governor's Chamber,
the House of Representatives, the Senate, the Cabinet,
or the White House, they entered with the sense that they
were representing constituencies that were not torn asunder
by a complexity of conflicting interests. They were not
subjected to the savage cross-fire of competing economic
groups, each with its separate stake in government. There
were, of course, broad cleavages of economic interest even
then, but nothing like the multitudinous array of grasping
groups that to-day level their but thinly disguised blackmail against political leadership. In these simpler days,
almost any honest and generally capable man could represent with decent adequacy the interests of all his constituents, for their interests were, in the main, his interests.
And these interests were not so complex as to over-tax
the ordinary unspecialized good judgment of a sensible
man. The geographical basis of representation was thus
admirably adapted to this early phase of American civilization when states and political districts did not present
much diversity of interests.

Physical science, industrial technology, and specialization in enterprise have completely changed this picture.
The agricultural phase of American civilization has been
brought to a definitive end by this trilogy of forces. The
technologic phase is well under way. And even the more
obvious differences between the initial and the current
phases of American development involve profound political implications. We are no longer a small nation. We
are a large nation. We are no longer an agricultural people
alone. We are an industrial people as well. The pattern
of our common life is no longer clear. It is confused by a
hundred and one contradictory lines that the immature
forces of the technologic age are drawing across it. The
problems of government are no longer simple. They grow
increasingly complex. The interests of men are no longer
similar. They come increasingly into conflict. The upshot

of all this is that our present social order bears little, if any, resemblance to the social order our political system was designed to serve.

It was a relatively easy matter to make representative government work in the initial era of American life when the problems of government were simple and the interests of men similar. It is a far more difficult matter to make representative government work in this technologic era when the problems of government are complex and the interests of men in conflict. Every year the problems with which government must deal grow more technical and less political in the older sense of politics. Every year the honest and intelligent amateur, who would have been an ideal political representative in the agricultural era, finds his equipment less and less adequate for the intricate enterprise of statesmanship in the technologic era. His plight becomes increasingly pathetic. His difficulties are, in large part, due to the fact that an old political order, designed to serve an agricultural civilization, is trying to administer a new social order, developed by a technical civilization. Tension between the two is everywhere evident from the politics of the neighborhood to the politics of the nation. And the outcome of this tension between the old political order and the new social order will, in no small measure, determine the progress or decline of American civilization which, in intenser terms, but dramatizes the problem of Western civilization as a whole.

As the student of statecraft visits Washington, he sees the virile forces of this new technical civilization straining against the theories and techniques of a political system that flowered from the soil of a non-technical civilization. The text-books on civil government, that the student of statecraft studied as a boy, told him that the legislative branch of the government was bi-cameral, that Congress was composed of two chambers or two houses. The Senate! The House of Representatives! For a long time he naïvely believed this. Political science, if its text-books are to be taken seriously, long went on the assumption that government in outline and government in action were the same. But latter-day political scientists are more interested in government as it is than in government as it is supposed to be. And now, when the student of statecraft visits Washington, he sees that the national legislature is not bi-cameral, but tri-cameral, that Congress is composed not of two houses but of three. The Senate! The House of Representatives! And a third house that is not even mentioned in the Constitution. In the special sense in which the student of statecraft sees it, this third house might, with measurable accuracy, be called The House of Technologists, for its members are in Washington to represent the forces of the new technical civilization that has arisen since the patterns of American politics were formed by the founders of the Republic. It represents the forces of our technical civilization sometimes blunderingly, sometimes selfishly, but it is nevertheless their national voice in a sense that neither the Senate nor the House of Representatives is.

This third house is new in form but not in fact. It has existed in one form or another since the beginning of our government. It was once no more than the old secret lobbies that played such a picturesque and powerful rôle in national legislation in those marauding days before the muckraking era. It was then but the crude instrument of plunder used by a business system that was still in its pioneer phase. In that form the third house interested the police power, but it carried little significance for the student of statecraft, save as he saw in it a threat to honest government. After a while an aroused public opinion swung the sword of blame against these lobbies and drove them out of Washington or, at least, further underground. And during the last decade or two this third house has assumed a more open and a more politically significant form.

To-day there is hardly a basic social or economic interest of the American people that is not represented by some highly organized occupational group that maintains expertly staffed headquarters in Washington. These expert staffs are not there as secret lobbies. They are there openly and aboveboard to represent their constituencies. They are not there to represent the conglomerate interests of a Congressional district. They are there to represent the clear-cut interests of this or that functional group. Business! Labor! Agriculture! And so on. The expert staffs of these national, occupational-group headquarters together constitute, in effect, a third house of Congress. With this difference: while the Senators and Representatives are officially elected on a geographical basis of representation, the members of this third house are unofficially selected on an occupational basis of representation.

Beyond the service that these national headquarters staffs render to purely selfish group interests, their existence suggests to the student of statecraft that the new social order, reflecting our technical economy, is instinctively feeling its way towards newer forms of representation that will bring to the current problems of government an intensity of interest and expertness of information that the old political system, born of an agricultural economy, does not guarantee. He suspects that as long as these expert representations of group interests are left lingering in the suburbs of government as but slightly fumigated agencies of lobbying their constant temptation will be to degenerate into nothing more significant than lobbies for limited group interests. He thinks a creative statesmanship might make them a point of departure for bringing into government expert representatives of the technical interests of the occupational groups of the country to supplement the amateur representatives of the general interests of the geographical areas of the country.

The student of statecraft thinks it is less than sincere for us to bring an idolatrous reverence to the Constitution, daring unholy hands to touch it with profane suggestions of fundamental change, while we are daily worm-

ing our way around its official scheme of geographical
representation with this unofficial scheme of occupational
representation. He is aware of the suggestion that we
should look upon lobbying as a necessary and respectable
method of bringing expert information before legislators,
who should content themselves with the rôle of referee
between competing experts, passing judgment on the evidence the lobbyists lay openly before them. As he thinks
of the intellectual quality and informational background
of the political leadership that the democratic processes of
selection and election, in the main, throw up, the student
of statecraft is skeptical of the assumption that this sort
of amateur refereeship can prove equal to the social management of a technical civilization.

The student of statecraft sees our technical civilization
calling for a kind of political leadership that democracy
is not habitually providing. He doubts that a technical
civilization can ever secure political servants, adequately
equipped to deal with its complexity of issues, until its
political procedures provide representation of the technical
interests of occupational groups as well as representation
of the general interests of geographical areas. But he sees
almost insurmountable obstacles to any such drastic reform
of the representative system in a nation like the United
States where a suggestion that certain aspects of the Constitution may be obsolete is, in the minds of many, equivalent to spitting on the flag.

The challenge of nomadism to democracy is this: The
theories and techniques of democracy in the United States,
let us say, were elaborated in terms of a settled people
that, despite the westward trek it was later to take in its
conquest of the continent, had outgrown the wandering
habits of hunter and herdsman, and was ready to set up
and to support social and political institutions that would
protect and promote the near-at-hand interests of its day-
to-day life and enterprise. But the technical forces of
facile transportation and far-flung economic enterprise

have radically altered this picture. The average American
is to-day but loosely rooted in any particular soil. He is a
come-and-go creature. He is less and less likely to live
and work and die in the locality of his birth. The old
homestead, with its unbroken continuity of local loyalties,
local interests, and local traditions, is a fading memory.
The modern American may be born in Massachusetts,
educated in Wisconsin, married in Virginia, harnessed to
a business career in Colorado, finally to die in California,
with children scattered to the four corners and on the
seven seas of the world. And even when the modern American lives out his entire life in the locality of his birth, his
major interests may be scattered throughout the nation
and the world.

Since the dawn of the technologic era, a steady delocalization of men's loyalties and interests has been under way.
In figurative terms, we have broken camp and begun
wandering again, as men wandered before they had evolved
the institutions or elaborated the constitutions of localized
governments. We pitch our tents for a time here and there
and yonder. We have shaken off the restraints of resi-
dence. An air of the tentative hovers, in consequence, over
everything American. We are satisfied with structural
shoddiness in our suburban building developments because
the mood of permanence is not ours. Along the canyons
of commerce we build towering buildings only to hustle
them off the scene a few years hence to make room for
still taller buildings. We are untethered and mobile. We
have ourselves turned nomadic again, and our interests are
no longer realistically related to such political units as
cities, states, and nations. The student of statecraft sees
this new nomadism of the technologic era creating new
difficulties of political mood and political organization.

The political mood of the new nomad does not augur
well for the future of Western democracy. The new
nomadism means that greater and greater numbers of
Americans, in particular, and of Westerners, in general,

lack that informed intensity of interest in government that marked the man of the pre-technologic era who, unless abnormally touched with the lust to wander, stayed put for a lifetime. The man who stays put for a lifetime is daily reminded that it is but intelligent self-interest to pay attention to the administration of the city, state, or nation that is to be his permanent environment. But men do not sit up nights worrying over the politics of a place they are likely to leave before another year rolls around. And so, in this unleashed generation, the social irresponsibility of the rovers of pre-political days reappears at a time when the complexity and interdependence of life make it perilous. Men are uprooted and politically listless. It is increasingly difficult to pin them down politically.

The political organization created in the agricultural era steadily loses reality as a result of the increasing mobility of modern enterprise. Greater and greater numbers of Americans, in particular, and of Westerners, in general, find such political units as cities, states, and nations meaning less and less to them, because their major interests are no longer concentrated in such circumscribed areas. There is a fatal disconnection between the organization chart of the American political order and the actual life processes of the socio-economic order that reflects the day-to-day enterprise of modern Americans. The geographical areas that we call states, bounded by arbitrary or accidental lines drawn on a map, no longer represent distinctive social or economic interests. Our states are not regions in which a special language, a special religion, a special culture, or a special economic life sets them apart from neighboring states. There are picturesque differences of dialect and demeanor between various sections of the United States, but, by and large, our states are highly artificial units. One has but to cross the line that separates, say, Missouri from Iowa to realize this. There is hardly an interest around which the daily lives of modern Americans revolve that does not cross and recross state lines. The ease

of transportation and the mobility of enterprise are playing havoc with political boundaries. The votes and the
ventures of men are in different worlds.

A cabinet officer, discussing some proposed fishery legislation, faced the stubborn reluctance of the representatives
of two states, across whose dividing line a river ran, to
agree on a common policy. Finally, in exasperation, he
said, "You must remember, gentlemen, that the fish do
not recognize your state boundaries." These fish effectively
symbolize the way in which our social and economic interests increasingly ignore our artificial political organization.
An hour before I sat down to write this paragraph I was
in conference with a man who lives in New York but whose
economic interests are all in Tennessee and in Arizona. We
compel this man to express himself politically in New
York, despite the fact that his major interests are in Tennessee and in Arizona. If he is active in the state politics
of New York, where his major interests are not, we call
him a good citizen. If he seeks to make his influence felt
in the state politics of Tennessee and of Arizona, where
his major interests are, we brand him an anti-social inter-
loper. We determine his political citizenship, not by where
his mines are, but by where his bedroom is. This pillow-
case politics grows increasingly ludicrous in a technologic
age.

It is observations of this sort that make the student of
statecraft pessimistic about the future of inelastic and
localized government in an era of fluid and delocalized
enterprise. He sees the living interests of Western man
everywhere straining against and breaking across the artificial lines that bound our cities, our states, and our nations.
On all hands he sees evidence of maladjustment between
the localized institutions and the delocalized interests of
the Western peoples. Men have been nomadic and their
interests have been delocalized before in history, but this
new nomadism of the technologic era is different. The
hunter and the herdsman of antiquity could carry his gov-

ernment, which was little more than a code and a chieftain, with him. Where his interests were, at any given time, there could his government be also. The newly nomadic Westerner has a harder problem on his hands. His interests may race about his nation or the world, as the ancient hunter's game ran fleetly through forest or across veldt, but, unlike the ancient hunter, the man of the modern West has an elaborate and inflexible political system, with its fixed frontiers, its seats of government, its patronage-hungry parties, and its tradition-dominated legislatures. This political system supports innumerable vested interests and is supported by innumerable vested ideas. It adjusts itself, at best, with glacial slowness to basic changes in the living interests of its citizens.

Some twenty years ago, in a casual essay called *Off the Chain,* H. G. Wells sketched the outlines of this growing maladjustment between a fluid social order and a fixed political order, pointing out that the invention of methods for the political expression and collective direction of peoples that were, in themselves and in their interests, essentially migratory would be one of the pressing political necessities of the twentieth century. The decades that have since gone by have enforced the pertinence of his prophecy. But his prophecy lies unused in the files of the academic observers of the political scene. The student of statecraft looks in vain for some political leaders, whose hands are on the levers of power, to put the correction of this maladjustment among the urgent items on the political agenda.

The challenge of the majority to democracy is this: One of the major objectives of democracy is the removal of all artificial restraints that might impede the release of the latent creativeness of men, regardless of the social, political, or economic quarter from which they may hail. High or low! Right or left! Democracy is thus the foe of tyrants who seek to make the national mind single-track. In its reaction against tyrants, democracy could not afford to lapse into an anarchic individualism, but a vigorously independent individualism of thought and expression was imperative if democracy was to be more than just another phase of the human venture, ending, as other phases had ended, in social and political crystallizations that nothing save revolution could shatter. Casting about for a regulatory device that would at once protect society against anarchy and the individual against tyranny, democracy hit upon the device of majority rule. But the best laid plans of political philosophers may go agley. To-day the majority has itself turned tyrant and threatens Western democracy with a treachery and an intolerance that the maddest of monarchs would find it difficult to match.

The student of statecraft is disturbed by this growing perversion of majority rule, which he sees in varying degrees operative throughout the West, but notably in the United States. The theory of majority rule is simply that we shall submit our difficulties and our difference to unhampered investigation and to unprejudiced discussion, vote on the various ways out that may be proposed, and then abide by the result of the vote until further investigation and further discussion change enough minds to change the vote. Majority rule is far from perfect. It is a device with clear limitations. Now and then a too literal loyalty to a majority decision may fasten upon a people a fanatic law that is subversive of the very ends it purports to serve. But, by and large, majority rule is the best instrument of decision yet invented for fighting the tyranny of the few. Its misuse by the majority may, however, result in an equally sinister tyranny of the many.

Unless its operations are administered and its results accepted in a sportsmanlike manner, alike by the majority and by the minority, majority rule may become an instrument of ruthless repression and an incitement to ruthless revolution. Majority rule can be socially creative only when there is a reciprocal sportsmanship between the majority and the minority. The minority must be sportsmanlike enough to allow the majority to settle contests. The majority must be sportsmanlike enough to allow the minority to stimulate controversy. We cannot have peace unless the majority controls institutions. We cannot have progress unless the minority creates ideas.

The student of statecraft is doubtful of the Western future as he finds this sportsmanship missing in the current operation of the majority rule. And in the general decline of sportsmanship, he suspects that the West is endangered more by the intolerance of its majorities than by the intransigeance of its minorities. The majority tends more and more to use the device of majority rule for silencing controversy as well as for settling contests. The besetting sin of the majority is its persistent passion for standardizing opinion. And the student of statecraft knows that this means death to the social order that permits it, for the simple reason that the majority has never taken an advance step on its own initiative, but only when prodded into progress by a minority.

The majority, save when it is greatly led, is jealous of its superior men. It hates the man who heckles its crowd-prejudices. It rarely selects its superior men for leadership save by accident or when the superior man succeeds in masking his essential superiority by the slouch of his hat, the mountebankery of his manner, or the vernacular raciness of his speech. The student of statecraft sees the democracies of the West nursed and nurtured on the doctrine that the voice of the people is the voice of God. *Vox populi, vox Dei!* But he suspects that the voice of the people is the voice of God only when the people are godlike. He knows that majority rule, save when too gravely abused, insures order. He doubts that it insures progress. He knows that over and over again the majority has been wrong and the minority right, even if he stops short of Ibsen's insistence that the majority is never right. He knows that progress is born, not in the moods of the swarming mass, but in the mind of the special man. He knows, however, that it is not enough for an idea to be right. Granted its rightness, enough people must believe an idea before it can become an effective factor in the life of a nation. He knows, therefore, that, if the future of the West is to be a progressive future, the minority must be patient and the majority tolerant in the administration of majority rule, for only so can society be protected against the uncritical acceptance of new ideas that are not right and the majority be subtly educated to the acceptance of new ideas that are right.

Instead of this socially sound administration of majority rule the student of statecraft sees a socially sinister mal-administration. The majority insists that its opinion is public opinion, although its opinion is but a part of public opinion, and very often not the best part at that. Majority opinion grows ever more inquisitorial and tyrannical. Not content to restrict majority rule to its valid function as a political procedure for settling contests, the majority noses inexpertly into the intricate processes of legislation and administration, threatening with expulsion from power the legislator or administrator who dares disobey its transient whims. Through derision and ostracism, when it does not resort to the more drastic disciplines of the tyrant, the majority seeks to terrorize into submission the minority man who is unwilling to be but an echo of the crowd. This tyranny of the many is more terrible than the tyranny of the few, because it is an anonymous tyranny against which it is difficult to strike. In times past men have freed themselves from the tyranny of kings by the unholy method of assassination, but how shall men free themselves from the hydra-headed tyranny of an unsportsmanlike majority? The student of statecraft considers the prevailing perversion of majority rule and the persistent refusal of the majority to recognize its limitations matters of serious import for the Western future.

The challenge of party to democracy is this: Political parties in the United States are extra-constitutional agencies which, if we take seriously the claims of their uncritical supporters, are designed (1) to dramatize and to direct discussion of issues that are vital to the national being by presenting, in successive election seasons, party platforms that reflect sincere and searching study of the living issues of the social order, (2) to discover and to draft into public service men and women equipped by temperament and training for distinguished and disinterested leadership, and (3) to serve as integrated groups, representing distinctive and alternative philosophies of affairs, that the people can hold responsible for the creative and courageous administration of government, rewarding or rebuking such groups as they succeed or fail in living up to these three reputed purposes. But, in the extra-constitutional system of permanent political parties that has been elaborated in the United States, these three objectives of organization have not been realized. The party system has confused rather than clarified the discussion of issues vital to the national being. The party system has lowered rather than lifted the quality of political leadership. And the party system has failed to produce parties representing distinctive and alternative philosophies of affairs. It has bred a political mind that gives more thought to the achievement of office than to the administration of government, a mind more interested in the pork than in the philosophy of politics. Clashing opportunisms take the place of competing objectives.

The student of statecraft believes that the future of Western democracies will be dark unless their political arrangements insure the sustained study and sincere discussion of living issues, the discovery and induction into office of men and women who will bring superior capacity and sustained courage to the administration of government, the maintenance of distinctive political groups representing clear alternatives of policy, and the development of a political type that does not exhaust its ingenuity in the game of vote-getting and come barren to the responsibilities of office. But he sees the existing party system effectively blocking progress towards these ends. He is tempted to believe that the permanent political party automatically destroys its own usefulness as an instrument of statesmanship, and that little in the way of creative and courageous leadership can be expected from any permanent political party after it has lived past the handling of the particular issues that called it into being, save in glowing moments of exception, when God lends one of his prophets to politics to dominate a party by sheer force of mind and personality, or in great crises, when men adjourn temporarily the motives of feeling and methods of thinking that normally move them. It takes an emergency to evoke reality in parties.

Political parties usually arise, in the first instance, out of real divisions of opinion on real issues. They are born out of a vivid battle over some single issue about which men feel keenly and in which their real interests are involved. In such moments politics is real and campaigns are realistic contests in which men fight for principles rather than for perquisites. But when such parties persist as permanent organizations, after the issues that called them into being have ceased to be living issues, there is a rapid and resistless decline in their reality. Why this must be is, to the student of statecraft, obvious.

Born from the womb of some social or economic crisis, a political party is, in its initial phase, a device for assembling men and women who think alike around definite issues. When a political party lives past the handling of the crucial issues that called it into existence, it becomes, in its later phases, a device for assembling indefinite issues around a motley membership of men and women who do not think alike. It is not in the cards that a political party can remain, generation after generation, a body of like-minded voters. That men in one generation of American politics come together in agreement on the issue of slavery and form a party to fight its extension does not mean that seventy-five years later their successors in this party will be in agreement on prohibition, foreign policy, tariff, taxation, and the whole medley of issues that haunt the party's platform makers.

It is only a question of time until every permanent political party reaches a point at which, in order to hold itself together and to win elections, it resorts to so many compromises that its platforms and its performances are alike robbed of reality. Its platform committees will sit night after night in smoke-filled rooms searching for the sort of colorless statement that will serve as the lowest common denominator of the aggregated prejudices of the party, hold together its warring elements, and seduce the largest number of votes on election day. Sincerity in the platform must not be allowed to endanger success at the polls! And, once in power, it will abdicate its leadership by submitting to the indirect blackmail of its dissentient constituencies, here and there and yonder throughout the nation, in a sorry attempt to please everybody in order to jockey itself into a favorable position for the next campaign. Born as a body of like-minded citizens, the permanent political party becomes, in time, a body of men and women, devoid of unity, but held together in an artificial and delusive union by a thousand subtle pressures for party regularity, by the lust for office, and by the lazy loyalty of inertia.

The student of statecraft suspects that, save in its early phase, a permanent political party cannot, if it is to capture and keep control of government, afford to be clear and courageous about issues, especially if they are vital issues. For the beliefs of men respecting vital issues, the real divisions of political opinion and economic interest, cross and recross the lines that separate the permanent party organizations. None save the naïve and the blind believes that political America, in the Republican and Democratic parties, is divided into two coherent groups of citizens who think alike about two clearly contrasted and competing programs of social and economic statesmanship. There are as wide differences of opinion on all

vital issues within our parties as between our parties. In
fact, wider! In each, some are members of the Ku Klux
Klan, and some its bitterest enemies. In each, there are
some who think we should join the League of Nations,
and some who think it would mean national suicide. In
each, there are some who worship at the shrine of St.
Volstead, and some who long for a somewhat moister
régime, or, at least, for a less furtively wet régime. In each,
there are some who think there is danger that the Catholic
church will get control of the government, and some who
think that the Protestant church has already got control
of the government. No wonder the man of intellectual integrity shudders a bit at the thought of trying to draft
campaign platforms for parties thus composed of clashing
interests and conflicting ideas!

When the Gilberts and Sullivans of the future set American politics to music, they will surely make the first line of
the opening chorus: *But that would split the party . . . !*
This phrase and the fear that fathers it is the rock against
which intellectual honesty, moral courage, and creative
statesmanship smash in the councils of all permanent political parties. The poor devil who must play political leader
under the existing party system must, to use a figure from
John Bright, produce like a conjurer port, champagne,
milk, and water out of the same bottle. The permanent
party system has exiled courage from American politics
and laid an embargo on political candor. The cowardice
of the leader demoralizes the led, and the submissiveness
of the led encourages the leader in his intellectually sterile
and morally shoddy strategies of vote-getting.

These destructive results of the party system, as the
student of statecraft examines them, are not due to factors
peculiar to the American political scene. They are inherent
in the permanent party system. Hamilton Fyfe, in his
*Archon or the Future of Government,* paints a similar picture of the results of the party system in England. The
party system was introduced in British politics in the latter

part of the nineteenth century, after its elaboration in the United States. There had been parties in England long before, but the bonds of party allegiance rested lightly upon political representatives. It was a common custom for members of Parliament to disapprove and drive out of office their party leaders. As late as the middle of the nineteenth century, Ministries were many times turned out by the votes of their own followers. Between 1832 and 1874, nine Ministries went to the wall by the votes of their own adherents in the House of Commons. Then the party system, with its rigid disciplines and its relentless demands for party regularity, came into the picture. And only once between 1874 and the present time has a Ministry been turned down by the votes of its own followers. With parties, but without the party system or the party machine, courageous political independence triumphed nine times in forty-two years. With the party system in control, independence has lifted its head effectively but once in fifty-seven years. Parliamentary debate has become but shadow boxing. The votes of the members are dictated, in the main, by the voice of the machine. The first Home Rule Bill, Mr. Fyfe thinks, was the last measure of major importance that the House of Commons debated in a serious uncertainty of what the vote on its provisions would be. Which means, if this judgment can be taken as measurably correct, that some forty-five years have passed since argument has vitally altered the vote on an important measure before the House of Commons. Mr. Fyfe's generalization is, I suspect, extreme, but I think it is, in essence, correct. Thus the party system standardizes British politics as it has standardized American politics into sterility. Thus Westminster follows Washington into a politics over which the dual curse of conformity and compromise hangs.

The student of statecraft sees creative and courageous statesmanship, which the West never needed more urgently than now, growing less and less possible under the permanent party system. And he is something less than hopeful that Western man will soon evolve workable substitutes for the existing permanent political parties.

The challenge of leadership to democracy is this: A simple civilization can survive a mediocre leadership. A complicated civilization, like the civilization of the United States, in particular, and of the West, in general, cannot. The success or failure of democracy in recruiting able leaders becomes, in consequence, a vital factor in any predictive assessment of the Western outlook. And as the student of statecraft subjects the democracies of the West to qualitative assessment, he sees them displaying an increasing inability to attract and an increasing reluctance to tolerate their ablest and strongest men in positions of leadership. This, as much as any other factor in the current life of the West, makes him doubtful of the Western future.

There is no magic in democracy that does away with the need of leadership. A democracy must both create and control its own leadership. And it cannot afford to neglect either half of this responsibility. If a democracy thinks only of the creation of strong leadership, forgetting its control, it may end the vassal of a dictator. If a democracy thinks only of the control of leadership, forgetting to encourage its creation, it will end the victim of mediocre leaders who are more interested in holding a job than in doing a job. The student of statecraft reminds us that democracy is still young, and that we may yet go on the rocks if we blunder in this business of creating and controlling a leadership that is at once able and fearless. When we smashed the twin traditions of the divinity of kings and the docility of subjects, the whole problem of finding and following leaders had to be worked out on a new basis. The student of statecraft cannot see that we have so far made much headway with this problem. We spend half our time crying for great leadership, and the other half crucifying great leaders when we are lucky enough to find them. The crowd-mind, which flourishes in democracies, has not greatly changed since some centuries ago, faced with a problem of judgment on leadership, it took its cue from the vested interests of traditionalism and cried out: *Away with this man, and release unto us Barabbas! Away with him, away with him, crucify him!* It still penalizes the man who challenges it.

Western democracy is gravely endangered by our tendency to select leaders who are similar to the rank and file of us, whereas the hope of democracy lies in our selecting leaders who are superior to the rank and file of us. This cuts to the heart of the problem of leadership in a democracy. Just what should we look for in our leaders? Should we look for leaders who will lead us or for leaders who will follow us? Should we look for leaders who will always think like us or for leaders who might, in a pinch, think for us? Should we elect men to office because they promise to vote for some pet measure of the moment or because we can trust their mental capacity and their moral courage to guide them aright on measures in general, once all the facts are before them? Shall we give our loyalty to leaders who will clarify our needs or to leaders who will cater to our desires? Is it either wise or safe to try to run a democracy on the theory that the patient should dictate the physician's prescription?

As the student of statecraft observes the current trend in Western politics, he sees the Western democracies failing, in the main, to grasp the point of these questions. He sees the Western democracies all too often filling their strategic posts with weather-cock leaders who turn swiftly with every wind of crowd-whim. He sees the Western democracies everywhere suspicious of their ablest men. He sees the Western democracies rebuking candor and rewarding compliance in their leadership. He sees the Western democracies so absorbed in the taming and tethering of their slippery leaders that they are giving little thought to the grooming of the strong leaders they must have if democracy is to be more than a pointless free-for-all devoid of statesmanlike direction. He need not leave the United States to find this sinister trend.

The student of statecraft sees this lack of insight into the function of leadership dramatically displayed in the later developments of American politics. Our Republic began as a government by trusted and uninstructed representatives. It has virtually become a government by mistrusted and instructed delegates. Like all human concepts, the notion of representative government held by the founders of the Republic was nobler in promise than in performance. Experience proved that representatives may all too easily become misrepresentatives. It soon became clear that a self-governing people must consider the control as well as the creation of its leadership. And popular recognition of this fact led to provisions that have radically altered the practical operation of our representative system.

There developed a growing conviction in the minds of many that the leadership-controls established by the founders of the Republic were inadequate. It was not enough, thought many, to set up popular controls at the entrance to office. It was necessary to establish popular control of men while they were in office. We began to throw all sorts of restrictions around the freedom of the leader to lead, restrictions we assumed essential to the protection of the led against the malfeasance of the leader. We devised the initiative, the referendum, and the recall. And we have resorted increasingly to the unofficial threat of the popular petition as an instrument of pressure upon leaders to defend or defeat particular measures. We began with the theory of responsible government, but we have gone over, bag and baggage, to the theory of responsive government. We began with the theory that representatives should be human substitutes for their constituencies. Our current practice is to convert our representatives into phonograph records of the fluctuating moods of the folk back home and automatic voting machines to register these moods.

The student of statecraft knows that strong men are all too often poisoned by their own power. He knows how easily men in office forget the essential distinction between representative and ruler. He knows that democracies must set up effective safeguards against such perversions of power. He knows that the initiative, the referendum, the recall, the informal popular petition, and other latter-day devices of leadership-control were called into being by the obvious dereliction of trusted, uninstructed, and relatively uncontrolled representatives. The student of statecraft himself helped to devise these instruments of control. And he has by no means recanted his belief in their value as clubs behind the door to be brought out when leaders prove too derelict in their duty. But he is not blind to the fact that the attitude towards leadership engendered by these control-devices is plunging us deeper and deeper into government by instructed and compliant delegates, which is a far cry from government by intellectually independent and politically fearless leaders.

The question that lies coiled at the heart of the problem of leadership-control is this: How can a self-governing people hobble its faithless representatives without hamstringing its faithful representatives? How can democracy protect itself against the strong man's irresponsibility without alienating the strong man's strength from public service? How can we defend ourselves against the treason of leaders without destroying the tradition of leadership that is too great to follow false orders from its followers? There may be no single and sufficient answer to this question, but the future of the West is seriously involved in the attempts the Western democracies make to answer it.

The student of statecraft is disturbed as he sees the Western democracies giving their most fervent allegiance to those leaders who most quickly carry out the orders of a post-card bombardment from the folk back home, for he knows that no form of government can endure that trusts only its compliant men in positions of power. The most difficult lesson American democracy has to learn is how to tolerate leaders who are great enough to differ from their constituencies when necessary. Until we learn this lesson we cannot hope for consistently great leadership in public affairs. For no man of authentic integrity of mind and character will purchase political power at the price of adjourning his own intelligence and becoming the errand boy either of Wall Street or of Main Street. The great leader will be the creative servant of every legitimate interest of both Wall Street and Main Street, but the cringing slave of neither. The student of statecraft finds his confidence in the Western future faltering as he sees the democracies of the West making subserviency of spirit a bigger political asset than superiority of mind.

The challenge of revolution to democracy is this: Revolution is, at best, a wasteful way to effect social change. Save as a last resort method of destroying utterly intolerable systems that have proved impregnable against all peaceful processes of change, revolution justifies itself only when it releases theretofore repressed superiority of leadership. Only so can revolution supplement destructive power with constructive policy. Of all forms of society, democracy can least afford to philander with the revolutionary process, because, in so far as democracy lives up to its promise of equality of opportunity for ability regardless of its social origin, democracy keeps is lower strata stripped of ambitious ability, so that revolutions in democracies release mediocre rather than masterful leadership.

In pre-democratic civilizations there was but little ascent of ability from the lower social classes into the higher social classes. Now and then the blood of prince and the blood of peasant mixed to the biological advantage of the princely strain and to the social advantage of the peasant strain. Now and then lowly genius fought its way barehanded to prestige and power. But these inter-class liaisons and these conquests of position by genius from below were exceptions that but brought into bolder relief the essential fixity of caste. The social frontiers were, in the main, sealed frontiers. To change the figure, there were few hatchways through which the able and the ambitious might crawl up or the weak and the worthless drop down from the class or craft status into which they had been born. But human greatness has always eluded monopoly by any single social class. The poor and the despised classes have always bred and will always breed occasional genius. In the rigidly stratified societies of the pre-democratic era, when the lower classes bred a man of superior capacity, he was obliged to stay below with his class. This meant that at all times the lower strata held men of significant ability whose authentic greatness of mind had never had the chance to show its mettle in positions of leadership. Thus, in rigidly stratified societies, while an upper class was degenerating, a lower class was becoming an untapped reservoir of ability. This is why revolution, for all its tragic wastefulness of method, has been salutary in stratified societies. Revolution in such societies has brought to the top the theretofore repressed and socially wasted greatness that the caste system had kept hermetically sealed in its disinherited classes.

In democratic societies the incidence of revolution is dangerously difference. Democracies are socially fluid. It is of the essence of democracy that it shall keep a career open to the talented, whether the talented be born in the alley or on the avenue. *La carrière ouverte aux talents!* But democratic opportunity for the talented lures men out of the lower social classes into the higher social classes as soon as their ability is discovered and demonstrated, thus keeping the lower social classes of democratic societies continually drained of their distinguished sons. In the democracies of the West, despite the powerful pressures towards stratification, men are going up and down the class ladder all the time. Yearly, monthly, weekly, and daily men are rising from the lower into the higher social classes. The result of all this is that the lower strata of democratic societies are actually lower in their stock of ability than the lower strata of aristocratic societies were, for the aristocratic societies forced even the ablest to stay on the lower social deck if they happened to be born there.

This is why democracies cannot afford to drift into revolution. The caste system sometimes needs revolution to tap a fund of unused genius in its lower social classes. Democracy does not. Democracy is doing this tapping all the while. Save for the fact that, when genius from below ascends to the upper social deck, it falls victim to the small-family tradition of the upper social classes and thus causes a progressive suicide of superiority, this free ascent of the able is a godsend to the peaceful processes of democratic societies. But it gives revolution a perilous import in democracies! Since democracy is all the while denuding its lower strata of their alert and able men, revolution in a democracy is more likely to spell ruin than to bring renewal, even when the objective of the revolution is worthy, because intellectually and biologically denuded classes, when they successfully prosecute a revolution, can but put the reins of power in the hands of the incompetent.

The student of statecraft does not find adequate recognition of these facts among the men whose hands are on the levers of political power throughout the West. He sees, on the contrary, the ruling forces of the West passively tolerating, where they are not actively defending, political maladjustments, social injustices, and economic instabilities that are open invitations to the revolutionary mood, despite the peculiar peril of revolution in democracies.

Here, then, are nine specific aspects of the political fear that has dictated so much of the post-war literature of despair: (1) the fear that a consistently intelligent readjustment of the tools of government to the changing tasks of government will be blocked by a political Bourbonism that cannot see the difference between social discontent with a government that has blundered and scientific discontent with government that seeks to keep it from blundering; (2) the fear that the realism of science and the opportunism of politics will cancel each other and leave the West robbed of the fruits alike of authentic science and of authentic democracy; (3) the fear that the vast stretch of the territory of a democracy like the United States will defeat the forces of national unity and make for a medley of warring regionalisms; (4) the fear that an old political order, designed to serve a simple agricultural civilization, will prove inept and inadequate in the administration of the new social order, created by a technical civilization; (5) the fear that localized governments, elaborated in terms of a settled people, whose families and fortunes were, in the main, concentrated in definite political areas, will prove incapable of administering the increasingly mobile civilization of the West, a civilization in which men and their major interests are more and more delocalized by the forces of fast transportation and fluid capitalism; (6) the fear that the majority will increasingly abuse its administration of majority rule, sealing the minority sources of fresh ideas, and fastening upon the West the fanatic legislation of the led-by-the-nose crowd; (7) the fear that the inevitable inner disunity of its permanent political parties will keep Western politics barren of reality; (8) the fear that the democracies of the West will jealously boycott their strongest men and fall victim to an increasing mediocrity of leadership; and (9) the fear that Western democracy, after denuding its lower social classes of their ablest men by giving them opportunities on the upper social levels, will tolerate conditions that will bring these denuded classes to revolt, throwing the control of the Western future into the hands of the social rejects whom democratic opportunity has left behind because they were incapable of taking advantage of it.

The political fears I have here catalogued and sought to clarify are not the propagandist products of the enemies of democracy. They rest rather upon the realistic observations of social analysts who believe in the validity of the democratic theory, but who are determined that their devotion to democracy in theory shall not blind them to the blunders of democracy in action. These fears have been repeatedly voiced by men who do not think democracy inherently incapable of achieving political adaptability to changing conditions or impotent to meet the eight arresting challenges I have analyzed. These are the students of statecraft who consider democracy the soundest philosophy of social organization yet advanced, but who fear that a perversion of politics will prevent democracy from bringing its beneficent ministry to the social direction of the Western future.

But, outside the circle of these anxious friends of democracy, there is a growing cult of determined disbelievers in democracy. These are the students of statecraft who consider the current plight of the West due, not to obstacles that have been thrown in the way of democracy, but to the inherent unsoundness of democracy itself. The peculiar stresses and instabilities of the war and immediate post-war periods brought the anti-democratic movement out of the libraries of the political philosophers into the arena of political action. Here it has expressed itself in a proletarian dictatorship that is frankly a class-government. There it has expressed itself in a personal dictatorship that disavows any such social monopoly by a single class and purports to effect a synthesis of the interests of all classes in an all-dominant national interest. The realist will judge these varied ventures in social control, not in the abstract, but in terms of the popular temper and peculiar conditions that made them possible at the time and in the place of their establishment. But those democracies of the West that have not gone socially bankrupt and made an assignment of their political liberties to some *de jure* or *de facto* dictatorship must reckon with the growing skepticism of the democratic dogma.

I need not here undertake an exhaustive survey of the anti-democratic literature that mirrors much of the political fear of the period. Such a survey would duplicate much that I have already recorded, for the anti-democrat sees and sets in the foreground of his analysis the same difficulties I have listed, but, unlike the anxious friends of democracy, he does not consider them challenges to democracy by factors external to it, but congenital defects of democracy itself, and thinks that a sounder political régime would have saved the West from many of its current dilemmas. It will be sufficient to sample the tone of the anti-democrat.

The disbeliever in democracy sees the believer in democracy holding two creeds. A spoken creed that describes his political beliefs! An unspoken creed that determines his political actions! The anti-democrat admits the allurement and appeal of the spoken creed of democracy. He is not surprised that uncritical millions will fight to make the world safe for democracy. They fight for its spoken creed. But he thinks the unspoken creed of democracy more important than its spoken creed. He thinks democracy is better judged in the legislature than in the library. He measures democracy against its actions rather than against its aspirations. He thinks political analysis is futile unless this distinction is kept in mind.

Here are some of the things he says he sees as he watches democracy in action: He sees democracy effective in the conquest of power and incompetent in the exercise of power. He sees democracy determining its policies by wholesale referenda of the judgments of millions of voters, most of whom do not know enough about the issues involved to form a trustworthy personal judgment. He sees democracy, that is to say, as government by a kind of ballot-box magic that purports to bring a right judgment out of the hat by stirring together several million uninformed judgments. He sees democracy putting in jail dangerous men who break good laws, and putting in office equally

dangerous men who make bad laws. He sees democracy
alternately falling victim to reckless revolution and reckless
reaction. One day insanity is in the saddle! The next day
inertia holds the reins! He sees free men, intoxicated with
the wine of democracy, reluctant to admit the necessity
of leadership. He sees democracy insistent upon the rights
of man and indifferent to the right man. He sees democracy
unwilling to be well led. He sees democracy making in-
eptitude in office an aptitude for office, since democracy
prefers pliancy to power in its leaders, and masterful
statesmen are not content to follow when it is their business
to lead. He sees democracy as government by organized
envy. Ignorance envying enlightenment! Incompetence
envying competence! Poverty envying wealth! Amateur-
ism envying expertness! And so on! He sees democracy as
a kind of *Götterdämmerung* of all that is excellent and
exalted.

The anti-democrat doubts that a social order can practice
equality and produce excellence at one and the same time.
At least equality as envisaged by the sentimental democrat!
He notes that nature makes excellence one of her major
objectives, but that she bothers little about any leveling
sort of equality. Excellence is her passion, but neither the
size nor the significance of the product seems to concern her
if the product is but excellent. She will lavish her creative
genius upon the fashioning of a sprig of larkspur as upon
the breeding of a Shakespeare. She takes as much pains in
painting a transient rainbow as in sculpturing the Andes.
She is satisfied if both be excellent. Democracy, in its
spoken creed, asserts its discipleship of nature in this
passion for excellence, but demands that excellence be
achieved in an atmosphere of equality. Democracy, in
other words, declines to be as unjust and as brutal as
nature in the quest of excellence. But, as a practical matter,
the anti-democrat asks, how far does democracy get with
this laudable idealism? He agrees that society should be
just and gracious in its quest of excellence. He does not

want society to be as red in tooth and claw as nature is. He insists, however, that a sentimentalized philosophy of equality is neither just nor gracious to the incompetent.

The anti-democrat thinks that democracy will always end by putting a nation's vast dead-weight of mediocrity in control of its affairs, that the envy of the crowd will always excommunicate the handful of folk who, because they think with greater precision, create with greater truth and beauty, and act with greater power, are the distilled essence of a nation's soul, and that democracy will always refuse either to acknowledge or to adapt itself to the inequality of persons that equality of privilege uncovers. As the anti-democrat balances the ledger between democracy and dictatorship, he finds, contrary to popular impression, that, since the days before the World War, democracy, loosely defined, rules a larger area of the world's surface than ever before. In the face of this fact, and feeling as he does about democracy, the anti-democrat takes his place naturally among the prophets of doom, save when he is the convinced servant of some religio-social passion like Communism.

The anxious friends of democracy do not deplore the agitations of the anti-democrats, for they know that contemporary democracy needs to be stung into awareness of its defects. They are not uncritical enough to assume that the retirement of democracy from the political stage of the Western world is impossible. They think, as I stated earlier, that Western man will long cling to democracy, in shadow if not in substance, but they know there is a limit to the muddling it can survive. "Few are the countries in which freedom seems safe for a century or two ahead," said the late Lord Bryce, a devoted adherent of the democratic philosophy. "When the spiritual oxygen which has kept alive the attachment to liberty and self-government in the minds of the people becomes exhausted, will not the flame burn low and flicker out?" There is no inevitable immortality that democracy can count upon. As

Lord Bryce pointed out, when popular government flickered out in ancient Greece and Rome, nobody thought of reviving it. "The thing has happened," he said, "and whatever has happened may happen again. People that had known and prized political freedom resigned it, did not much regret it, and forgot it."

### The Economic Fear!

Two groups of observers of the Western economic scene face the future with confessed fear: (1) the anxious friends of the Western system of free capitalism and political liberty, who believe it to be sounder in principle than any alternative system yet proposed, who consider that under statesmanlike direction the machine economy of the West can come nearer than any other instrument to emancipating the race from drudgery, poverty, and insecurity, but believe that this social ministry of the machine economy is dependent upon basic shifts in economic policy which will mean, in effect, a new capitalism, that will be at once more profitable economically and more productive socially, and whose fear is that the business and industrial leadership of the West will not effect these shifts in economic policy quickly enough to avert an increasing appeal of alternative systems to the uncritical millions whose increasing insecurity is rendering them increasingly uncritical; (2) the avowed enemies of the Western system of free capitalism and political liberty, who would substitute for it an extensive application of the principle of State Socialism or a complete reorganization of the economic West in terms of Communism or a syndicalist Fascism, and whose fear for the future is less a fear than a feverish glee over what they consider the inevitable failure of Western capitalism and the nearness of their historic opportunity to seize the reins of power.

Since the traditional indictment that the proponents of Socialism have long leveled at capitalistic industrialism is well-known, since the presses are gorged with pamphlets and books both hailing and hammering the philosophy and propaganda of Communism, since the syndicalistic program of Fascism has not lacked insistent dramatization, and since in the last four chapters of this book and elsewhere in its argument I deal in detail with the balance sheet of assets and liabilities of the machine economy of the West, as this balance sheet is cast up by the anxious and analytical friends of the capitalistic industrialism of the West, I shall say no more, at this point, respecting the economic fear than to record its obvious existence.

### The Administrative Fear!

As the student of administration seeks to forecast the Western future, he is sometimes harassed by the fear that the scale and complexity of the organized enterprises of Western life have outstripped the existing managerial capacity of Western man. He harks back to a principle stated with stark simplicity by Mr. Justice Brandeis a score of years ago when, in a paper on *Trusts and Efficiency,* he said, "While a business may be too small to be efficient, efficiency does not grow indefinitely with increasing size. There is in every line of business a unit of greatest efficiency. . . . The unit of greatest efficiency is reached when the disadvantages of size counterbalance the advantages. The unit of greatest efficiency is exceeded when the disadvantages of size outweigh the advantages." The student of administration is impressed by the general impotence, both in analysis and in action, displayed by reputedly great business, industrial, and financial leaders in the presence of the forces of economic retardation and relapse. He wonders whether he is witnessing a confirmation of a further statement by Mr. Justice Brandeis, when, in the paper from which I have just quoted, he said, "Man's work often outruns the capacity of the individual man; and no matter how good the organization, the capacity of an individual man usually determines the success or failure of a particular enterprise—not only financially to the owners but in service to the community. Organization can do much to make concerns more efficient. Organization can do much to make larger units possible and profitable. But the efficacy of organization has its bounds. There is a point where the centrifugal force necessarily exceeds the centripetal. And organization can never supply the combined judgment, initiative, enterprise, and authority which must come from the chief executive officer. Nature sets a limit to his possible accomplishment."

The student of administration may not concur in all the implications with which Mr. Justice Brandeis invests this philosophy of organization and scale, but he is disturbed by the fact that the scale of Western enterprise seems to have grown far more rapidly than the statesmanship of management. During the last decade, in particular, he has seen a mania for volume sweep the world of Western enterprise, resulting in an economic elephantiasis that does not, as he sees it, augur well for the health of the Western social order. The student of administration distinguishes between a far-sighted philosophy of volume and a short-sighted passion for volume. He is quite aware that mass production and mass distribution, those engaging twins born of the marriage of science and technology, can prove neither profitable to the manufacturers nor beneficial to the masses apart from unprecedentedly large volume of output and sale, and he is not at all alarmed by the large-scale operation that a statesmanlike administration of mass production involves. It is the rapid growth in scale and complexity outside such phases of Western enterprise, where bigness is at once economically essential and socially salutary, that disturbs the student of administration.

The student of administration, again harking back to a distinction drawn by Mr. Justice Brandeis, is not disturbed by the bigness of enterprises that have *grown* big, but he looks differently upon the bigness of enterprises that have been *made* big. A normal growth to bigness favors the presumption that statesmanship of management has led rather than lagged behind increase in scale. The sheer manufacture of bigness, which marked the epidemic of mergers during the abortive New Era, may mean the quick creation of a scale and complexity of enterprise that outrun existing managerial capacity. The first is an authentic bigness; the second an artificial bigness. The student of administration suspects that the West is over-stocked with artificial bigness.

He finds the American, in particular, given to quantity mindedness. Our two major sports, he thinks, are weighing and counting. The national coat of arms might well carry a statistician caressing an adding machine. Everywhere and always the quest of bigness! Big businesses! Big industries! Big banks! Big churches! Big universities! This mania for bigness led the luminous minded William James, in a letter to Mrs. Henry Whitman, in commenting on G. E. Woodberry's discussion of democracy, in *The Heart of Man,* to cry out, "As for me, my bed is made: I am against bigness and greatness in all their forms, and with the invisible molecular moral forces that work from individual to individual, stealing in through the crannies of the world like so many soft rootlets, or like the capillary oozing of water, and yet rending the hardest monuments of man's pride, if you give them time. The bigger the unit you deal with, the hollower, the more brutal, the more mendacious is the life displayed. So I am against all big organizations as such, national ones first and foremost; against all big successes and big results; and in favor of the eternal forces of truth which always work in the individual and immediately unsuccessful way, under-dogs always, till history comes, after they are long dead, and puts them on top." The sober student of administration hardly follows James in this emotional secession from an age of large-scale enterprise, but he is convinced that Western enterprise tends to grow in size and complexity beyond the control of available executive genius.

The student of administration recalls the observation

of the late Lord Bryce that our modern states have grown so big as to be virtually unmanageable by existing means of human control. He sees city administration after city administration resembling nothing so much as a nervous spinster weakly clutching at the reins of a runaway team. He sees state government after state government wrestling wistfully with the threat of insolvency. He sees university administration after university administration excuse failure to face a manifest challenge to educational reconstruction by pleading the unmanageability of numbers. And so, the student of administration is, at times, haunted by the fear that many of our empires, states, cities, industries, universities, and other enterprises have reached the point at which the disadvantages of size outweigh the advantages. The failure of many gigantic mergers to live up to the lush promises of their lavish prophecies of super-efficiency may be, it seems to the student of administration, in his more disillusioned moods, but the symptom of a more widely prevailing sickness—the sickness of unmanageable bigness—that has fallen upon Western society.

The administrative fear is felt by many students of administration who do not agree with the Brandeis philosophy of organization and scale, that is to say, by students who do not think that the existing maladministration of much of the large-scale enterprise of the West is due to any inherent unsoundness of large-scale organization itself, but to stubbornly surviving managerial traditions that are maladjusted to current economic forces and to laggard educational traditions, formulated and fixed in the pre-machine era, that have not been consciously redirected to the discipline of men for life and leadership in an age of large-scaleness of enterprise, complexity of relationships, and unprecedented rapidity of tempo. And, of course, some expressions of this administrative fear have been dictated by an unreasoning resentment of bigness *per se* and by an uncritical reaction to the graver malpractices of certain large-scale economic leaderships.

At any rate, in the midst of an age of large-scale enterprise, there is a manifest reaction against large-scaleness. In the field of economic enterprise, there is a bitter lashing back, by those who have suffered from the practice of centralization and by those who are convinced by the philosophy of decentralization, at such fresh manifestations of large-scaleness as the tendency towards mergers and the triumphant advance of chain systems of merchandising and banking. In the field of political enterprise, there is a growing skepticism of the wisdom of swelling the power of the Federal Government, which found an ardent advocacy in the new nationalism of the Rooseveltian era, and the emergence of a new interest in the potentiality of State governments, a resurgence of the philosophy of localism in the midst of the practice of large-scaleness. In the field of educational enterprise, there is a mounting criticism of universities and school systems that have, during the last quarter century, mushroomed into magnitude. The student of administration, where he has been swept into this reaction against large-scaleness, suspects that we are headed towards an increasing maladministration of Western life unless we either breed and train more great administrators or reorganize our life in terms of smaller and more manageable units. The alternative, as he sees it, is complexity falling into chaos.

### The Moral Fear!

A great fear freezes the hearts of many student of the individual and institutional conduct of the contemporary West, the fear that we have fallen into a moral apostasy that seems to some the cause and to others the result of the night winds of political and economic anarchy that now howl about the windows of the Western world and chill the marrow in the bones of Western leadership generally. The frightened moralist has added many fat tomes to the literature of despair. He is uneasy in the presence of a post-war generation that seems to him to have gone

renegade to all wholesome standards of thought and conduct and to be morally adrift without rudder or compass.

If this generation could speak with a single voice, he
thinks its *Confessio Fidei* would be: We are children of a
rebel generation. We have sniffed the air of freedom. We
have drunk deep of the wine of liberty. We have declared
our independence of inherited proverbs. We have traded
the spirit of the fireside for the spirit of the frontier. We
have burned our copy books. We have revolted against
rules. We are apostles of the experimental life. In terms
of this elastic credo, the frightened moralist sees this
generation engaged in the pursuit and practice of three
morally dangerous enterprises: (1) a new liberty; (2) a
new levity; and (3) a new looseness. And he does not
concur in the defence the post-war generation makes of its
libertarian mood and manners. Its defence and his dissent may be simply stated.

He sees the boy of to-day reading in the parlor a book
that the boy of a generation ago would have read in the
hay mow. The apostles of the new liberty contend that this
is a good thing even if it is a bad book, for, to them, it is
the sign of a generation that prefers candor to concealment.
And candor, they think, is preferable to concealment as a
guiding principle of conduct. But strychnine is quite as
poisonous, the fightened moralist thinks, when swallowed
in the village square as when swallowed behind the barn.
And he suspects that this generation is not quite candid
about its interest in candor. He quotes to the experimen-
talists from H. G. Wells, himself an apostle of experimentalism, who, in his *The World of William Clissold,*
says, "To bring a thing into the light is the first step to
dealing with it sanely; but mere frankness and exposure
will no more cure our troubles than they will heal a broken
leg." If the new libertarians would use their candor
honestly as an instrument for clearing the ground for a
more responsible and realistic meeting of the issues of
their lives, the moralist would, he says, feel differently

about the new liberty, but he is fearful that much of modern candor is evaporating in merely unhampered talk about things hitherto taboo.

He sees the youth of to-day treating with breezy familiarity things their fathers refused to touch save by whispered indirection, and walking with their hats on into the holy of holies, where their fathers halted reverentially in the ante-room. The apostles of the new levity contend that the seeming irreverence of this generation is but a reaction against the intellectual and moral laziness of earlier generations that found it easier to reverence their creeds and constitutions than to reform them, that the new levity is but a half-way house on the road to a new reverence that will reserve its respect for reality rather than form. The moralist insists that he is in sympathy with any battering ram that beats down a bogus reverence compounded of laziness, fear, and mere compliance with custom if those who swing the battering ram will set seriously to work to create on the ground thus cleared a genuine reverence compounded of quick appreciation and lasting loyalty in the presence of the real, the true, and the creative, but he is disturbed by what seems to him the degeneration of much of the new freedom into a sterile flippancy.

He sees the youth of to-day indulging, without serious sacrifice of respectability, in a looseness of conduct that would have meant social ostracism in earlier generations. Some of the less candid advocates of this moral modernism contend that there is simply more *open* looseness in this generation, while the more candid protagonists of the new freedom contend that the looseness that frightens the moralist is inevitable in a generation that is moving out of a philosophy of concealment into a philosophy of candor, that in any era of enlarged freedom there are weaklings who will not keep to their feet, that weaklings never have known, do not now know, and never will know how to use liberty, that society cannot give to the weakling a strength that the imperious forces of heredity have denied to him, and that a rational social order dares not organize itself, set its standards, and determine its relationships in terms of the weakling unless its wants, sooner or later, to pull the strong down to the level of the weak. The frightened moralist does not follow this argument. He thinks the new looseness roots in a deeper soil. He contends that, even if what seems to him the brutality and fatalism of the new freedom towards the weakling were justifiable, the whole experimentalism of this generation overlooks the imperative necessity for stabilizing traditions and the continuing challenge of standards.

The superficial moralist sometimes identifies the, to him, unhappy aspects of the outlook and conduct of the time as a transient aftermath of the war, but the more realistic student of emerging folkways senses causes more remote and varied. The current attempt to effect a reorientation of conduct, blind and blundering as it may be, would to-day be under way even if the war had never come to shake the Western world to its foundation. The heady wine of the new freedom was fermented in the laboratories of scientists, the closets of philosophers, the council chambers of industrialists, and the cabinet rooms of statesmen who may not themselves have foreseen the transitional unsteadiness its drinking would bring to the moral conduct of this generation.

Far fetched as it may seem at the first lay glance, the realistic student of the springs of behavior traces the libertarian mood and loose manners of the current generation to seven sober enterprises prosecuted during the century past by scientists, philosophers, industrialists, and statesmen who were seemingly quite oblivious to the fact that they were manufacturing ethical explosives. These seven enterprises are: (1) the new politics; (2) the new economics; (3) the new theology; (4) the new biology; (5) the new philosophy; (6) the new psychology; and (7) the new physics. The escapade mood of post-war youth may have been exacerbated by war and prohibition, but these seven basic movements in thought and action, rather than gun fire or gin, must, the realistic student of behavior thinks, be looked to as the causative sources of the "unmoralism" that runs rampant in the post-war West. Let me indicate the specific and limited sense in which I use the seven phrases with which I have directed attention to the seven major sources of the current ethical unsettlement.

By the new politics I mean the democratic movement. Whatever new integrations it may finally achieve in any given field, democracy's initial impact upon an undemocratic organization of relationships makes for disintegration. It breaks up the old hierarchies. It means the release of persons and powers before repressed. It stimulates the dreams of the theretofore disinherited. It looses all sorts of latent envies that undemocratic stratifications of society inevitably induce. With its insistent emphasis upon the centrality of the individual, democracy pulls the props of reverence from under the royal and ruling groups that before gave a kind of stability to social organization and fitted the conduct alike of classes and masses into well-understood and generally accepted formulas. At its onset, democracy confers new rights upon everybody, and, in consequence, all sorts of persons undertake all sorts of things—politically, socially, economically, religiously, educationally—from the doing of which they had before been excluded by the accepted inhibitions of pre-democratic régimes. For the doing of these new things these new groups may or may not be fitted either by nature or by nurture, the results may mean creativeness or confusion, but the doing of new things by new groups is inherent in the democratic enterprise. It is thus that the democratic movement, by breaking up the old integrations, has played its part in bringing about the phase of experimentalism through which the West is now passing.

By the new economics I mean the policies and processes of the machine economy of the industrialized West, a new organization of work that has involved a new organization of life. Western industrialism, under the dual sponsorship of science and technology, has changed life outside its factories even more than it has changed work inside them. Adjourning for the moment the social aspect of religion and morals, as this aspect appears in the ground-plan and guiding principles of the socio-economic order, modern industrialism must share with modern intellectualism responsibility for landing the current generation in a vast confusion respecting even the personal aspect of religion and morals. To the man of the pre-scientific and pre-technological age, religion and morals were predominantly personal matters. He lived in an earth-centered universe and on a man-centered earth. Before the rise of modern science and modern industry, the metaphysician and the moralist alike thought in intensely personal terms. Both the cosmos and the conduct of pre-machine man were personalized. Modern intellectualism has depersonalized the universe. Modern industrialism has depersonalized society. The advance of science has left the individual depressed as it impresses him with his relative insignificance in a universe of titanic forces that he cannot feel, as his father felt, are amenable either to his will or to the caprice of gods. The advance of industrialism has debased the individual as it has impressed him with his relative insignificance in a society the work of which is organized in increasingly impersonalized large-scale units, a society in which he, as an independent craftsman, and his family, as an independent economic unit, seem doomed to a losing fight for the right to stand on their own feet.

There is a large part of the current ethical unsettlement that is not due to the new ideas in terms of which men think but to the new conditions under which men work. The new economics throws off a new ethics as a by-product. Under modern industrialism the family as an economic unit, in which parents and offspring shouldered and shared a common responsibility in a common enterprise, has disappeared. The home-economy which preceded the factory-economy kept the older and younger generations in continuously intimate contact. Youth was not set early adrift to be exposed alike to new temptations and to new theories. Young and old, the women of the household as well as the men of the household, were kept at home and kept busy. Conduct-changes, from generation to generation, were thus effected gradually and without the sense of drastic and dramatic break between the moral codes of the older and the younger generations. But the advance of industrialism has wholly changed the stage-setting of morals. The master-apprentice relationship between father and son is gone, and with it has gone the chance that relationship gave for continuous moral tutorship by the father, for the father's contact with the son, who is now absent from home so large a part of the time in school or factory, has become a touch-and-go contact. The advance of industrialism has meant the emancipation of the mother from the absorbing economic activity she knew in the pre-machine age home and the opening up to her of the possibility of independent economic activity outside the home. This dual emancipation of women, from an old economic status into a new economic status, has meant for women at once a new idleness and a new activity. And both the new idleness and the new activity have raised for women new moral problems of baffling complexity. The newly idle modern woman, who no longer busies herself with the spinning and weaving that was part of her grandmother's program and who is under no necessity to become herself a breadwinner, is faced with the problem of finding satisfying ways of absorbing her energies and investing her days with interest. The more intelligent she is the more restive she must become under an organization of life that offers but social diversion at the end of the day. In the quest of a solution to this problem a thousand and one relationships may be run into that raise new moral issues. The newly active modern woman, who is by necessity or choice a breadwinner outside the home, finds herself in daily relationships that

would have seemed strange and dangerous to her grandmother, relationships that are effecting marked changes in
the manners if not the morals of women. The moral incidence of both the new idleness and the new activity of
women falls upon the daughters as well as the mothers of
the machine age. Fathers and sons and mothers and
daughters are all alike faced with the problem of fitting
themselves into a new scheme of working and living.

Out of the struggle to preserve the home-nurtured values
of the pre-machine age in the midst of the home-shattering
circumstances of the machine age a mass of moral dilemmas
arise. As modern industrialism has increasingly centralized
economic enterprise in congested cities, the older and
ampler houses have given way to the rabbit warrens of
slums and small-apartment houses. This has meant the
progressive ejection of the social life of the young out of
the home and away from its oversight. The entrance alike
of mothers and of daughters into the day-to-day relationships of office and factory has shattered the old sheltering
of women which was an accompaniment of the earlier and
stricter codes of conduct. As the cost and complexity of
life in this industrialized age have increased, young men
have felt under increasing pressure to postpone marriage.
And the economically independent young woman tends to
think twice before she marries a young man of slender income unless she can continue her career as an income-earner
after marriage. And if she does continue her career as an
income-earner after marriage, it involves a drastic reconstruction of the concept of the feminine function and domestic relationships which seemed sacrosanct to earlier
generations. All this means a growing army of young men
and young women cut off from the normal sexual relationships, sanctioned by religion and the social code, that
marked the life of earlier generations less harassed by a
costly and complex existence. Even when he is most deeply
appreciative of the dilemmas these new conditions of work
put to contemporary youth, the moralist is disturbed as

he sees this growing army of youth, cut off from the normal
life of the home, clutching at what seems to it new sanctions
for easier moral codes.

The moralist sees profound ethical implications not only
in the economic arrangements of the machine economy but
in the machines of the machine economy as well. One
modern machine, the automobile, may serve to symbolize
the direct effect machines may have upon morals. The
cheap private car is establishing new relations between the
sexes and between parents and children. "Both sexual
conventions and social castes are affected by motor trac-
tion," C. Delisle Burns observes in his *Modern Civilization on Trial*. "When a man or a woman driver can escape
out of range of local gossip and caste-acquaintance, there
is no telling what may happen; for most traditional morality depends upon the control over the individual by the
little local group to whom he is personally known. The
impersonal atmosphere of the city area destroyed village
morality in the nineteenth century; the life of the road
may now create a new morality of nomads. . . . Again,
the car has made it possible for a man and wife and perhaps
the children to take enjoyment together. . . . When, however, the children grow to adolescence, they seem to take
refuge in other cars from the company of parents. The
private car, then, is changing the relationship of members
of a family, especially in America." A hundred machines
and devices are, like the automobile, registering effects in
the field of conduct.

But the moralist is most deeply disturbed by the fact
that the tempo of economic evolution is producing an ever
more swiftly and sweepingly changing life and that, dizzy
with his ceaseless effort to keep his conduct effectively
adjusted to the changing circumstances of his world, Western man is moving towards a more and more elastic concept of morals. "The society of the future," he finds a sober
sociologist like W. F. Ogburn saying, "will be one of
greater and greater change. And as the environment

changes, the habits of man change. Under these conditions morality, as it is generally conceived, will have no place. For the general notion of morality is that it is the following of a set of rules or commandments. Such commandments can be laid down with great specificity in a stationary society where experience leads to guidance in minute detail. But in a society undergoing great change, there is little guidance to be gained from the past. The situations that arise are new, and ethical conduct is a matter of intelligence and forecast, and the fixity and detail, right and wrong, give way before social expediency." The frightened moralist sees this as a dangerous philosophy of moral improvising. He cannot feel that we are safe unless we can see some immutable Sinai shining through the smoke of the factories that symbolize our changing economic scene and the moral dilemmas it throws up.

By the new theology I do not mean any particular set of newly evolved doctrines, but the general emancipation, which took place in the latter half of the nineteenth century, from the traditional orthodoxy that had until then held the relatively uncritical allegiance of the overwhelming majority of the Western peoples. Historical criticism, as a new method of approach for the scholar in the fields of the history of religions and scriptural exegesis, struck heavy blows at the dogma of authority and stimulated unprecedented activity in independent investigation and private judgment. For the generation that effected this emancipation from traditional dogmas, it remained an intellectual emancipation only. The traditional ethics that went along with the traditional theology remained. The new theology meant to its pioneers a new way of thinking rather than a new way of living. They were engaged in the conquest of intellectual self-respect. But they ratified the old morality while they railed at the old theology. Unless some exceptionally zealous defender of the faith booted them from the temple, they still went to church. They still prayed about their family altars. And in the dining room they

still thanked God for their daily bread. They may have
doubted the traditional theory of the authorship of *The
Ten Commandments,* but they did not doubt the validity of
their moral demands.  If these pioneers in theological reconstruction could return to watch their descendants busy
with what seems to them the more important enterprise of
ethical reconstruction, bringing the same independence of
judgment to asserted authorities in the field of conduct that
they themselves once brought to asserted authorities in
the field of creeds, they would, the disturbed moralist
thinks, be surprised if not shocked by the harvest that has
sprung from the seeds of their nineteenth century dissent.
One generation cannot emancipate itself from imposed
creeds and expect the next generation not to emancipate itself from imposed conduct.  In fields as intimately related
as religion and morals, it is impossible to release the forces
of free investigation and independent judgment in one and
isolate the other from their impact.  The current reconsideration of ethics is but a later installment of the story
that began with the reconsideration of theology.  And here,
as elsewhere, the men who started the story did not foresee
how it would end.

By the new biology I mean the evolutionary outlook associated in the popular mind with the researches of Darwin.
The doctrine of organic evolution shattered the one-week
carpenter theory of the making of the world and man and
substituted therefor the conception of a developing world
in which we are not mere Tony Sarg marionettes, but ourselves progressively both creatures and creators of new
values and new vitalities.  This idea of evolutionary change
was not the private plaything of biologists in sequestered
laboratories, but a provocative and productive force that
altered men's attitudes in every field of action.

The idea of evolutionary change registered its effect in
the field of group conduct.  Even the misinterpretations
of its major implications colored the thought of the West.
Men jumped to many premature conclusions after their

first reading of Darwin's observations. Under the spell of the "struggle for existence" and "survival of the fittest" phrases, superficially interpreted, they coined dangerous catch-words that still serve as rallying cries for the designing few and the deluded many. Competition! Class Conflict! Commercial Antagonism! War! Darwinism was twisted into a mandate for political imperialism and economic brigandage, despite the fact that coöperation has played as big a rôle as conflict in animal evolution, and in the face of the indisputable testimony of the Dinosaur that force and bigness may come off rather badly in the game of evolution.

The idea of evolutionary change registered its effect likewise in the field of personal conduct. It resulted in a fresh approach to the study of morals. The history of morals has come to be looked upon as one continuing illustration of the evolutionary idea. To a generation viewing life as a becoming, morality becomes less and less a matter of arbitrary rules and more and more the changing forms that reflect the successive responses of human impulses to the changing circumstances of successive generations. The history of morals is strewn with all sorts of now reprehensible conduct that were, at one time or another, sanctioned by religion and held respectable by society. To the evolutionary-minded this means that there is no once-for-allness about morality, but that morality is forever in the making. The idea of evolutionary change has thus brought into being a generation unafraid of the idea of change in morals.

By the new philosophy I mean those philosophical tendencies of the last quarter-to-a-half century that may, with measureable accuracy, be described as a revolt against reason. The pragmatism of William James and the creative evolution of Henri Bergson will suffice as illustrative identifications of this philosophical influence. Truth is that which works! The trueness of truth is not to be proved by dialectics or by appeals to authority, but by trust-

ing your life to it! If it brings ruin it is false; if it brings
radiance it is true! Life is not a picture puzzle with the
pattern predetermined by a master logician! Life is a
continuing experiment! Life is not a creation; it is a
creating! Not the surface intellect, but the sub-surface
intuitions, must be looked to for the dependable driving
force of our lives! *L'élan vital!* Intelligent living involves
a refusal to lean too heavily on the intellect! Trust and
test your instinct and your intuition! These exclamatory
exhortations and assertions fall far short of an accurate
and comprehensive interpretation of the philosophies of
James and Bergson, but they reflect, with decent faithfulness, what has filtered down to the crowd, to fashion its
conduct, from the benignant sage of Harvard and the
brilliant savant of Paris. The essence of the James-
Bergson influence upon contemporary conduct is that it has
made for a sense of life as a going experimentation. It
helped to spoil a world of clear landmarks and comfortable
moorings. A John Dewey comes into the picture with a
practicality and an air of immediacy to current affairs that
is almost wholly missing in a Bergson and was never quite
captured by the pragmatic James. And Dewey, too, with
his eager concern to help his contemporaries adjust their
conduct, individual and institutional, to the changed and
changing circumstances of the time, adds to the sense of
life as a going experimentation.

I am quite aware that James and Bergson and Dewey
do not tell the whole story of modern philosophy. They
are outside the current absorption of philosophers in
mathematics. I cannot resist the conclusion that many
modern philosophers turned to mathematics as a city of
refuge from the too exacting demands of a philosophy that
sought to wrestle with human problems. But even here they
are doomed to disappointment. Mathematics, like conduct,
has gone fluid. There is little more of certainty in modern
mathematics than in modern morals. So that philosophy,
whether wrestling with the concrete problems of conduct

or the abstract speculations of mathematics, both contributes to and reflects the increasing unsettlement of modern life.

By the new psychology I mean those tendencies in psychological theory that have lifted the idea of self-expression to a parity with, if not to predominance over, the idea of self-control. Jung and Freud may here serve as illustrative identifications of these tendencies. These and their colleagues lifted the sunken and suppressed instincts and impulses to a new dignity. I do not undertake to interpret Jung or Freud. I am interested here only in what the crowd has caught from them. And this, I think, is a fairly accurate statement of the Jung-Freud influence upon current conduct. Too much self-control! Too little self-expression! Needs and desires, real if not respectable, are clamped down and covered up by social conventions! Down in the dark they fester and ferment! Take the lid off! Be candid at all costs! Pull your hidden thoughts into the sunlight! Clarify, even if you do not carry out, your impulses! There is, the disturbed moralist admits, much sense and soundness in all this. He is disturbed, not by the responsible application of the findings of the new psychology to the diagnosis and direction of conduct, but by their misapplication. He thinks he sees these sober scientific conclusions being turned by the many into a mandate for a new wantonness.

By the new physics I mean those tendencies in the thought of modern physicists that have largely disestablished the old reign of rigid laws of the physical world. In a paper read before the American Philosophical Society in 1926, Robert A. Millikan, by a bald listing and brief defining of the twenty-one major discoveries in the field of physics during the fifteen to thirty years preceding, gave even to the layman a vivid sense of the rapid disintegration of many long established notions respecting the behavior of the physical world. As late as the end of the nineteenth century, there were at least six principles which, as Mr. Millikan put it, acted as "police officers" to keep the physical world in a state of law and order, but these six principles, once thought to have universal validity, are to-day in varying stages of disrepute.

The six principles of the old physics that once held sway were: (1) the principle of the conservation of the chemical elements; (2) the principle of the conservation of mass; (3) the principle of the conservation of energy; (4) the principle of the conservation of momentum; (5) the principle involved in Maxwell's equations in the field of electrodynamics; and (6) the principle of entropy or the second law of thermodynamics. Each of these six principles has suffered loss of prestige at the hands of the new physics. Doubt has been thrown upon the universal validity of all of them, and most of them, we now know, are subject to exceptions and refinements overlooked by the old physics. The new physics discovered radioactivity, and the principle of the conservation of the chemical elements became questionable if not obsolete. The new physics discovered that the mass of the electron increases as its speed approaches the velocity of light, and the principle of the conservation of mass, as such, went into the museum of superseded concepts. The new physics found it increasingly difficult to maintain the old sharp distinction between energy and mass, and the principle of the conservation of energy, as such, if not dethroned, at least had to alter the theory of its reign. And the quantum theory has seriously restricted the validity of the principle of the conservation of momentum. And so on down the list of laws and principles that once pretended to universal validity.

The old physics was *macroscopic*. It saw things in the large. It gave us a picture of the physical world drawn with bold lines that the layman, at least, thought of as laws invested with universality and immutability. The new physics is *microscopic*. It sees the little happenings as well as the large habitual performances. It sees variations that the old physics missed. It is not accurate to say that the new physics has repealed the laws that the old physics assumed. It has discovered exceptions to and refinements of these laws. It has come upon whimsicality in a physical world that was once supposed to be governed by immutable laws, but it has not become a physics of anarchy. In the large macroscopic sense a law of the old physics may still be held true, despite the exceptions and refinements that the minuter microscopic researches of the new physics have revealed.

There has, however, filtered down to the crowd a certain sense of lawlessness from the new physics as from the loosening of old formulas that has taken place in other fields of research. The crowd has, for instance, heard the sound of the word relativity, if it has not caught its technical meaning, and has begun to thrust the notion of the relative rather than the absolute into its world of values once presided over by the notion of fixity and immutability. The crowd hears even the most conservative of the new physicists say that by and large the old laws are true but that in this or that case exceptions must be noted. And the crowd begins to say similar things about long established concepts in the field of conduct. Monogamy! Chastity! And so on! The apostles of the new freedom begin to say that by and large these concepts are useful and true but that in this or that circumstance exceptions must be noted. The combination of *by-and-largeness* and *in-this-caseness* that marks the new physics begins to mark the new morals. The logic of all this may be faulty, but the fact is obvious. The new physics thus affects folk who know nothing of the new physics.

The moralist sees these seven major enterprises of the modern mind registering very definite effects upon the conduct of the current generation. These effects are due to the fact that in all these fields—the new politics, the new economics, the new theology, the new biology, the new philosophy, the new psychology, and the new physics—there has been a breaking up of the old fixities, a fluidizing of concepts, a sense that the cards are being reshuffled, that the books are not closed, that a thing thought immutable law a generation ago may have been but the expression of limited insight, a sense that the race is everywhere experimenting with values. The effect of all this upon conduct is definite if not direct. These seven enterprises of research and restatement have changed the climate of opinion in which Western man now considers questions of conduct along with all other issues.

The moralist thus sees the experimentalism of the laboratory inducing an experimentalism in life. And he comes upon one life after another that has met shipwreck in the process. Even the most realistic moralist, who admits the inevitability and assumes the rightness of the progressive adjustment of conduct-standards to changing insight into values, recognizes the shipwreck incident to the process, and wonders whether, in the difficult days ahead for the Western social order, we shall make intelligent moral use of modern knowledge.

In sketching this bird's-eye view of the six fears that have arisen out of six fields of modern research and modern experience, I have sought sedulously to keep my own judgments out of the picture. I have sought to serve simply as an amplifier through which the prophets of doom might speak. I am quite willing to say now, however, that I think these six fears rest upon very real grounds. But I do not think the story of modernism ends with the prophets of doom. The book of modernism has another story to tell. And it is to this other story that I want now to turn.

# III

# The Literature and Leadership of Hope

OUR observation flight over the basic fields of research
and experience has revealed at least six soils from which
the deadly nightshade of post-war fatalism flowered. We
have examined with measurable thoroughness the six social
fears that have been confessed in turn by the biologist, the
psychologist, the student of statecraft, the economist, the
administrator, and the moralist, as each, in terms of his
special field, has sought to sense the direction in which
Western civilization is moving. Must Western man accept
as final the fear-colored forecasts of these social analysts?
It is to this question that I want now to turn.

It is not necessary to deride the story that the prophets
of doom have told in order to doubt that the prophets of
doom have told the whole story. There are, I think, valid
grounds for most of the fears that have led responsible
scholars to list a new dark age among the possibilities that
lie ahead. "But, after all," admits Dean Inge, as a kind of
after-thought to one of his particularly fatalistic prophecies, "we judge our generation mainly by its surface cur-
rents. There may be in progress a storage of beneficent
forces we cannot see. There are ages of sowing and ages
of reaping. The brilliant epochs may be those in which
spiritual wealth is squandered; the epochs of apparent
decline may be those in which the race is recuperating after
an exhausting effort." The contention I want now to argue
is that, in the midst of the indisputable decline of the West,
to which the prophets of doom rightly direct our attention,
there has been in progress a storage of beneficent forces

which, if the West can but recruit the requisite statesmanship for their direction, may mean rebirth rather than death for the Western social order.

Alongside the existing literature of despair, in which the prophets of doom see the West entering the twilight of a new dark age, there is an emergent literature of hope, in which the West may, if it will, discover the road to a new renaissance. These contrasted literatures are not the products of a temperamental competition between confirmed pessimists and congenital optimists. They are simply the dual record of two separate sets of results that have been produced by the enterprise of modern research. The same basic researches that have produced the literature of despair are producing the literature of hope.

Scientific research has a double function when it deals with the processes of a civilization. In biology, in psychology, in political science, in economics, in all fields where the forces that make and unmake civilizations are subjected to critical assessment, modern science has done two things: (1) it has analyzed social tendencies, and (2) it has elaborated social techniques. And, alike in its analysis of social tendencies and in its elaboration of social techniques, research has sought to exclude from influence upon its conclusions such factors as the innate pessimism or the inveterate optimism of the researcher.

In dealing with the prophets of doom and the prophets of hope, we are not, therefore, dealing with sullen *Cassandras* and smiling *Polyannas* whose manifestoes are dictated by their moods. We are dealing, on the one hand, with responsible scholars whose analyses of social tendencies have revealed a West moving with dangerous momentum towards a new dark age, and, on the other hand, with equally responsible scholars whose researches have resulted in new social techniques by the use of which the West may reverse its direction and realize a new renaissance of social and spiritual energy. Modern research, in its most valid form, is at once investigative and inventive. Its investigative activity has produced the literature of despair. Its inventive activity is producing the emergent literature of hope.

This emergent literature of hope is not yet a coherent literature in the sense that the literature of despair is a coherent literature. It would be a relatively simple matter to select the titles for a five-foot shelf of the literature of despair, for the literature of despair has been reduced to clear-cut generalizations and confident forecasts. Its authors have deliberately set out to predict the future of Western civilization. It is, by design, a literature of prophecy based upon a critical exploration of the biological, psychological, political, economic, administrative, and moral blind alleys into which Western man has wandered. In contrast to this clearly formulated literature of despair, the literature of hope is as yet quite formless. It is really too early to call it a literature save as a device for bringing the possibilities it suggests into vivid relief against the probabilities the literature of despair sets forth.

This emergent literature of hope is as yet but an incoördinate mass of raw materials of fact and idea from which Western man may, if he will, construct redemptive policies. These raw materials of redemptive policy are hidden away in the mass of detailed results that have been thrown up by the spade-work of modern research. Biological research, for instance, has thrown up certain ideas which, disentangled from the details of the long and labored investigations that produced them, constitute biology's net contribution to the science of the management of the human future of the West. Modern psychology has, in like manner, made its contribution to an improved direction of Western affairs. So has economics. So has political science. So has sociology. So has the experimental study of ethics. So have all the sciences and philosophies springing from the loins of realistic research. So have the innumerable experimentations that critical intelligence has prosecuted in the practical processes of politics, of industry, and of the professions. When he has searched out these seminal ideas, produced by intensive researches and proved in isolated experiences, Western man will have before him a dependable inventory of the raw materials of social renewal. The now formless literature of hope will assume form and influence when these raw materials of social renewal have been assembled, interpreted, and translated into practical policies for the development and direction of the family life, the politics, the economic enterprise, the education, and the religion of the West.

The West can escape a new dark age and realize a new renaissance only through a social statesmanship that makes comprehensive and consistent use of these creative ideas that have been thrown up out of modern research and modern experience. What are these ideas? I shall not, as a layman, presume to select and to set them down here. That is an undertaking that must be managed by men in whom specialized knowledge of varied fields and a flair for social engineering meet and merge. That is a job for specialists who, rising above the limitations of specialism, are able to see the human implications of their fields and to relate their findings to the social processes of their time.

But of this much I am sure: there is no other road to renaissance for Western man. Intelligence actively applied in the scientific discovery and social utilization of knowledge is the only guaranty of survival for his social order. He must find his messiah in his mind. This is as true biologically of man, in general, as it is true socially of Western man, in particular. It is not safe for man to assume that he has title in perpetuity to the lordship of the earth. He must ponder the fate of his predecessors. Mammoth but virtually mindless mammals roamed and ruled the earth many million years longer than man has existed. But their bigness did not save them from biological break-down. Man is still an amateur in the long gallery of creatures who have ruled the earth only at last to make their bed in oblivion. But, happily, he has an instrument of protection that the dinosaurs and dinoceras of the dark past did not have. The means and methods of scientific research stand between him and the fate of his forerunners. Unlike them, man may, if he but puts his intelligence to the task, be the creator rather than the creature of his destiny. Through the discovery and application of scientific knowledge, it is conceivable that man may achieve biological immortality for himself as a species. Certainly it is only through the scientific discovery and social application of knowledge that the survival of his civilization can be assured.

Neither the literature of despair I have sketched nor the literature of hope I have suggested has brought Western man to clarity of decision respecting the road he is to take into the future. He stands confused and hesitant between two huge piles of materials. As he looks at the pile on his left, he finds an obvious jumble of materials, utterly lacking in coördination. As he examines this pile more closely, he understands why it lacks coördination. It is a pile of wreckage. It is made up of the débris of an order of life and thought to which modern-minded men no longer feel a convinced and eager allegiance. As he pokes about in this pile, he finds in it the worm-eaten and shattered timbers of many ancient shelters in which the minds and hearts of men were once at home. Dead doctrines, obsolete opinions, irrational inhibitions, cowardly cautions, foolish fears, silly superstitions, atrophied authorities, and other bits of wreckage are there. It is the dump-heap on which have been thrown all the things that have been bowled over and discarded by the critical intelligence of the modern man. In this pile the modern mind is getting ready for its bonfire of vanities.

But we must not push the analogy of the dump-heap too far. The modern mind has taken the timbers of many ancient shelters apart and piled them here. The really scientific minds of the time have emancipated themselves from many formerly regnant doctrines, opinions, inhibitions, fears, superstitions, and authorities, and have thrown them on this pile as if they were but lifeless relics and reminders of a dead order of thought and action. But we must reluctantly admit that there is life in the old order yet. Over this pile of wreckage there flickers a fitful light, a kind of unstable aura, that represents the lingering ghosts of once powerful intellectual, social, and political traditions. And these ghosts still dominate more minds than we like to admit. The scientific achievements of critical intelligence are still the working capital of a minority.

As Western man turns to his right, he sees another pile of materials. This pile seems, at first glance, to be about as jumbled, about as incoördinated, as the pile on his left. And it is. But, as he pokes about in this pile, he discovers a difference. This pile on his right is not a pile of wreckage, but a pile of raw materials. In it he finds all the new ideas, new idealisms, and new spiritual values that have been thrown up as by-products of the sciences, philosophies, and practical experimentations of the modern mind. He is looking now not on the dump-heap of an old order, but on the assembling-ground of the building materials for a new order of Western life.

These two piles of materials symbolize a high-tensioned conflict that is going on to-day throughout the Western world between what H. G. Wells has described as "very powerful social and political traditions" and "a spreading tide of new knowledge and an unprecedented onrush of new inventions that are entirely incompatible with these social and political traditions that still dominate men's minds." It is in this "spreading tide of new knowledge" and in this "unprecedented onrush of new inventions" that the raw materials of a literature of hope lie waiting the transforming touch of a new statesmanship.

The men whose researches have produced this flood of knowledge and this onrush of inventions have not been sentimentalists seeking to stir in Western man the spirit of hope, but scientists giving to Western man a chart of the anatomy of hope. They have not exhorted Western man to conjure up a blind belief in a bright destiny. They have been quite aware that the maladjustments and muddlings that justify the fears of the prophets of doom cannot be corrected by any such emotional incantation. They have not been social cheer leaders naïvely assuming that Western man can stand still, look up, think beautiful thoughts, and wish himself into a stable and significant civilization. It is a literature of hope that their researches have made possible, not a literature of optimism. Plugging away in their obscure laboratories and venturing bravely out on the far frontiers of knowledge, they have given to Western man the factual materials from which he may and must now fashion a realistic literature of hope that will do two things: (1) tell him how to go about removing the grounds upon which the biological, psychological, political, economic, administrative, and moral fears of the prophets of doom legitimately rest; and (2) tell him how to set going, nationally and internationally, those biological, psychological, political, economic, administrative, educational, and moral forces which alone can renew, enrich, and stabilize his civilization.

Unlike a literature of romantic optimism, this literature of realistic hope will uncover for Western man the unused resources of social health in his civilization and suggest to him workable techniques for using them. This literature of hope will have nothing to do with four false dawns that were heralded by four transient optimisms that flourished during the war and in the immediate post-war years: (1) the false dawn of a spiritual renewal to be inspired by the idealism of the war period; (2) the false dawn of a new mysticism which post-war spiritualism sought to materialize; (3) the false dawn of an attempted revival of a religion of dogmatic doctrinalism; (4) the false dawn of an atavistic idea of progress. It will not be the carrier of panaceas. It will be a practical manual of social engineering. It will go beyond and beneath the moods alike of optimism and despair. It will not be concerned at all with the moods of Western man as he speculates upon the future of his civilization. It will be concerned solely with his methodology as he sets about the business of renewing, enriching, and stabilizing his civilization. The buckling down to realistic social statesmanship, that the literature of hope will call for, will not be easy for Western man, because he has been notoriously a creature of whims, now marked by uncritical hope and now by uncritical despair.

In an exquisite little volume called *Ariel,* José Enrique Rodó retells from Guyau the story of a woman touched with a strange and wistful madness which consisted in her thinking that every day was to be the day of her marriage. In the blackness of every night she nursed and nourished this dream. Every morning, in the pale light, she put upon her pale forehead the marriage crown and draped herself in the marriage veil. Meticulously gowned, she invoked a smile to greet the imaginary bridegroom, and waited through the day for his coming, until another night threw its black blanket over her bright hope. For a few hours her madness became melancholy. But her inveterate hope would rise again with the dawn, and no memory of yesterday's disillusionment would cross her heart. Again she would set the marriage crown on her forehead. Again she would drape herself in the marriage veil. Again she would smile in confidence that her bridegroom would come. "It is to-day that he comes," she would insistently murmur until night again proved the vanity of her hope.

This is a faithful parable of the heart of Western man. He has been strangely unrealistic about his destiny. Incorrigible romancer that he is, despite his pretensions of *realpolitik,* he has displayed a mad genius for renewing his active hope generation after generation. He has suffered less from shortage than from surfeit of uncritical optimism. His self-esteem has outrun his self-criticism. He has been the consistent victim of what Rodó calls that "sublime stubbornness of hope which is born all winged from the very breast of delusion." This inveterate hope has, it is true, been punctuated by interludes of fear. Western man is in such an interlude just now. But, at best, he has alternated between uncritical hope and uncritical fear. He has never quite risen to that realism which is beyond hope and fear. Unless he can rise to this realism, the Western spirit would as well go defeatist now.

It is this realism which is beyond hope and fear that informs the now emergent literature of hope. This literature, when responsibly formulated, will suggest that Western man set coolly to work using its ideas and techniques to determine his destiny instead of wasting his days speculating upon his destiny, with his speculations now colored by the enervating mood of optimism and now controlled by the paralyzing mood of despair. "Hope and fear," says Benedetto Croce, is a casual essay in his *The Conduct of Life*, "are precious parts of life and precious aids to living. But they lose their value, they become sources of weakness and embarrassment, when they are fixed as attitudes, habits, points of arrival. If anxiety lays hold on a man and comes to dominate his personality, he is paralyzed; he is reduced to impotence. Losing confidence in himself, he finally thinks of himself as finished, as dead. And hopefulness operates in the same way. It blunts the acuteness of our vision; it saps the energy of our action, lulling us to repose in the fatuous confidence that things will turn out right anyway." All this is as true of a people as of a person. And this is why I am concerned to emphasize the radical difference between the literature of hope here dealt with and a literature of optimism. A literature of optimism is a literature that does little more than seek to stir in us a spirit of expectancy bolstered by a blind belief that there is a good time coming. Western man must beware this facile and foolhardy sort of optimism. It blunts the acuteness of his vision. It saps the energy of his action. It lulls him to a fatal repose. And, in like manner, he must

refuse to let an uncritical despair unnerve his determination
to be the conscious creator and controller of a satisfying
destiny.

If I may now summarize and bring to conclusion the
simple thesis I am advancing, the still distressingly incoördinate mass of results produced by the critical intelligence of modern man constitutes the beginnings of a literature of hope, but its constructive formulation is still to be effected. The age of analysis has given us the raw materials for a new order of Western thought, organization, and
action, but we are still lingering in the ante-room of an age
of synthesis that shall take these achievements of specialism and coördinate them into the marching orders of a way
of life for modern man.

I can hear coming through the thick brick walls of my
study a thousand skeptical protests against the feasibility
of a formula of social renewal that depends for its fruit-
fulness upon the acceptance and application by the Western
masses, in the governance of their common life, of the realistic results of critical intelligence in the fields of modern
research and modern experience. It is maintained, and
rightly so, that a new credulity has paradoxically arisen in
this skeptical age of science. And the fact of this new
credulity has made many social analysts more cynical than
ever of the possibility of achieving anything like social
realism to an extent sufficient to dictate the character of
Western civilization. For this reason it is important to
examine closely the nature of this new credulity.

There is no escaping the fact that we are citizens of an
age at once the most skeptical and the most gullible in
human history. Science, in putting to rout the old superstition, has given rise to a new superstition, which has
taken the form of a near-universal belief in the infallible
and inexhaustible ingenuity of scientists. The ancients met
their perplexities with the assertion that the Lord will
provide. The moderns meet their perplexities with the
assertion that Science will provide. The scientist main-

tains a hold upon the confidence of the commoner that would have been the envy of the medicine men of primitive generations. Almost anything, however bizarre and beside the point, can get a hearing to-day, if it but comes with a laboratory label. A supposedly sophisticated generation pours barrels of money annually into the coffers of the purveyors of mental and medical quackeries that come with an elaborate air of research and wear the borrowed finery of a scientific vocabulary. The scientist has worked such marvels in the physical transformation of our world and its enterprise that the masses of modern men slip easily into a tacit assumption of the omniscience of scientists. And this new credulity is leading Western man into many blind alleys.

That all this puts new hurdles across the road to a realistic statesmanship cannot be denied. But there is a good side to this new gullibility that the cynics may be overlooking. If the modern masses are facile in accepting scientific quackeries, they are also facile in adopting scientific realities. Insulin caught the popular imagination almost as easily as a fake cancer cure raises fresh hope in the fear-stricken hearts of victims of that subtle and as yet mystic malady. The validities of authentic science as well as the fakeries of pseudo-science race across the modern mind like a prairie fire. Whether Western man renews, enriches, and stabilizes his civilization will depend entirely, I think, upon whether he breeds and brings to power leaders with the requisite intellectual capacity and social insight for piloting such a modernization of his social order. If there are men to lead, the masses will follow. I cannot in any wise concur in the contention, insistently made by many intellectuals, that there is in the Western masses either an incapacity or an unwillingness to follow a leadership of social realism.

It lies, I am sure, within the power of Western man to insure the historic stability and human enrichment of Western civilization by sinking the roots of his social policies in the results that have come from the patient and productive investigations of biologist, psychologist, statesman, economist, administrator, educator, moralist, and kindred pioneers in the quest for new insight into nature and human nature. And the imperative preliminary to this West-wide venture in social statesmanship is the capture and correlation in a coherent but ever-changing literature of hope of the socially creative ideas and techniques these fields have given.

Little is to be gained by inadequately informed lay speculation upon the technical nature and social meaning of the contributions the separate sciences have made towards redemptive policies for the Western social order. This is, as I have said, a task that must be taken over by uniquely gifted scientists and statesmen with specialized knowledge in their respective fields of learning and leadership. I turn aside from this crucial next step in the thesis I am here developing, not only because it is a step I lack the expertness to take, but because this book is not concerned primarily with the content of policies, but with the sources of power and strategies of progress for the Western future.

In suggesting this emergent literature of hope, I have directed attention to what seems to me one of the major sources of power for the Western future. I want now to turn to what seems to me an important preliminary stroke of strategy for the Western future by discussing a bit more in detail the leadership needed to bring the latent vitalities of this literature of hope into active play.

The West faces the definite possibility of a new dark age because Western man has not used these raw materials of renewal, as he might have used them, in the building of a family life at once rich in human values and realistic in its social adjustment to an altered world, in the elaboration of an education designed to fit men for life and leadership in an age of breath-taking change and baffling complexity, in the vivification of religion as a sweetening and strengthening force in his secular affairs, in the practice of a politics sensitively attuned to the changing life-processes of his social order, in the harmonization of his business and industrial policies with the new forces of science and technology, and in the organization of his international relations in terms of the newly intricate interdependence of the modern world. It is more than economic depression that afflicts us. There is a profound and pervasive maladjustment between the traditional structure and policies of Western society and the new processes of working and living instigated by modern research and instituted by modern experience. It is this hiatus between the leap of new processes and the lag of old policies that has produced the prevailing malaise of Western society. But Western man must not go fatalist and assume that it is an incurable sickness that afflicts his society. It will be far from easy to effect, and there is no guaranty that it will be effected, but the cure is, I think, clearly indicated.

We can, I am convinced, realize a sweeping renaissance of Western civilization if we consciously set ourselves to the task of making these raw materials of renewal, progressively thrown up out of modern research and modern experience, the basis of policy and action throughout our common life. Western civilization must choose between social control by design or social suicide by default. And the only sound social control is a control developed and administered in terms of the best knowledge we have. The problem of our generation is to bring modern knowledge into contact with modern life in a manner that will make it socially effective. The men and the women who can help us do this will be the engineers of a new renaissance. How are we to go about this Gargantuan task? What sort of leadership do we need? It is with some aspects of this problem of procedure and leadership that I want now to deal.

We should be able to effect this progressive adjustment of man to his changing social environment through the

normal ministries of church and school and state. Candor
compels us to admit that we are not. The disease of institutionalism that afflicts church and school and state
hampers these institutions in this their major function.
The cosmogonies and theologies of the church, the curricula and teaching formulas of the school, the compromises and traditions of the state, with a seeming
inevitability, play for fixity rather than fluidity save when
lashed and led into imperative readjustments. The renaissance of the West must, I am convinced, find its initiative
and its driving force outside the routines of Western institutionalism. It must be captained by that growing band
of men and women, scattered throughout the West, in
whose blood the fires of the future burn unabated by the
dampening futilities and frustrations of the blind orthodoxies of their time. And it must begin, at least, by seeking to remake the adult minds that are exercising control
or may exercise control of Western affairs either as leaders
or as the supporting mass that gives leadership its mandate,
with the hope, lurking in the background of the enterprise,
that its impact may make for productive change in the
normal ministries of church and school and state. The
problems of procedure and leadership involved in releas-
ing the latent creativity that is locked in contemporary
knowledge call for a volume all by itself, a volume I hope
some day to foreshadow even if I may be unable adequately
to write it. I am content here to advance two suggestions,
the first having to do with the formulation of the raw
materials of renewal for the adult popular mind, the
second having to do with the fostering of interest among
the people generally in these raw materials.

I suggest that we need to have done for contemporary
knowledge something analogous to what Diderot and
the Encyclopedists did for the knowledge of the eighteenth
century. Western civilization would profit greatly from
the labors of a group of men who would go, with expertness
and conscientious care, through the findings of the natural

and social sciences and through the results of experiment and experience in political, social, and economic administration, pulling out, tabulating, and reducing to readily understandable terms the net contributions each of these ventures of the modern mind has made to the future of the West. This would give us, as I suggested earlier, something approaching a comprehensive inventory of the raw materials of social renewal upon which we must depend to invest with reality our enterprises of social creation and social control.

All of the sciences have lying in their laboratories, relatively unused, socially significant ideas which would, if put to work, lift the whole tone and temper of Western life. Unfortunately many of these ideas are now buried under the jargon of technical scholarship and effectively insulated from contact with the common life. Now and then fitful and fractional glimpses of these ideas find their way into the press to be misinterpreted and manhandled by the obscurantists in their misguided warfare against the whole salutary output of the modern mind. If we are to save the results of research from slander at the hands of the demagogue and prevent the sterilization of science as the mystic arcana of monastic savants, there must be some soundly conceived attempt to winnow out from the chaff of attendant detail the social and spiritual contributions of scholarship and to translate their values into the vernacular. We have little right to complain of the victories won by the evangelism of superstition until we have matched it with an equally insistent evangelism of science.

Research may unearth all of the necessary raw materials for a Western renaissance, but these raw materials of policy will be about as significant as so much sawdust if they are allowed to lie unused in our laboratories or remain buried in technical brochures that none save the initiated can decode. And they will not be used promptly enough or in any socially effective manner unless the man in the street is given at least a bowing acquaintance with their broad implications. Applied science, no less than practical politics, must capture and convince constituencies. This is the price it must pay for the chance to play directly upon life. If we are to realize a renaissance of the West, we must somehow contrive to thrust the results of research into the stream of common thought and make them the basis of our social action. The productive scholar is the hope of civilization, but his contributions do not become active social assets until they get beyond the stage of inarticulate accuracy. We have no right to damn the commoner for his cavalier disregard of science until science has talked to him in terms he can understand. He is not a mind reader.

Two aspects of the scholar-mind stand in the way of any such sweeping socialization of science by scholars themselves: (1) the scholar's altogether admirable habit of holding his conclusions continuously open to revision, and (2) the scholar's priest-like devotion to pure science as distinguished from applied science. These qualities are vital to the enterprise of scholarship. I review them here, not in their relation to scientific progress, but in their relation to social progress.

In holding his conclusions continuously open to revision under the successive impacts of fresh insight and further information, the scholar is protecting the conscience of scholarship from the temptation to dicker with dogmatic assumptions or to give stubborn loyalty to vested ideas. In his priest-like devotion to pure science, the scholar is protecting the chastity of scholarship from seduction to sheer utility. It is necessary to recognize, however, that these habits of mind which are assets to the scholar in the scientific discovery of knowledge may become liabilities to the scholar in the social application of knowledge.

The scholar's habit of floating his conclusions in a stream of qualifications and forever reminding us that he may have to change them tomorrow, and his intellectual preference for the uncompromising processes of pure science over the blurring compromises that inevitably attend the application of ideas in human affairs, tend to withdraw the scholar from contact with the going processes of the socio-economic order, to cut the nerve of action in him, and to retard the ministry of knowledge in the affairs of an age. The scholar-mind is apt to shy away from the sort of venture in summary, synthesis, and social interpretation I am here suggesting. To select and to seek to interpret to the lay mind the net contributions the sciences have severally made to the Western future smacks of a definitiveness and cocksureness inconsistent with the practice of suspended judgment which is of the essence of scholarship. Any practical program of action, looking towards the stabilization and enrichment of Western life through the social application of modern knowledge, is bound to be marked by elements of compromise and over-simplification that will irk the scholar, whose breadth of knowledge makes it difficult for him to bring devotion and drive to those limited and feasible programs that seem essential in the practical politics of progress. I realize the importance of suspended judgment in the work of the scholar. To this modesty of scholarship the world owes a debt it can never discharge. But we must also face the fact that a civilization will starve on a diet of suspended judgments alone. The scholar dares not turn dogmatist. He must hold his conclusions forever open to revision in the light of further research. But this does not obviate the fact that, unless Western civilization is to play into the hands of selfish interests and social inertia, Western man must evolve a better technique than he has yet employed for using the results of scholarly research in the determination of its basic policies.

I am not sure but that the scholarly fraternity has overdone its insistence that pure science and applied science must be kept severely apart, as if great advances are not likely to be made if the researcher keeps a weather eye on

the possibility of humanly usable results. I am not sure
that the advance of science depends upon any such immacu-
late conception of ideas. Pasteur, who did a rather decently
distinguished job in the field of pure science, did not scorn
to bend his energies to the solution of the practical problems of the farmers and distillers of the region he served
as scientist and schoolman. And some of his purest scientific results came out of his most practical investigations.
Research that is rooted in the problems that beset and
baffle the Western masses is, I suspect, neither unworthy
of scientists nor inimical to the advance of science. Western man cannot, in fact, afford a science that is remote
from life, technical beyond intelligibility save to the specialists, and pursuing its explorations in serene aloofness
above the battles of a headless and haphazard West. He
stands to gain little from a theory of pure science that is
perverted into a rationalization of the scientist's escape
from his social responsibility.

"The true purity of knowledge," as John Dewey has
said, in his *The Public and Its Problems*, "exists not when
it is uncontaminated by contact with use and service. It is
wholly a moral matter, an affair of honesty, impartiality,
and generous breadth of intent in search and communication. The adulteration of knowledge is due not to its
use, but to vested bias and prejudice, to one-sidedness of
outlook, to vanity, to conceit of possession and authority,
to contempt or disregard of human concern in its use. . . .
To make physical science a rival of human interests is bad
enough, for it forms a diversion of energy that can ill be
afforded. But the evil does not stop there. The ultimate
harm is that the understanding by man of his own affairs
and his ability to direct them are sapped at their root
when knowledge is disconnected from its human function.
. . . Knowledge is communication as well as understanding. . . . The schools may suppose that a thing is known
when it is found out, [but] a thing is fully known only
when it is published, shared, socially accessible. Record

and communication are indispensable to knowledge. Knowledge cooped up in a private consciousness is a myth, and knowledge of social phenomena is peculiarly dependent upon dissemination, for only by distribution can such knowledge be either obtained or tested. A fact of community life which is not spread abroad so as to be a common possession is a contradiction in terms. . . . A glance at the situation shows that the physical and external means of collecting information in regard to what is happening in the world have far outrun the intellectual phase of inquiry and organization of its results. . . . Democracy . . . is a name for a life of free and enriching communion. . . . It will have its consummation when free social inquiry is indissolubly wedded to the art of full and moving communication."

But quite aside from the outcome of an academic debate about the difference, real or imagined, between pure and applied science, we may agree, I think, that the final justification of all analysis is synthesis, and that the goal of all scientific discovery is social application. And this means, it seems to me, that every now and then we must gather up the results of a period of research into what, for want of a better term, may be called tentative dogmatisms upon which society can act until further research reveals sounder bases for social action.

Such tentative dogmatisms would not do violence to the scientific spirit. They would, on the contrary, if intelligently used, faithfully express it. The scholar may be pardoned the fear that the popular mind is so accustomed to the tenacious dogmatisms of superstition that it would misinterpret the purpose of the scholars if they sought to set up a series of tentative dogmatisms of science, that society would cling to these tentative dogmatisms long after the scientists had been forced to change them, leaving the scholars responsible for social policies they had themselves outgrown. The risk here is real. But the solution of this difficulty does not lie in the scholar's refusing to accept responsibility for social leadership; the solution lies rather in the development of an education that will stimulate in students the spirit of science as well as set before them the discoveries of science. A generation truly trained in the scientific spirit will not be afraid to act, in social affairs, upon tentative dogmatisms and to scrap them as soon as further knowledge proves them inadequate.

The really important results of research invariably get used socially, but only after a long and wasteful period of resistance. The question that Western man, face to face with the threat of a new dark age, needs to answer just now is: Might not a more alert social statesmanship speed up this transfer of knowledge from the stage of discovery to the stage of application instead of leaving the transfer to the slow fortunes of a snail-paced infiltration into the popular mind or to the manipulation of purely materialistic interests? If Western civilization is a race between education and catastrophe, might we not help education to win the race by ferreting out and making intelligible to the commoners the major results of modern research and modern experience? I think we can. And I think one of the first moves in this enterprise is the making of a comprehensive, but avowedly tentative, inventory of the socially usable ideas that have been produced by the natural and social sciences and by experiment and experience in political, social, and economic administration. The New Encyclopedists are overdue!

Where shall we find the men and women for this venture? If an evangelism of science is needed, can we effect a working partnership between the accuracy of the scholar and the appeal of the evangelist? Effective evangelism has long served the sensational and the traditional. Can it be made the servant of the realistic and the creative? This is the problem that will confront the New Encyclopedists. It is a problem that the productive scholars may not be able to solve by themselves, for two fairly obvious reasons:

(1) in many instances, the productive scholar may not be the best judge of what his net contribution to the future has been, and if he undertakes to distil from his achievements the socially usable essence, he may dissipate his own energies, distract the attention of the people, and obscure the main point by spending too much time on collateral aspects of his ideas, aspects that may be important to him as a technical scholar, but of minor significance in terms of social application; (2) the spirit of propaganda and the spirit of research do not work well together in the average scholar-mind, each tending to reduce the effectiveness of the other. This does not mean that the tentative summary and interpretation of the socially usable ideas of the time must be made by facile laymen who may take a few months off to brush up on the sciences. Here and there and yonder, inside and outside our universities and research institutes, there are unusual scholars who combine the burrowing qualities of the mole with the singing qualities of the lark, men who are masters alike of the science of research and the art of expression. It is from the ranks of these scholar-geniuses that we must draw the leaders of the New Encyclopedists. Such men will know how to make use of good minds and facile pens that lie outside the ranks of the professional scholars.

Science has two obligations: (1) the obligation to discover, and (2) the obligation to disseminate. Scientists have never taken the second obligation as seriously as they have taken the first. They have, in fact, been a bit patronizing to the man who has sought to translate his scientific values into the social vernacular. They have respected the burrowing mole. They have been suspicious of the singing lark. It may be a survival of the Puritan distrust of anything save the austere, but the man who has put artistry into his activity has not been looked upon as safe and sane and sound. The scholar-world has preferred his more leaden-footed brother. But the West is now in the midst

of a confusion and complexity which require a leadership of
clarification, and such leadership must rest upon a power of
interpretation as well as a power of investigation.

"It has often been said," says John Dewey, in the discussion from which I have just quoted, "and with a great
appearance of truth, that the freeing and perfecting of
inquiry would not have any especial effect. For, it is argued,
the mass of the reading public is not interested in learning
and assimilating the results of accurate investigation. Unless these are read, they cannot seriously affect the thought
and action of members of the public; they remain in se-
cluded library alcoves, and are studied and understood only
by a few intellectuals. The objection is well taken save as
the potency of art is taken into account. . . . Presentation is fundamentally important, and presentation is a question of art. . . . The freeing of the artist in literary
presentation, in other words, is as much a precondition of
the desirable creation of adequate opinion on public matters as is the freeing of social inquiry."

It is important that the scholarly world bring the enterprise of social interpretation to a parity with the enterprise
of scientific investigation. The West cannot afford to have
the two torn apart, with the enterprise of interpretation
damned by the doctors as superficial journalism. The New
Encyclopedists must marry scholarship to journalism. And
in the union each must learn from the other. The scholar
is inspired by the passion to understand. The journalist is
inspired by the passion to be understood. Functioning in
isolation each falls short of his maximum ministry to his
time. The passion to understand without the passion to
be understood has given us the jargon of the researcher.
The passion to be understood without the passion to understand has given us the journalese of the reporter. The
New Encyclopedists must be at once men of insight and
of intelligibility. They cannot afford either jargon or journalese. "The great men of culture," Matthew Arnold
once wrote, "are those who have a passion for diffusing,

for making prevail, for carrying from one end of society to the other, the best knowledge, the best ideas of their time; who have labored to divest knowledge of all that was harsh, uncouth, difficult, abstract, professional, exclusive; to humanize it, to make it efficient outside the clique of the cultivated and learned, yet remaining the best knowledge and thought of the time." Here are the marching orders for the New Encyclopedists!

The New Encyclopedists will labor under a handicap from the outset unless the scholars are willing to recognize the function of interpretation as not inferior to the function of investigation. That they have not so recognized it is one of the major sins of the scholar-mind. Count Hermann Keyserling has spoken penetratingly of this in his *The World In The Making.* "It is true enough," he says, "that journalistic technique seldom serves the finest spirit. But this does not in any wise alter the fact that to-day this is the kind of technique which can achieve most. Very few have the time and the taste for the reading of heavy volumes. For them, scientific values must be prepared in the compactest and most practical form if they are to assimilate them. And further be it noted that this circumstance does not in itself indicate superficiality on the part of the reader, but rather a higher development of the intellect. He who catches the drift of a matter in the content of a brief phrase is as absolutely superior to the one who needs laborious argumentation as the man of pithy expression is to the man of pompous phraseology. That the journalistic gift is in itself no indication of inferiority is proved by the single fact that, without exception, all great statesmen were, in their manipulation of the masses, masters of the journalistic method, and that the ablest directors of our time have come from the ranks of the journalists. The gift in question means in itself nothing more nor less than the capacity for brief, telling, and effective expression. What else, indeed, was characteristic of the most effective among the profound spirits of all times—be they kings or sages—if not this very gift? Were they not all to this extent not simply journalists, but indeed superjournalists? With our present-day rapidity of intercourse . . . it is only the superjournalist who can, in any event, achieve significance for the good." Scholarship must come to acknowledge its larks, no less than its moles, as reputable members of its household.

Much of what I am suggesting is already being done by the scholar-geniuses I have described and by a small band of really responsible lay interpreters, who know the difference between the vulgate and vulgarity, but it is as yet a scattered enterprise, lacking the impact of a coherently organized attempt to interpret the major findings of the modern mind. This is an enterprise that deserves the sponsorship of some great university or some great publishing house, for, despite the almost insuperable difficulties that will attend its execution, it is, I think, socially imperative. I cannot but believe that the victories of intelligence will be insecure, liable to periodic defeats by strange revivals of obscurantism, until, as I put it earlier, we match the evangelism of superstition with an equally insistent evangelism of science.

I have said that I think we have at hand most of the necessary raw materials for a renaissance of Western civilization, and that the question is: Will we have the wisdom to recognize, the genius to coördinate, and the will to utilize these raw materials on anything like a grand scale for the renewal of our common life? I think that an affirmative answer to this question will depend largely upon whether there arises some leader-genius who will be able to capture the attention of the Western world and fire its imagination with the spiritual and social possibilities that are locked up in these new ideas, new idealisms, and new spiritual values with which modern research and modern experience have provided us. I am quite aware that this leaning upon great personal leadership will, in the minds of many, date me as distinctly pre-modern. Let me report a typical conversation with a distinguished scholar who agrees fully with the suggestion that the renewal of the West can come only through the social use of the results of modern research and modern experience, but disagrees emphatically with the suggestion that any such movement of social renewal needs or is likely to find a single great leader to inspire it.

"You are entirely right," he said, "in saying that modern research and modern experience have furnished Western civilization with the raw materials of a new renaissance. And I am not without hope that we shall get around to using these raw materials. I think you and I may live to see this new renaissance, but, if and when it comes, there will be no single leader around which its forces will rally. I think you are being misled by your memory of great historical movements. The Renaissance had its Erasmus. The Reformation had its Luther. The Revival had its Wesley. But the new renaissance you suggest is a different sort of movement and must work itself out in a different sort of age. And these two facts underlie the two reasons why Western civilization will not find renewal in the trail of a great personal leader."

"Let's take your two reasons one at a time," I suggested.

"All right," he said, "here is the first reason. Your New Encyclopedists, if there were enough of them, might roughly and tentatively list the major results of modern research and modern experience in a helpful manner, but the mere bulk of modern knowledge has become so great that it is intellectually impossible for any one man to come to know enough about the varied fields of human thought and interest to enable him to bring anything like general leadership to the situation in which the West finds itself. With knowledge increasing by leaps and bounds while the intellectual capacity of mankind remains stationary, we have reached a time when the individual mind must be content with specialisms. There can never be another Aristotle, or even a Descartes or a Humboldt. The next renaissance must be a renaissance by piecemeal. A movement that means the propagation of a set of doctrines or the contagion of a new emotion may still be promoted by a great leader, but a world-wide movement that means the synthesis and social application of modern knowledge can have no single leader. It can have only leaders in the various fields of knowledge. And this brings me to the second reason. The time has passed for trusting to great leaders. Humanity has had its fill of Napoleonism. And a Napoleonism in the fields of the mind and the spirit would be the worst of all. We are out of the age of great personal leadership. We are in an age of group leadership."

I cannot bring myself to agreement with these contentions. We have allowed ourselves to be unduly awed by the mere bulk of modern knowledge, damning as a dabbler the man who seeks a thread of coherent meaning in the complex mass of its details. I am quite aware that we have gone past the great systematizers. We do not want an Aristotle to lay out an authoritarian pattern of modern knowledge to chill and chain the Western mind with its orthodoxy. Modern knowledge with its vastness, its variety, and its vitality is not amenable to that sort of synthesis. Another Aristotle, in the sense of a master of the minutiae of all knowledge, is manifestly impossible. But this is not to say that the sheer mass of modern knowledge makes impossible a general leadership in the social utilization of its central values. If the specialization that marks modern scholarship is not to spell social suicide, Western man must rescue the modern mind from the fatalism it displays in the presence of modern knowledge when it refuses to attempt any intellectual generalship on the assumption that anything beyond a meticulous truck-farming of tiny tracts of knowledge must be superficial. The generalship of a single great Western leader in the enterprise of harnessing modern knowledge to modern needs is not impossible. In any field of knowledge the truly seminal ideas are few and simple, at least susceptible of simple statement. And I believe that one of those rare, intuitive minds that the race seems to throw up at historic intervals could, even at this late date, range over the whole field of modern knowledge, arrive at a fairly accurate sense of the few seminal ideas the sciences have severally contributed to the social and spiritual future of the West, and render a distinguished service to civilization by playing generalissimo to the scientists and recruiting officer to the masses who must be won to a willingness to plant their common life in the soil of science.

This distillation of the essence of modern knowledge, which must precede such leadership, is as urgently needed in scholarship as in statesmanship. And it is neither impossible nor inimical to sound scholarship, for, as H. G. Wells has accurately said, in the varied sciences as in history, as the gaps fill in, the outline simplifies, and as the outlook broadens, the clustering multitude of details dissolves into general laws. The sort of leader I here project would in no sense supplant group leaderships; he would but supplement them, as impresario of the organized statesmanship of the varied functional groups in Western life. He would play ringmaster to the specialists, luring them out of their sometimes thought-tight compartments and welding them into a fighting fraternity for the common good. He would have to be a combination of Francis Bacon and Theodore Roosevelt. He would have to be a man of vast catholicity of interests, an omnivorous reader, who had ranged widely over the fields of human knowledge, and had made himself more or less at home with the great generalizations that have emerged and are emerging from the sciences, philosophies, and practical experiences of mankind. And there would have to be just enough of the alloy of mountebankery in him to enable him to touch the imagination of the masses. At home with the creative minds and at grips with the crowd mind, such a leader, rightly placed, might invest the whole adventure of the modern mind with that absorbing passion for humanity which has characterized all great epochs of civil and religious progress.

I am not thinking of such leadership in terms of a secular messiah who would play miracle man to a muddled world. I am thinking only that such leadership might awaken an effective popular impulse to search out, to interpret, and to weave into social policy these new ideas, new idealisms, and new spiritual values that have been thrown up out of our laboratories, our class-rooms, our philosophers' closets, our industrial institutions, and our political experimentations. Such impulse, in any wide-spread and effective sense, is to-day lacking. We stand outside our laboratories eagerly waiting for any result of research that we may apply to the material enterprises of our time, but we display a strange reluctance to bring science, in like manner, to the guidance to our larger social policies. It is not chimerical, I think, to suppose that even one great personality, with a genius for leadership, might stir the whole Western world to a realization that the same scientific spirit that has enabled us to remake our civilization materially can help us to remake it socially and spiritually. The civilization of the West is in a state of delicate balance. The scales may tip towards retrogression or towards renaissance. Even one superb leader, with a devotion to science and a passion for humanity, might, I believe, tip the scales towards renaissance.

To say that humanity has gone past the age of great personal leadership sounds strangely unconvincing in a generation that has seen the rise to power of a Lenin and a Gandhi. As one sees these two rebels extraordinary in, say, René Fülöp-Miller's *Lenin and Gandhi,* they are at once widely different and singularly alike. Here are two men through whom the "dumb world of the disinherited" found voice. Both set out to be high-priests of the humble. Both achieved hynotic power over their followers. Both achieved sway over the crowd without the cleverness and cadence of the orator. Lenin's weapon was the sword; Gandhi's weapon is the spirit. They flowered from different soils—Lenin from the soil of the peasant's cruelty, Gandhi from the soil of the saint's gentleness. Lenin chose violence as an instrument for realizing his dream; Gandhi scorns violence. Lenin sought to emancipate Russia's millions through machinery; Gandhi seeks to emancipate India's millions from machinery. Lenin dreamed of a Russia gone forward into the age of giant power; Gandhi dreams of an India gone backward into the age of the spinning wheel. Lenin preached the submergence of the individual; Gandhi preaches the supremacy of the individual. But both have proved by their dramatic leaderships that, regardless of the social philosophy involved, the masses still respond to the powerful personal leader.

I doubt that the sort of leader I suggest is likely to appear as a wandering free-lance. The modern West seems organized against the itinerant prophet. We are so busy, so distracted, and so obsessed with the idols of respectability and exalted position! Humanity seems even readier than it was nineteen hundred years ago to crucify, at least by ostracism and neglect, a leadership that appears with no authority save the intrinsic authority of its own sincerity and insight. We have difficulty in recognizing great leadership apart from the glittering regalia of high office and the clamorous cry of mob approval. This probably means that the Erasmus of any new renaissance, the Luther of any new reformation, the Wesley of any new revival of Western civilization will have to be a man whose official position gives to his voice a sounding-board with world-wide resonance and invests his pronouncements with an automatic prestige. An American President or a British Premier, possessing the qualities I have suggested, might light the fires of renaissance by putting the prestige and attention-getting values of his office back of the new ideas, new idealisms, and new spiritual values that the New Encyclopedists might uncover.

The function of this leader will not, however, be merely to press-agent the New Encyclopedists. His function will be more creative than that. There are, in addition to the technical contributions the sciences have made towards the equipment of the new statesmanship, which the New Encyclopedists will assemble and interpret, certain broad concepts of policy, flowering from the soil of these technical contributions, which it will be the business of a general leadership to formulate and force upon the attention of the Western masses. These concepts are readily reducible to a simplicity of statement that even the ill-informed millions can grasp. They are concepts that creative leadership might readily infuse with that emotional content which even the most realistic ideas must have if they are to be made regnant in the life of an era. The milling masses in the midst of their confusion can be made to feel vividly the urgent importance of these concepts in the current distraction that is making the Western world nerveless and insecure. These broad concepts, ably and insistently propagated by the sort of leader I have projected, may be made the spear-head of a thrust that will open the way for a widespread social application in Western life of the more technical contributions of the sciences.

These broad concepts, rather than the detailed ideas and techniques that science has given to Western man as the tools of reconstruction, are likely to prove the arousing words that will call the West to action. For the ideas that whole peoples blazon on banners and make the rallying cries for a fresh advance in their common life are invariably simple ideas. Involved and abstruse ideas, however vital they may have been to the policies of a period, have never moved vast masses of men either directly or quickly, but only by indirection and slow seepage into the common mind. The peoples of the West cannot, in their present plight, await the slow seepage of ideas. They dare not trust themselves to guidance by indirection. It is the business of Western leadership to find the few flaming ideas that will recruit the emotional energies of the Western masses in a West-wide reconstructive effort.

This is a task that a single great leader with the peculiar genius this particular juncture in Western affairs calls for might do triumphantly. It is to this problem of finding and following these contagious rallying cries that I want now to turn.

## IV

# Rallying Cries of Western Advance

JOSEPH CONRAD, who caught the music and the madness
of the sea in his imperishable prose, and in whose tales the
sea sings with its joys and sobs with its griefs until it
ceases to be a body of water and becomes a vivid human
thing, had a word-sense that approached wizardry. He
was himself so transcendently gifted in bending and binding words to his purposes that it is small wonder he appre-
ciated the creative power of the right words at critical
junctures in human affairs.

"He who wants to persuade," I find him saying in *A
Personal Record,* "should put his trust not in the right
argument, but in the right word. The power of sound has
always been greater than the power of sense. I don't say
this by way of disparagement. It is better for mankind to
be impressionable than reflective. Nothing humanly great
—great, I mean, as affecting a whole mass of lives—has
come from reflection. On the other hand, you cannot fail
to see the power of mere words; such words as Glory, for
instance, or Pity. . . . Shouted with perseverance, with
ardour, with conviction, these two by their sound alone
have set whole nations in motion and upheaved the dry,
hard ground on which rests our whole social fabric. . . .
Of course the accent must be attended to. The right accent.
That's very important. . . . Give me the right word
and the right accent and I will move the world."

Without confirming its implied undervaluation of reason
and response to reason, here is a sound generalization of
social statesmanship. Words have precipitated creative

revolutions and sent whole peoples into cataclysmic wars. In the forefront of every historic march forward in the common life of a people there have been electrifying words —rallying cries—that have given voice to theretofore dimly felt needs and inarticulate aspirations of the masses. The right selection of the words, the aptness with which they have been built into phrases, and the accent with which they have leaped from the mouth of leadership have had much to do with their power to recruit men to a common cause. These magic words have not made history by their own power alone, but only when the minds of men have been prepared for their reception either by the drift of events or by the design of statesmen. Words are magic when the stage is set for them. They fall powerless on unprepared hearts.

There is, I think, a four-fold formula that underlies creative advances in the common life of a people: (1) the old philosophies and old procedures of the politico-social order fall into futility by failing to keep alive to the changing circumstances of the civilization they were designed to serve; (2) new philosophies and new procedures, alert in their motivation and adapted in their method to the new circumstances of the time, are meanwhile hammered out by the scientists and seers whose historic mission it is to be the unofficial statesmen who keep fresh and flowing the streams of living insight from which the official statesmen may drink if they will; (3) after a long period of maladjustment between the old policies and the new problems of the civilization in question, a period in which the vast majority of the people, despite increasing difficulties, cling uncritically to the traditional order, the masses of men, who may be quite in ignorance of the preparation the elect minds of the time have made for fresh ventures in policy, grow openly skeptical of the philosophy and leadership in control of affairs, but continue to fumble for the clue to a new departure in their common life; and (4) a new leadership appears to put into words that towards which the masses have been blindly groping, words that flower from the soil the scientists and seers have plowed and sown, words that rise above the technical terminologies of the new social processes they herald, words that walk up and down in the hearts of men, words that become the rallying cries for a fresh advance of the human spirit.

When this happens, if solid genius is waiting to assume managerial responsibility, the clock strikes twelve, a thousand and one hitherto divergent forces come together in collaboration, the distractions of the time disappear in a new coherence of purpose, the common life thrills to a sense of common aim, and a whole people finds itself in a new phase of its social evolution. But the moment of pause before a new leadership gives voice to the inarticulate hungers of a harassed age is a moment when almost anything may happen. The civilization in question hangs in delicate balance. If the new leadership is laggard in its coming or proves inept in translating the nature of the needed advance into terms that call contagiously and compellingly to the masses of the people, the scales may tip towards ruin. If the new leadership meets its appointed hour and coins with creative genius the right rallying cries, the scales may tip towards renaissance. This coining and crying of recruit-calls, in those moments when profound historic change impends in the life and polity of a people, is the first phase of that social engineering which is statesmanship.

The Western peoples seem to me to be now in one of these moments of pause, a phase of expectancy that may or may not find fulfilment in a new leadership that can recruit the Western masses for the West-wide reconstructive effort I sought to chart in the preceding chapter. Western affairs have reached and are ready for the final step in the four-fold formula I have suggested.

Many of the old philosophies and the old procedures of the political, social, and economic life of the West have obviously fallen into futility through the failure of Western leadership to keep them progressively adjusted to the new circumstances of the age of science and technology. The West has not been wanting in unofficial statesmen who, as scientists and seers, have blazed the trails towards the new philosophies and new procedures needed to check the decline of the West and to give firmness and fresh significance to its political, social, and economic orders. There has been a long period of manifest maladjustment between the old policies and the new problems of Western life. Manifest, that is, to the more penetrating minds of the West! The tether of traditional loyalty has been slow to weaken, however, and Western man, until a world-wide economic disturbance shook him from his serenity, was reluctant to question the major assumptions upon which his life had long been organized. To-day his mood changes. The tether of traditional loyalty slips as the ground-stakes of his social order loosen. Western man grows ever more openly skeptical of the philosophy and leadership in control of Western affairs, while he fumbles in a kind of wistful futility for some clear lead out of his confusion.

Thus the stage is set for the emergence of a leadership that can sense and sound the rallying cries of a redemptive statesmanship. It may be, as I have argued at length, that the raw materials with which such statesmanship must deal lie locked in the mass of results thrown up by modern research in the fields of nature, human nature, and social organization, but it is hardly probable that the Western masses will be swept into a vast reconstructive effort by technical descriptions of the contributions the sciences have severally made towards realistic social policy. The masses will be moved, if moved at all, by a few broad and simple ideas towards which the needs of modern society and the nature of modern knowledge have alike led. And these broad and simple ideas will be the stuff of which the rallying cries of a Western advance may be made. In a new renaissance of the West, as in the French Revolution, the masses will not be directly or quickly moved by the subtle and erudite theses of their scientists and seers. They must have their *Liberté! Egalité! Fraternité!* to evoke their enthusiasms and to recruit emotionally their loyalties.

That this contention may not be left a sheer abstraction, I venture to suggest seven broad and readily understandable concepts that might, I think, be made the rallying cries for a new renaissance of the West: (1) the idea of a cultural nationalism; (2) the idea of an economic internationalism; (3) the idea of a rationalized politics; (4) the idea of a mass-conscious industrialism; (5) the idea of a socialized religion; (6) the idea of a well-bred race; and (7) the idea of a realistic pacifism. These are, I am convinced, among the major clues to a renewal and reënforcement of the Western social order.

I should be profoundly skeptical of the possibility of thrusting these ideas into the social policy of the Western future but for the fact that the drift of Western affairs has prepared the way for their appeal to the minds of men. The more I probe into the past and the more I watch the passing show the more I doubt the ultimate effectiveness of trumped-up propagandas that seek to impose an alien idea upon the affairs of a time. If half the beauty of a sunset is in the painter's eye and half the glory of a tale in the listener's ear, half the effectiveness of a social concept is in the social conditions that surround its announcement. Abstractions lie inert until events make them leap into life. Every age lives under the lordship of a few dominant ideas, but the ideas are less creators than creatures of its events. It sometimes seems, I know, that the destiny of a people is at the mercy of whatever propaganda can commandeer the greatest cleverness of appeal. But, in the long view of history, it may be doubted that any propaganda has ever registered more than specious and tentative triumphs save as it has come to interpret and make articulate a lesson the race had already learned, even if its implications had been but obscurely sensed. New and productive ideas do not win their way by grace of their theoretical soundness. They come to ascendancy in the policy of an age only when the people, disillusioned with the prevailing status of their social order, see in them a promising alternative.

The seven ideas I have here suggested are not abstract theories conceived *in vacuo* by seers and soothsayers aloof from the rough-and-tumble of Western affairs. They are not mere hypotheses of the social philosophers, the feasibility of which is shrouded with uncertainty. They are inevitable deductions drawn from the inescapable facts of the current plight of the West. And the manifest failure of their opposites has verified them by indirection. Who, save the frightened custodians of vested interests, remains to argue the social value of an intransigeant nationalism that persists in running amuck in an interdependent world? Who will insist that the economic life of the West can escape collapse if its interrelations are ignored? Who can longer, save with tongue in cheek, worship at the shrine of a weather-cock politics at the mercy of every wind and whim? Who is still so blind as to believe that Western capitalism can meet the challenge of Communism save by serving the masses better and more dependably than any alternative system promises? Who can believe that religion must be insulated from the secular struggles of the race and made the secret luxury of the saint? Who can doubt the necessity of Western man's conscious assumption of responsibility for his trusteeship of the germ plasm of the race? And who will contradict the contention that Western man, not daring to risk his civilization in the gamble of another world war, must set himself realistically to the task of ridding his political, social, and economic orders of the things that make for war?

The furtherance of the seven ideas I have advanced will obviously not be an adventure in imposing alien ideas upon Western affairs. It will be but an attempt to interpret and to make articulate seven lessons the Western masses have lately been learning under the stern schoolmaster of social necessity. Events have set the stage for the triumph of these seven socially productive ideas. They await some Conrad of public affairs to give them the wording that will send them singing through the hearts of men. Each of these ideas sends a thousand roots into all the obvious and obscure soils of Western life. Their implications are interlocked. Each demands a volume for its adequate analysis. And a book would be all too small to hold a comprehensive study of their possible interplay in the hands of a creative statesmanship. I shall content myself with saying just enough about each of these seven ideas, in turn, to suggest their peculiar pertinence to the present exigent juncture in Western affairs.

*Cultural Nationalism!*

It is hardly probable that Western civilization can survive if Western man persists in his allegiance to the prevailing concept of political nationalism, which has converted all Europe into a bear-garden and keeps the conduct of world affairs consistently aloof from the new realities of this sensitively interdependent age of science and technology. Nationalism as we have known it must go, or Western civilization will go! This is not to say that nationalism must go, but only that the political perversion of nationalism, into which Western man has permitted an essentially noble concept to fall, must go.

Nationalism, like science, is neither moral nor immoral; it is but an instrument waiting to be used for high ends or low at the will of the user. I agree with the incomparable Mazzini, who once said to the hot-headed and high-hearted Italian youth answering the call of his contagious spirit, "Without the nation there can be no humanity. Nations are the citizens of humanity, as individuals are the citizens of the nation. And as every individual lives a two-fold life, inward and of relation, so do the nations. As every individual should strive to promote the power and prosperity of his nation, through the exercise of his special function, so should every nation, in performing its special mission, according to its special capacity, perform its part in the general work, and promote the progressive advance and prosperity of humanity. Nationality and humanity are, therefore, equally sacred. To forget humanity is to suppress the aim of our labors; to cancel the nation is to suppress the instrument by which to achieve the aim." Here is a voice of sanity to which the chauvinistic nationalists of the West would do well to listen. Here speaks the spirit of cultural nationalism.

Political nationalism has given us nations conceived primarily as units of power and measured by the common standard of military and economic might. It has made its idolatrous worshipers narrow, exclusive, smug, and swashbuckling. It has resented and repressed the spirit of sustained self-criticism. It has never quite believed that men could be critical of their national ideals and loyal to their legitimate national interests at one and the same time. It has standardized the minds and motives of peoples, thereby preventing different individuals, classes, races, and religions from making their distinctive contributions to the common life of the nation. It has been through the generations more a threat of power than an expression of culture. It has never quite succeeded in making adequate preparation for national defense without exalting the ideals of war and war-making.

Western man faces the difficult and delicate task of destroying political nationalism without destroying nationality in the process. Great civilizations are not built by rootless nomads with their transient loyalties. Great civilizations are born of men rooted in particular soils whose sap sings in their veins. There is nobility in the national tradition of a great people busy with the building of a distinctive social order and its supporting culture. We must preserve this priceless instrument of nationality, but we must purify the concept of nationalism. Civilization is the net result of a triple collaboration between the individual, the nation, and humanity. The problem is to create and maintain nations that will neither browbeat the individual nor betray humanity.

Throughout the Western world to-day political nationalism is debasing the individual and disregarding the manifest necessity of a moral and intellectual reunion of mankind if the civilization of the West is not to collapse. It stands in stubborn opposition to all those modernist forces of science and technology that are making for the unity of mankind. Nationalism rose to magisterial power in the politics of the nineteenth century. It, more than all else, dominated the politics of the period. It was the vessel that held the neo-paganism that led the West to the World War. There seemed, for a time, a chance that the war might demonstrate, alike to the masses and to their ministers, the incompatibility of the political nationalism of the chauvinists with the new relationships made imperative by transformations effected by the advancing forces of science and technology. The ending of the war, however, left political nationalism more powerful and pervasive than ever. And all this at a time when the forces of credit, contract, capital, corporate organization, and the lithe arms of rapid transportation and swift communication were welding the world into an intimate neighborhood. This resurgence of political nationalism has stilled the voice of sanity and tied the hands of realism in the economic and financial operations of the post-war West. And belated attempts to bolster up, by common action, the credit structure of a Europe threatened with bankruptcy have hardly changed this picture. Political nationalism, obviously obsolete in a world whose economic relations constitute one vast and sensitive nervous system, is to-day riding the West to ruin. As the price of survival for his social order, Western man must come to see that, in this new world of interlocked interests, there are no shock-proof frontiers behind which nations may hide like hermits. Even the United States is not exempt from the incidence of this interdependence.

European insecurity is a standing threat to American security. A permanently prosperous America is out of the question in a poverty-stricken world.

Swiftly and surely the forces of science and technology are internationalizing every material aspect and action of modern life. This need not mean the death of nationality. It should mean the restriction of the rôle of nationalism to that of carrier for the distinctive cultures of diverse peoples, and the allocation to international action those aspects of world affairs that science and technology have made manifestly international in their implications. There is no intrinsic incompatibility between a creative nationalism and a constructive internationalism. We may safely intensify our differences of national genius if we are intelligent enough to organize the world in terms of a cultural division of labor, with its common problems subjected to the suzerainty of common policies. Western man must, in short, erect upon the ruins of political nationalism a cultural nationalism that will convert world politics into a competition in excellence instead of a competition in power. It is not a question of choosing between nationalism and internationalism; it is a question of determining the respective rôles of nationalism and internationalism in the light of the new realities of the age of science and technology.

### Economic Internationalism!

In 1815 the statesmen at Vienna stood on the threshold of an era of nationalism. Nationalism was entering world thought as a new motive force, but the statesmen at Vienna ignored it. Nationalism went on working, nevertheless, and has dominated world politics from then until now. In 1918, little more than a hundred years later, the statesmen at Versailles were standing on the threshold of an era of internationalism. Internationalism had entered world thought as a new motive force, but the statesmen at Versailles, in the detailed provisions of the treaty there fabricated, gave it but timid acknowledgment, bowing to it one moment, cynically check-mating it the next. Internationalism will go on working, nevertheless, for it has about it an historic inevitability that has marked but few forces in the long evolution of organized society. Statesmen who ignore it will, in the end, prove traitors to their time. Historic inevitability attaches to internationalism not as an ethical ideal, but as an economic imperative. It is the economic complexity and interdependence of the modern world that has rendered political nationalism obsolete and made some measure of economic internationalism obligatory if the structure of civilization is to stand.

The modern West is a single economic body of which the several nations are the separate cells. There is something more than a figure of speech here. The biology of death throws a revealing light upon the issue of economic internationalism upon which events now challenge Western man to act.

The biologist assures us that the separate cells of the human body are potentially immortal. They might go on dividing and subdividing forever, if lodged in a congenial medium, properly nourished, adequately warmed, and safeguarded against injury. But, despite this potential immortality of separate cells, all men everywhere sooner or later die. Man dies, according to the biologist, simply because the cells from which man comes, as they differentiate and divide to make the various organs of his body, become so sensitively interdependent that the fate of all the organs may hang upon the failure of one. The human body is a complex and interdependent community of cells. Having become a unity in fact, the human body must function as a unity or die. Man does not die because *all* of his cells die, but only because *some* of his cells die and, in dying, pull the rest of his cells into the grave with them. Much of a dead man may still be alive. The cells of the heart muscles stop functioning; death comes; but other parts of the dead man's body may not actually die for some time to come. Such

parts, under laboratory care and control, have been kept
alive for a good stretch of years.

The preservation of the life of the human body calls for
a kind of physical statesmanship that shall keep the parts
of its complex and interdependent organization functioning
as a unity. This physical statesmanship, whose other name
is hygiene, cannot afford to declare a separate sovereignty
for the brain cells, for these cells live or die according to
the success or failure with which the heart cells play com-
missary of subsistence and garbage disposer to them. The
private ability of any single cell or group of cells to keep
alive for a time cannot prevent the death of the body. Life
can be assured only at the price of a working harmony between the interdependent cells of the body. No single cell
can save itself by declaring a policy of splendid isolation.
It cannot avoid entangling alliances with the other cells of
the body. Only single-celled creatures can practice a policy
of isolation.

I do not want to belabor the point or ride the analogy
too far into the enemy country of details, but the advancing
forces of science and technology have made the Western
peoples as interdependent as the cells of the human body.
World politics becomes a kind of social biology. And in
politics as in biology it seems that the wages of complexity
is death. Western man must master the perils of his new
interdependence or be mastered by them. The ascetic
nation is an anachronism in the modern world. The diseases of civilization, with mercurial swiftness, overleap
every frontier, cross every ocean, and filter through every
foreign policy. Any security that America, for instance,
may attain apart from a stabilized Europe will be but the
temporary security of one healthy cell extracted from a
dying body and artificially kept alive in a laboratory.

This means that Western man must frankly and fear-
lessly go international with respect to certain phases of
Western affairs. But he must be realistic about his internationalism. He must follow the facts of his world, not

race ahead of them. He must begin his setting up of the agencies of international counsel and control in those fields which science and technology have already made manifestly international, even if national policies have failed to reflect the change. These fields of obvious international import are, in the main, physical and economic. Western man's best chance to make progress in adapting his policies to the new realities of the age of science and technology lies, therefore, in the direction of economic internationalism.

The West stands to gain but little from premature ventures in political internationalism. The orgy of self-determination that swept the Western world, just when the realistic forces of science and technology were making greater unification imperative, has made it difficult to do more, in the field of political internationalism, than to provide new arenas in which still stubborn nationalisms can carry on their conflicts with a somewhat improved etiquette. To approach the crucial issue of internationalism from the political angle is but to give the chauvinist a fresh chance to dramatize his lack of insight and to misinterpret the fathers whose political catch-words, coined in a time when separatism was not suicidal, are his stock-in-trade. Chauvinism is still too deep-seated to be dislodged by argument. Events must educate Western man respecting the obsolete elements in the dogma of political sovereignty.

The economic interdependence of the Western world is a more obvious matter that even the chauvinist begins reluctantly to admit. The phase of depression that to-day dampens the spirit of every Western people is proving, even to the most parochial, that the economic interests of the Western nations are inextricably interlaced. The Western world *is* an economic unity, despite the philosophy of separatism that animates its administration. Injure it at any point and it quivers entire! No nation of the West went into the current depression alone; none can come out of it alone, save for tentative and relative recoveries. No nation of the West can single-handed achieve dependable exemption from the all-Western insecurity that preceded, produced, and persists in the existing economic disruption. Having become an economic unity in fact, the West must function as an economic unity, or resign itself to the certainty of an era of increasing insecurity that will end in the collapse of Western civilization.

This need not mean an economic super-government set up to serve as receiver for the several national economies of the West. Any such sweeping surrender of national controls seems quite out of the question. The present economic plight of the West does, however, demand a measure of common policy and common administration in its economic enterprise that the political nationalisms of the West have as yet been unwilling to concede. Adherence, in some degree, to an economic internationalism is the price that Western man must pay for the survival of his socio-economic order.

C. K. Leith's small but significant volume on *World Minerals and World Politics* is a vivid and convincing exhibit in proof of the increasing necessity of some measure of international control, whether public or private in its nature, in the mineral field to which the nations must turn for the major raw materials of their industrial and military power. Nature obviously did not have political nationalism in mind when she distributed the world supply of minerals. Mr. Leith's survey of the geography of mineral sources and his analysis of the mineral position of the nations make this clear.

With the dominating centers of mineral production few in number, some thirty major mineral districts accounting for more than three-fourths of the value of the world's mineral output; with even the most favored nations dependent for essential minerals upon sources beyond their frontiers; with a growing tendency towards national specialization in minerals, as the United States dominating the oil and copper industries, Great Britian the tin industry, and Germany the potash industry; with the factors of exhaustion, discovery, technology, substitution, and governmental policy not likely to make any decisive change in these specialized mineral positions of the nations; with mineral trade routes, as arteries carrying nearly one-third of the world's mineral tonnage, which is life-blood to the industries and armies of the nations, crossing and recrossing national boundaries; with the main mineral deposits gravitating into fewer and larger units of commercial control which, in notable instances, approach world monopoly, it becomes obvious that in the world's mineral supply, upon which the economic welfare, the industrial prestige, and the military power of the several nations rests, Western man faces a fact that laughs at his political frontiers.

No one can predict how fast or how far Western man will go in relating the development and control of mineral supplies to the new interdependence of the age of science and technology, but, if he is to check waste of these exhaustible and irreplaceable resources, bring the forces making for over-production under control, prevent the relative mineral starvation of important phases of the industrial life of some of his nations, wisely conserve the mineral heritage of the race for his posterity, and make the mineral supply of the world a stabilizing factor in peaceful enterprise instead of an incitement to war, it is safe to say that he must move from an excessive nationalism towards some measure of economic internationalism. And what is true of mineral resources, in particular, is true, in varying degrees, of natural resources, in general. Stubborn nationalism and a statesmanship of resources are incompatible.

The economic relations as well as the economic resources of the modern West require policies and administrative procedures that go beyond nationalism. The virile industrial nations of the West, in terms of their varying circumstances, from time to time find their fortunes and their futures vitally dependent upon their securing one or more or all of four basic economic opportunities: (1) the oppor-

tunity for transit; (2) the opportunity for trade; (3) the
opportunity for investment; and (4) the opportunity for
migration. The unhampered development of the modern
industrial nation ideally requires these four things: first,
that the inter-state railways, the canals, the seas, and the
ports of the world shall be open without undue toll to the
entry and transit of its goods; second, that in access to
markets it shall not be unduly discriminated against; third,
that its free capital shall not be denied adequate play and
equal privilege in the constructive exploitation of the backward territories of the world; and, fourth, that its surplus
population shall not be barred from entering more sparsely
settled regions of greater opportunity.

There is dynamite in each of these demands. Their
satisfaction puts difficult and, in some instances, it may be,
insoluble problems to Western statesmanship. Fluidity of
migration for surplus populations, in particular, is a re-
quirement that the West is never likely to be able to meet
save in special cases and under special circumstances. The
fact remains, however, that for these four opportunities
peoples have always fought and will continue to fight until
the statesman excels the soldier in devising generally for
the nations guaranties that the needs represented by these
demands shall, as far as feasible, be met. Nations will not
lightly cast aside the instruments and methods of the old
order until there is convincing evidence that these four
basic economic needs can be better dealt with by a new
order.

It is in the handling of these crassly material things,
rather than in the high dreams of the political peace-
makers, that Western man must look for security from war
and for the stabilization of his economic order. He can
make but little headway towards rationalizing his military
policies until he has harmonized his economic relations.
Here is an enterprise for an economic engineering that
takes the whole West and the whole world for its field.
A statesmanship that cannot, in dealing with the economic

resources and the economic relations of the West, rise above the limitations of political nationalism will fail the Western future.

### Rationalized Politics!

The unpardonable sin of Western politics has been its reluctance to find and its refusal to face facts. At worst, Western politics has been dominated by inherited opinion, uncritical crowd-mindedness, irrational hatred of peoples and of personalities, limited class interests, and the organized insincerity of campaign strategy. At best, Western politics has been animated by an idealism that has mistaken desires for realities, and gone recklessly into combat or conference in ignorance of the facts and forces that inevitably condition the procedure of the moment and the policy of the future. This schism between facts and politics has committed politics to an intellectual celibacy that has borne bitter fruit in Western affairs.

The outstanding fact of the contemporary politics of the West is that Western man knows better than he does. He is content to conduct campaigns of emotional claptrap, with facts standing lonesomely in the suburbs of his discussions. He must rationalize his politics if he wants his social order to survive. He must bring science to the service of social management. The prophets of doom have rightly indicted him for permitting the knowledge of the scientist to languish for lack of political power, and the power of the politician to run amuck for lack of scientific knowledge.

During the last hundred years a new force has arisen with which the state must reckon. This new force is scientific research. The one problem in which all of Western man's social and economic problems take root is the problem of transforming his rhetorical politics into realistic politics. And this transformation can be effected only by his establishing a sound and sustained relation between his laboratories and his legislatures. Only so can the West bring into being a league to enforce objectivity in the analysis of social issues and in the administration of governments.

In working out this relation between science and politics, Western man must not assume that scientists are infallible and politicians incompetent. Science, like politics, has its mountebanks as well as its masters. Its words are sometimes longer than its vision. It has sometimes been more concerned with the classification of social forces than with the creation of social power. It has sometimes mistaken its knowledge for wisdom. It has often presented as much confusion and contradiction of counsel as the politics of prejudice and passion has ever produced. The fulsome flattery that has lately been showered upon science has sometimes gone to the scientist's head and caused him to don the dictator's garb and swagger irritatingly through the discussion of social problems with dangerous oversimplifications. In the imperatively desirable alliance between politics and science, it is important that the scientist as well as the politician recognize the limitations of his rôle.

It is an alliance between politics and science, not a domination of either by the other, that the rational regulation of Western affairs demands. Each must serve the other. Each must check the other. The statesman must ground his policies on facts. Politics without science must be sterile and may be sinister. But the absolute necessity of the scientist's service to the state in this era of unprecedented complexity does not mean that the state must bow in servile and unquestioning submission to dictation by scientists. The state dares not, for the simple reason that scientists, for all their priesthood of realism, are human beings subject to the prides and passions and prejudices of the rest of us, once they step outside their specialisms. The use of science by the state, not the usurpation of the state by scientists, is the venture in which hope for the Western future lies.

In making this plea for a rationalized politics, I am

under no delusion that the Western masses will ever go scientific by wholesale. I am quite aware that the complexity of the social order and its system of government has long since outstripped the information and the insight of the man in the street. I realize that the omnicompetent citizen, whether he was ever more than a fiction of the philosophers even in the simpler days of the pastoral era, is manifestly a myth in this technologic age. I do not expect subtly refined judgments upon detailed policies of government and economics from the rank and file of Western voters. The Western masses must register their will in broad and brusque verdicts upon men and measures. The most they can do politically is to approve or disapprove the general direction in which their leadership is leading them. They cannot deal in details.

The rationalization of Western politics must be an achievement of the elect, by the elected, for the electors. And I am convinced, by first-hand observation of isolation cases of rational leaderships and mass-reactions to them, that the Western masses can be made to rise to the challenge of a rationalized politics, if its leadership will but match the demagogue's artistry of appeal. Shoddy political leadership is born of the conviction that the politician must play down to the masses. Too little is said of the necessity the masses are all too often under of living down to their leadership. The political leadership of the West is to-day reading its own timidities and time-servings into its constituencies. It is not, I suspect, the fanatic temper of the masses so much as the faulty technique of otherwise fine leadership that delays the coming of a rationalized politics. I venture the judgment that a transcendent political leadership, should it appear in the midst of the current confusion, grounded in science and graced by the gifts of clear interpretation and contagious appeal, would reveal the Western masses hungry for realism. The crowd-mind can be stolen from the demagogue and given new idols of phrase and personality. And the future of the West hinges upon the capture of the crowd by the advance agents of a rationalized politics.

*Mass-conscious Industrialism!*

The industrial system of the capitalistic West is to-day on trial. It is challenged from the outside by Communism and threatened from the inside with collapse. Competitive capitalism set itself up in the West as a system that promised to provide, without preachment from the church or paternalism from the state, the livelihood of the people. It did not promise to make this service to the masses its primary aim. It unblushingly confessed that private profit was its major incentive. And it took but little pains to conceal the spirit of the buccaneer that brooded over its early conquests. It contended only that the masses could best secure their bread and circuses as by-products of the enlightened self-interest of the owners of the instruments of production. It staked its future upon its ability to give the masses a better living than they could secure under any other system. Its early promoters may not have been consciously aware of this gamble that capitalism was taking, but this was the gamble it took nevertheless. And to-day events are forcing a show-down of the cards. What do the cards show?

Despite the criticisms that have been levelled against it by the radical theorists and the social unfortunates, the capitalistic industrialism of the West, during the hundred years that ended about the middle of the nineteenth century, produced an amazing advance in the material aspects of Western civilization. But, roughly reckoned, from the middle of the nineteenth century, capitalistic industrialism has been increasingly harassed by social problems that begin to threaten its stability. It has known interludes of exceptional prosperity that have made it forget, for a time, the stubborn social issues that confronted it. The seven fat years that lately lifted American business to new levels certainly postponed for most Americans any realistic assessment of the basic health of their economic order and outlook. But that bright boom ended in the blackest depression that Western capitalism has yet known. And to-day its anxious friends wonder whether the initial success of capitalistic industrialism is to be followed by inevitable self-defeat, while here and there among its ablest administrators this puzzled wonder gives way to gravest skepticism. Montague Norman, Governor of the Bank of England, as he watched Western finance and Western industry flounder towards crisis, is reported to have written Clément Moret, Governor of the Bank of France, "Unless drastic measures are taken to save it, the capitalist system throughout the civilized world will be wrecked within a year. I should like this prediction to be filed for future reference." It is not necessary to argue the accuracy of this forecast to realize that such skepticism at the very center of Western capitalism is symptomatic of a seriousness not necessarily indicated by similar forecasts inspired in other years by the wishful thinking of wild-minded agitators.

The capitalistic industrialism of the West is, as I have said, to-day challenged from the outside by Communism as well as threatened from the inside with collapse. The challenge from the outside is made real by the threat from the inside. A vast system of social and economic organization such as capitalism, to which, in its varied stages of development, the peoples of the West have been committed for a century and a half, cannot be seriously challenged by an alternative economy unless the alternative, however unsound it may be in totality, has in it some valid and vital element that the system under fire does not have. I am not, at this point, concerned with a critique of the soundness or unsoundness of the detailed working program to which, as in Russia, Communism has reduced its philosophy. I am, for the moment, concerned only to call attention to one fundamental difference in the respective points of view from which Communism and capitalism approach the problem of devising and directing an economic system of production and distribution. For this difference centers around the valid and vital element which, present in communistic philosophy and absent in capitalistic philosophy, is the core of the communistic challenge to capitalism.

Whatever may prove to be the outcome of Communism in practice, in its philosophy, Communism makes the welfare of the masses the primary aim rather than a by-product of business and industry. Communism is mass-conscious. The Communist contends that capitalism is, on the contrary, money-conscious and inherently insensitive to the human requirements of the masses. I am quite aware that this stump-speech sharpness of distinction the Communist makes is less accurate than he assumes. The masters of Western industrialism are not money-mad monsters moved by an every-man-for-himself-and-the-devil-take-the-hindmost philosophy. Private profit is not the major incentive that holds the majority of industrial captains at their posts. I number among my personal friends a score of industrial captains who have long since passed the point of interest in the income they personally derive from their captaincies. They are as deeply interested as any Lenin in the part they and their industries may play in lifting the labor and leisure of the toiling millions to new levels of social satisfaction.

But two swallows do not make a summer. The basic assumptions of a system are more powerful than the mood of a few of its servants. And, despite the trend towards a socialized mind among the abler captains of industry, Western capitalism is still functioning under the mandate of the philosophy elaborated by Adam Smith and his colleagues in politico-economic interpretation who, taming the militant French doctrine of natural rights, created and carried to popular acceptance in eighteenth century England the theory that the free pursuit of private ends was the royal road to the public good, and that the mechanism and movement of economic life transformed "as with an invisible hand" this exercise of individual rights into humanity's best instrument for the achievement of mass-welfare. Western capitalism has, in consequence, developed around the doctrine of the private rights of industrialists rather than the doctrine of the public function of industrialism.

Industry has a social function that quite transcends the special interests of the industrialists at its helm. It is first the function of industry to feed, clothe, and shelter mankind. And, once these minimum necessities are provided, it is the further function of industry to make materially feasible the conquest of leisure and loveliness in the life of the masses. During the last two decades, in particular, Western capitalism, without recanting its doctrine of private rights, has increasingly acknowledged the fact that industry has this social function of assuring the physical support and social enrichment of the life of the masses. And, when its economic curve has been in the ascendant, Western capitalism, despite inequalities and injustices it has engendered, has gone far towards discharging this social function. Its prosperity, although dishearteningly spotty and disturbingly insecure, has been more widely distributed than the prosperity of any alternative system that has had to serve swarming millions of population. But, at the moment, the economic curve of Western capitalism dips menacingly downward. And, rightly or wrongly, the impression grows in the popular mind that this current drop in the economic curve reflects a situation markedly more serious than the phases of temporary maladjustment that have heretofore produced periodic depressions in the economic life of the West.

This impression is not confined to the cloistered intellectuals, who are habitually over-facile alike in their despairs and in their hopes, or to the unskilled and the ignorant, who are readily victimized by deliberately subversive missioners of revolution. It haunts the minds of the innumerable white-collared servants of business and industry, invades the reflections of the vast concourse of salaried executives, and enters an unbidden guest into the council chambers of the directorates of economic enterprise throughout the West. Millions of men and women, who have no disposition to quarrel with capitalism, and who are still employed, are chilled by the fear of unemployment.

The net result of all this is that Western man is ready, as never before, to listen tolerantly to a skeptical critique of an industrialism animated by a philosophy that makes the pursuit of private ends its primary aim, with the security and support of life for the millions left to follow as a by-product. And an undue continuance of the drastic depression that has fallen upon the West will render him increasingly and uncritically sensitive to the lure of an alternative philosophy of industrialism that promises to make the welfare of the masses its primary aim, with the current doctrine of private rights either ruthlessly subordinated or completely cast aside.

The masses are not given to hair-splitting. They are content to let the philosophy of their industrial system be what it will, if its practical results but minister to the increase, the enrichment, and the stabilization of their lives. It is, I am convinced, quite immaterial to them that a system like Western capitalism rests upon a philosophy of individual rights, with the assumption that mass-welfare will follow the free pursuit of private ends, as long as the mass-welfare really follows. They have no objection to their welfare as a by-product as long as the by-product is assured and adequate. I have long since outgrown the delusion that the masses are eager to share in the risks of ownership and the responsibilities of management. Man is more enamoured of security than he is excited about liberty. A capitalism that successfully discharges the social function of industry while in pursuit of private ends is in little danger of overthrow from without or breakdown from within.

But this is hardly the picture the Western scene presents at the moment. There is no blinking the fact that millions of erstwhile uncritical servants of Western capitalism to-day find their faith in its underlying assumption of mass-welfare by indirection, as the by-product of the exercise of private rights, seriously shaken by events. A régime of free capitalism and political liberty is, I am convinced, basically sounder than the Communism and the Fascism that to-day stand as its most contagious alternatives, how-ever necessary these alternatives may be, as interim econ-omies, at certain historic junctures in the life of particular peoples, and however practical they may prove in the light of particular racial psychologies. But Western capitalism must, if it is to survive, effect one deep and drastic change in the still regnant philosophy it inherited from the Adam Smiths who rationalized its initial impulses. It must be-come as mass-conscious as Communism! It must, generally and not sporadically, put the social function of industrial-ism above the special interests of industrialists. Its primary and its secondary objectives must change places. It must make the increase, the enrichment, and the stabilization of life for the millions its first business. Private profit must be found as a by-product of the statesmanlike administra-tion of this social function. Capitalism must, I repeat, be-come as mass-conscious as Communism. For it becomes in-creasingly the mood of mankind to judge industrial systems by this criterion.

If the achievement of this mass-consciousness by West-ern capitalism necessitated the wholesale recantation of private rights, there would be little chance of its coming to dominance in the mind of industrial leadership. Men do not make such sweeping surrender of traditional privileges save under the duress of revolution. If this mass-con-sciousness had to come as the knight-errantry of social enthusiasts, I should not trouble to give its consideration space here. But it becomes increasingly apparent to the exceptional industrialist, if not as yet to the average industrialist, that this mass-consciousness is not only the best insurance policy for capitalism, but the best business policy for capitalists. Putting the social function of industrialism above the special interests of industrialists is a policy of enlightened self-interest for the industrialist.

In the long generations of the handicraft era and in the early decades of the machine age, mass-consciousness was not vitally related to the development and stabilization of business. Until the machine age brought to measurable maturity the processes of mass-production, captains of industry could be cold to the call of the crowd for adequacy and security of income, could largely ignore the cry of the working millions for a decent measure of leisure, and still build vast businesses and pile up huge incomes. But the moment mass-production became the major method of Western industrialism, the situation was radically altered. Mass-production is without point or purpose save as the servant of mass-consumption. And so to-day, quite apart from any social considerations, the captain of a mass-production industry must concern himself with the economic status of the masses who are to buy his goods quite as much as with the efficiency of the machines that are to produce his goods. He cannot otherwise build a permanently successful business. The speed and scale of the machine age have made necessary a new capitalism that shall be mass-conscious in the first place even if it be money-conscious in the second place.

This new capitalism is in the making. It differs at important points from the old capitalism. The old capitalism thought profits lay in high prices and low wages. The new capitalism thinks profits lie in low prices and high wages. The old capitalism thought profits were helped by long hours. The new capitalism thinks profits are helped by short hours. The old capitalism believed in class conflict despite its damning of the class conflict theory. The new capitalism believes in class coöperation, knowing that the prosperity of the buying masses is its best guaranty of

profits. The old capitalism thought of wealth as a static
something to be captured. The new capitalism thinks of
wealth as a dynamic something to be created. For a long
time it seemed to many of the more sensitive spirits of the
West that the only hope of redemption from the sins of
the old capitalism was either a social revolution or a
spiritual reversal of the nature of business men. The beginnings of this new capitalism, however, give hope that
the West may find redemption from the sins of the old
capitalism by modern business men's finding out that the
old capitalistic methods of low wages, high prices, and
long hours are, in a mass-production age, unbusinesslike
and unprofitable.

Western man must not be naïve about this new capitalism. It is still far from ascendancy in Western industrialism. The most dependable judgment to which I have access
estimates that approximately one-fifth of the economic enterprise of the United States was, when depression struck,
operating under the policies of the new capitalism, with
the remaining four-fifths still following the philosophy of
the old capitalism. This new capitalism, which effects a
synthesis of the mood of Communism and the motivation
of capitalism, is still but an emergent force in Western life.
To make it an established force dominating the economic
order of the West is one of the major tasks of contemporary leadership. This new mass-conscious capitalism can,
I am convinced, actually do what Communism dreams for
the millions, and, in the doing, still leave to Western man
the lure of vast individual achievement and personal
reward.

### Socialized Religion!

It is with deliberate intent that I follow a consideration
of Western industrialism with an observation on the rôle
of religion in the renewal of the West. I cannot concur in
the contention of a certain school of sophisticated moderns
that religion is an irrelevant and impotent factor in West-

ern man's current problem of survival. At the very outset of man's religious venturings, religion was intimately related to the practical business of survival in a little understood and largely unfriendly world. Religion was a functional tool that primitive man used in his half-instinctive efforts to adjust himself to his natural and social environments. And so it must again be made, I think, in Western man's currently imperative task of creating and controlling his social environment, even if the advancing forces of science have rendered religion obviously irrelevant to man's problem of the conquest of his natural environment.

The diverse rituals of primitive religions reflect the distinctive struggles that their practitioners had with their diverse environments. The primitive rituals of peoples who wrested their living from the soil were cast in terms of agricultural issues. The primitive rituals of peoples who lived by the sea were colored by their attempts to dominate the problems that life put to fisherman and sailor. The primitive rituals of peoples who lived within the shadow-terrors of the jungle were designed to exorcise the devils that haunted its depths and to bring emancipation from its fears. At all times and everywhere in the early eras of man's evolution, man turned to religion as a tool to help him come to terms with his natural and social environments.

Primitive man, it must be admitted, functioned crudely in the field of religion, as he functioned crudely in all other fields. But, in essence, his religion was an important part of his attempt to penetrate the mystery and to perfect the mastery of life. In his attempts to penetrate the mystery of life, he fell easy prey to superstition. His notions of life seem pathetically naïve in the light of modern knowledge. In his attempts to perfect the mastery of life, he leaned credulously upon the supernaturalism that lurked in the shadows of his dimly lighted world. His belief alike in the capricious and in the controllable interventions of his gods in human affairs seems childish to us now. But it must be remembered that primitive man's dual striving for the conquest of mystery and the achievement of mastery was a vital factor in his struggle for survival. Religion was not a thing apart from the secular lives of our remote ancestors. Primitive man's ponderings upon the difficulties and dilemmas that infested his world were, like the patient investigations of the modern scientist, efforts to get at the meaning of life. His confident appeal to his gods for rain was, to him, as much a practical effort to control his natural environment as the construction of a flood-control system is to modern man. His cry to his gods to give conquest to his armies and to spread confusion in the ranks of his enemy was, to him, as much a practical effort to control his social environment as the prosecution of the Five Year Plan is to the modern Russian.

Primitive man's religion was, then, marked by two things: (1) it was concerned primarily with the control of man's environments, and only incidentally, if at all, with their creation, and, it should be said in passing, concerned more with the control of man's natural environment than with the control of his social environment; (2) it was thus intimately related to primitive man's secular problem of survival and success in his day-to-day life and work, the emotional drive back of his effort to make himself safely and congenially at home in his world.

But something happened to religion in the long trek man took from the age of superstition to the age of science. As man progressed in the direction of rational controls of his environments, he leaned less and less upon religion as a factor felt to be vital to his secular ventures. Religion was progressively insulated from living contact with practical affairs. Intimately involved in the secular life of primitive man, religion became a thing apart from the secular life of modern man. I do not mean that man went confessedly renegade to religion. He continued—as he still continues—to lavish gifts upon his temples and to pay a lip-service, even more richly elaborated, to the gods and gospels to which he was professedly still allegiant. I mean only that the rituals of his religion became more and more symbols and less and less tools in his secular struggle for survival and success in his day-to-day life and work.

It is a common but, I think, questionable generalization that religion has suffered because man has secularized his civilization. It is, I suspect, more accurate to say that civilization has suffered because man has de-secularized his religion. I mean, by this confessedly loose use of the term secular, that civilization has suffered because man has drained away into less socially significant channels the emotional drive of religion that once went, however blindly, into man's effort to make and to master his environment. Man has more and more tended to make religion one of the special businesses of his life rather than the spiritual breath of his life, a dynamic infusing with purpose and power the whole of his enterprise. He has increasingly identified religion with special persons, special places, special periods, and special practices.

Special persons may be useful as religious guides, but we cannot hire men to be holy for us. This is an undertaking at once personal and social. It cannot be executed by proxy. Special places in which we may voice our common aspirations are useful, but religion is as much at home in the carpenter shop as in the cathedral. Out of a carpenter shop, in fact, came the initiating impulse that ended in Mont-Saint-Michel and Chartres. Special periods in which we stop long enough to take stock of ourselves are useful, but fast days and feast days cannot exempt us from the challenge of religion for the rest of the year. Special practices that help us to concentrate our minds on the spiritual issues of existence are useful, but high religion, after all, does not consist in doing special things, but in doing all things in a special way and with a special quality. Western man has tended to turn these specialized arrangements respecting religious persons, religious places, re-

ligious periods, and religious practices into a series of
Ellis Islands upon which he detains religion from fruitful
entry into his everyday affairs.

Now and again this tendency to sterilize religion by
setting it apart from the sweat and struggle of the day's
work has been challenged by the rise of prophets who have
called man back to a realization of the social function of
religion. The rise of the prophets has always meant a demand that the routines of the priests be relinked to man's
secular struggle for survival and success in his day-to-day
life and work. But between these interludes of prophetic
challenge religion has always settled down to routines that
have affected man's secular life remotely and by indirection
only.

Western religion is now in one of these phases of settling
down. Even in the ranks of religious modernism there is
a significant diversion of the emotional drive of religion,
so urgently needed to animate an ethical reconstruction of
the Western social order, into concern with speculative
theology, individualistic psychology, and aesthetic ritual-
ism. Happily this diversion does not go unchallenged.
Alike in America and in Europe, the last two decades have
seen the development of an apostolate of scholar-prophets,
like the Walter Rauschenbusches of twenty years ago and
the Harry Wards of to-day, who have sought to rescue
religion from an aloof pietism and relate it to the human
perplexities and hungers of the workaday world. These
latter-day prophets, worthy successors to those ancient
prophets whose words are still winged as they fly from the
pages of the Old Testament to plague the formalists, are
urging Western man to effect that imperative inter-relation
of ethics and economics without which the church grows
anemic and the social order aimless. They do not dispute
the fact that occasional saints may achieve a modified
goodness and mystical godliness in cloisters safely distant
from the social battle-fields of their time. They contend
only that the good life for the millions cannot be achieved,

in this intricately interdependent age, apart from the achievement of the good society. They want religion to play a productive rôle in fashioning a society that will fortify instead of frustrate the quest of the individual for the increase, the enrichment, and the moral unification of his life.

Western man must listen to these prophetic voices. He need not still the restless questionings of his curious mind as he faces the cosmic riddles that have haunted man from the dim beginnings of human history. But he must not be deluded into thinking that ventures in sheer intellectualism constitute vital religion. Speculative consideration of the nature of God divorced from statesmanlike consideration of the needs of man produces a religion irrelevant and impotent. He need not close his mind to anything that psychology and allied sciences have to say about the tragedies of maladjustment and the techniques of adjustment in the field of human personality. But he must not become so absorbed in the psychological tangles of individuals as to forget that the lives of individuals may be made or marred by the impact of social and economic forces operative in the society of which the individual is a part. The social statesman as well as the psycho-analyst should be within ready reach of the confessional. He need not turn his back upon beauty or halt the embellishment of his hitherto austere and aesthetically barren rituals. But he must remember that beauty may be a harlot luring man from his profounder duties unless it is an authentic flowering from his common life. The achievement of beauty in its churches and the acceptance of ugliness in its factories can hardly be considered the mark of a well-conceived civilization.

The Western future depends in no small measure, I think, upon the extent to which Western man makes his religion ethical in its implications and social in its focus. Western man cannot hope to spiritualize his social order save as he socializes his religion. He must make his religion less a mirror to reflect and more a force to redirect his social order.

## A Well-bred Race!

The civilization of the West is a battle-ground for the conflicting claims of dead ancestors and unborn descendants. Transient atoms of creative energy between the womb and the tomb, we are the living links between the dead and the unborn. We are the physical carriers of a flickering light of life that illuminates for a time the narrow tract of conscious existence between the darkness that precedes birth and the darkness that follows death. We may turn this light of life that we carry either backward or forward. We may center our interest either upon those who gave us birth or upon those to whom we shall give birth. We may, in short, become either ancestor worshipers or descendant worshipers. Wisdom bids us balance these rival claims upon our devotion, but, with our strange Western incapacity to follow the Confucian rule of the golden mean, we become either ancestor worshipers or descendant worshipers, with ancestor worship getting the better of the bargain.

We are not, of course, followers of the cult of the dead in any conscious or formal sense. We should repudiate the grim aspects of this cult as practiced by the ancient Scythian king of whom Herodotus tells us, at whose tomb were strangled his concubine and his cup-bearer, his cook and his groom, his lackey and his envoy, together with several of his horses. We should refuse to adopt even the more gracious aspects of this cult as reflected in the folk-traditions of China and Japan, where the unseen presence of the ancestral dead guards men's homes, fructifies their crops, and steels their arms in battle. Nevertheless we Westerners are ancestor worshipers. Despite the flexibility of his mind in the fields of physical science and industrial technology, Western man, in those deeper matters of social and biological significance that determine the direction his civilization takes, is more a slave of the past than a servant of the future.

The Western future will be largely determined by the outcome of this contest between the forces making for ancestor worship and the forces making for descendant worship. The wisdom or the folly he brings to the adjustment of these conflicting claims becomes a crucial matter for Western man, for what he does or fails to do in behalf of the physical, intellectual, and spiritual quality of the yet unborn populations of the West will ultimately dictate the survival or collapse of his social order.

Concern with the biological quality of the unborn becomes almost hourly more imperative as Western life increases in scale, complexity, and tempo. The biologist sees the Western social order suffering from structural overloading and Western man finding it difficult to carry the increasing burden his civilization has been creating. This is the theory of "the burden of civilization" that has been stated with simplicity and clarity by many sociobiologic analysts. Sir Francis Galton put this theory briefly when some years ago he said, "Our race is over-weighted. It will degenerate under circumstances which make demands that excel its powers." Galton pointed out that savage peoples in Australia, Cape of Good Hope, New Zealand, and elsewhere have been swept away within the biologically brief span of three centuries as a result of their having come into contact with a civilization they were incapable of supporting. And events increasingly confirm the Galton contention that we civilized moderns begin to show signs of being unable to understand the complexity, control the scale, keep pace with the speed, and bear the burden of the civilization we are creating.

As social observers of the Galton sort assert, the tendency among civilized peoples seems to be that each succeeding generation elaborates the social environment, increases the number of demands made upon the members of society, and complicates generally the problem of living and working. With the biological strength of the race at a standstill or on the decline, while the burdens it must carry are on the increase, it is obvious that, unless steps are taken consciously and successfully to reverse the biological trend and to increase the physical, intellectual, and spiritual virility of its population generally, a time is likely to come in the life history of any civilized people when the structural overloading will become so great that the civilization in question will either collapse by an involuntary lapsing of the processes of society into chaos or be overthrown by a deliberate revolt of the people against civilization in the interest of a simpler and more bearable economy. Either or both of these alternatives may, in a given civilization, be averted by the rise to power of a saving remnant of the superiors who, animated by a Caesarian will-to-order, may succeed for a time in imposing a stabilization from above. But, unless these Caesars can actually set the forces of biological renewal at work, they cannot permanently postpone a social judgment day for the civilization they are captaining.

This is, I think, accurately descriptive of the current status of Western civilization. And this is why it is crucially important for Western man to shift the balance of interest from the dead to the unborn. The much derided science of eugenics seeks to effect this shift. Eugenics is not a materialistic reduction of the home to the level of the barnyard. It is a quest of the Holy Grail of superiorities of body and mind to the end that Western man may be assured of the capacity to understand the complexity, control the scale, keep pace with the speed, and bear the burdens of the civilization he has created.

Although there is little likelihood of his doing it, Western man would be ill-advised to try to write a comprehensive eugenics program into legislation. It is increasingly obvious that organized society should have the power to prevent, under proper safeguarding, the unrestricted reproduction of the manifestly unfit. Even this power runs the risk of misapplication, but the danger here is not as great as the danger that would be involved in eugenics legislation that would give officialdom the power to determine the evolution of desired types as well as the elimination of undesired types. Reforms instigated by responsible scientists come under the administration of the politician who all too often takes his mandate from the mood and adjusts his policies to the mind of the least intelligent among his constituents. I am not sure we should want our world peopled with the types a congress of present-day eugenists might select. I am quite sure we should not want our world peopled with the types a political bureaucracy might select.

The imperative quest for an improved human quality in the Western peoples must, I think, remain an unofficial quest. Western man must subject himself to a ceaseless self-education in the nature and necessity of increasing his biological strength which to-day bends under the burden imposed upon it by the vastness of scale, the complexity of process, and the rapidity of tempo that mark his civilization. His concern with this issue must be based upon something deeper than his being logically convinced that only a well-bred race can pilot a civilization of this size, intricacy, and speed. Despite the distortions that habitually creep into crusades, something of crusading passion must animate this quest for biological enrichment, if biological enrichment is to overtake biological enervation in time to insure the survival of the Western social order. Western man must actually shift his loyalty emotionally from the past to the future without letting it be waylaid by self-indulgent considerations in the present. He must emancipate himself from his half-conscious ancestor worship, which is but another name for his reluctance to follow the gleam of science and the goading of common sense. He must put an emotional drive back of conscious conviction in the rational development of a descendant worship.

When Sir Francis Galton said that eugenics must "sweep

the world like a new religion" he was but projecting this hope that Western man might harness the profound emotional forces of his loyalty in a descendant worship as peoples here and there have harnessed their deepest allegiances in ancestor worship. Western man must, at least and at last, understand that even the most transcendent genius of statesmanship cannot insure the survival of his social order unless there is a well-bred race to answer its call.

### Realistic Pacifism!

We are not fools. We are quite aware that, in this imperfect phase of the human venture, we may have to fight now and then because we are not wise enough or our neighbor nations are not wise enough to devise a better way of resolving conflicts of interest and intent. Despite our sense of war's insanity, we must, when we blunder into it, accept its tragic obligations and play our part as men. But we must not blunder into it! We must not, that is, unless we are willing to run the risk of a quick and complete collapse of Western civilization.

I need not, I am sure, rehearse the long array of convincing facts that make it doubtful that civilization could survive another World War, the scale of which, and the swiftness with which it would consume men and materials, would far exceed the last. Men who have even an inkling of the strategies and instruments of combat now being perfected by the war colleges of the several Western nations can hardly consider war a feasible instrument of national policy or a school of character either for citizen or for nation.

It becomes increasingly clear that, as part of the price he must pay for the survival of his social order, Western man must elaborate and bring to realization a program of realistic pacifism. I use the term realistic pacifism in contrast to a merely romantic pacifism of protest and abstention. I do not mean to speak slightingly of the heroism of

protest and abstention that braves the brutality of the mob
mind when war has conscripted the emotions and adjourned
the sanity of most men's minds. I mean only that, whatever its educative effect may be, romantic pacifism is not
broadly enough based to meet the full challenge that war
flings to the Western social order. The realistic pacifism
I project must be a science of peace as well as a sentiment
for peace. Its objective must be the scientific organization
of peace rather than a sentimental opposition to war. Its
proponents may, in fact, say little about the menace of war
as they go about their business of solidifying the foundation
and securing the superstructure of Western civilization.
Realistic pacifism cannot be a single crusade. It must be a
richly varied enterprise of social and economic statesmanship. It will flee from the folly of over-simplification. The
World War was called a war to end war. We now know
that this valiant phrase was the abortive offspring of good
intent and bad insight. War will never be ended by war.
The disease is too complicated for so simple a remedy.

Henry Kittredge Norton, in his *Back of War,* vividly
dramatizes the bewildering variety of causes that lead
peoples into conflict. He finds at least five *primitive* causes
of war: (1) plunder; (2) land; (3) conquest; (4) honor;
(5) revenge. He finds at least five *social* causes of war:
(1) dynastic ambitions; (2) racial rivalries; (3) religious
intolerance; (4) patriotism; (5) nationalism and self-
determination. He finds at least five *economic* causes of
war: (1) food supply; (2) surplus population, with its
emigrative impulse; (3) trade, with its run of problems
involved in shipping, tariffs, restrictive controls, and varied
combinations and cartels; (4) colonies, with their implications as markets and as sources of oil, cotton, rubber, and
other raw materials; (5) imperialism at once or in turn
predatory, strategic, administrative, and financial. He
finds at least eight *political* causes of war: (1) national
unity, with its intermittent crusades of irredentism; (2)
national prestige, now driving nations to fight for what is

felt to be national honor, now setting whole peoples sullenly out to seek national revenge; (3) internal unrest, tempting ruling but harassed governments to precipitate a foreign war in order to unite their own peoples and solidify their domestic authority; (4) foreign intrigue; (5) armaments, which may not only register but reënforce national fears; (6) alliances and treaties that crystallize the *status quo* into a balance of power that nothing save war can break if progress requires its breaking; (7) diplomacy which, struggle as it may, can hardly rise above the rôle of retained attorney for more or less intransigeant national interests; (8) propaganda, creating moods that easily capitulate to war cries.

There are other and more elaborately detailed analyses of the causes of war, but Mr. Norton's analysis suffices to emphasize the baffling complexity of war at its source. A social scourge like this, that may come from any one or a combination of any number of twenty-three or more causes, will clearly not succumb to a pacifism that is less varied in its attack than the scourge itself is varied in its origins. I said, a moment ago, that war will never be ended by war, and yet, figuratively speaking, there is no venture quite so imperative just now as the organization and prosecution of a war to end war. It is this non-military war to end war that I mean when I speak of a realistic pacifism.

This war to end war must be fought with volunteers. Although, if sense and insight do not lead us to volunteer, the conscription of necessity may hasten our entrance into its ranks, with the instinct for self-preservation acting as a kind of draft law. This war to end war cannot be won on a single front. It must be fought wherever any one of these twenty-three or more forces making for war are operative. It is a war that can be fought without firing a gun or flying a bombing plane. Its generals must be scientists, statesmen, and seers. Its regiments must be filled with biologists, psychologists, geologists, economists, captains of industry, labor leaders, bankers, social inventors, and teachers who have gone beyond the safe orthodoxies of the text-books to wrestle with the living problems of their generation. Its objective must be a world organized for adventurous peace rather than for annihilative war.

The business man must play his part in the furtherance of this realistic pacifism. The radical critic of big business has long considered the business man a war maker. Some time ago, an American Rear Admiral said, "If I read history aright, we are nearer war to-day than ever before, because we are pursuing a competitive trade policy, and crowding other nations into the background. A policy of this kind inevitably leads to war. . . . The penalty of national efficiency, either in commerce or in arms, is war." The business man must look into the validity of such judgments. Is foreign trade necessarily a cut-throat enterprise that must make for war? The business man has slowly but surely civilized the competitive processes of domestic trade. It is true that he still has much to do in the domestic field, but he has gone far on the road from buccaneering to enlightened trade practices. Cannot foreign trade be similarly civilized? One of the major social obligations of the modern business man is the development of a business ethics in foreign trade that will make business less and less a source of international conflict.

The geologist must play his part in the furtherance of this realistic pacifism. His expertness in the crucial field of resources gives him his chance. As they lay their plans for preparation against the possibility of war, the military staffs of modern governments must give serious and sustained attention to the problem of the adequacy and assurance of resources other than man power. Modern war becomes increasingly a contest in material resources. In the small-scale wars of earlier centuries, man power was the decisive consideration. In the large-scale wars of to-day, copper, nickel, manganese, nitrate, graphite, tin, mica, brass, aluminum, sulphur, asbestos, iron, lead, zinc, potash, and other material resources are more decisive than brave soldiers and bright uniforms that stand in the foreground of idealized pictures of war. The World War consumed mineral resources at a staggeringly rapid rate, but men at all conversant with the current war preparations of the major powers know that a next war would outstrip the last war in consumption of mineral resources far beyond the extent to which the World War outstripped preceding wars. We are rapidly approaching the time when the ever-increasing difficulty of maintaining adequate and assured mineral supplies for the prosecution of a modern war may prove a near-decisive consideration in the peace-or-war problem that confronts Western man.

In his *World Minerals and World Politics,* to which I have already referred, C. K. Leith calls attention to the fact that the blockade respecting copper, manganese, nitrate, nickel, and other basic minerals not adequately available within their frontiers, had much to do with the ultimate defeat of the Central Powers; that German occupation of the iron ore fields of Lorraine affected profoundly the conduct and course of the war; that the Allied Powers felt the pinch of shortage in minerals, notably potash, available only in areas under enemy control; that in the half-year immediately preceding the war Germany accumulated unprecedentedly large stocks of manganese, brass, nickel, tin, aluminum, asbestos, sulphur, graphite, and mica; that since the war France has been accumulating reserves of manganese and other minerals quite beyond her commercial needs, while Italy has been storing large oil reserves and building refining plants seemingly in excess of her commercial requirements. All of which emphasizes the key rôle that material resources play in modern war! There is far-reaching social significance for Western man in Mr. Leith's contention that "no nation is really self-contained as to war supplies" and that "with the vastly increasing demands of modern warfare, essential supplies in huge quantities must be obtained from all quarters of the globe, even by the nations most favored with domestic supplies." The problem of war will assume a new aspect as the major nations increasingly realize that no one of them alone has or can secure adequate and assured material resources for carrying out the ambitious plans of its war college.

We used to think that the increasing horror of modern war would lead men to renounce it and nations to evolve guaranties against its outbreak. Most of us doubt this now. The memory of the madness of any given war has but a slight carry-over to succeeding generations. There is already at the threshold of maturity in the Western world a generation of young men and young women to whom the tragedy and terror of the World War are but rhetoric in the books of reminiscence. There have always been romantic pacifists who thought that intelligent indict-ment of war as political insanity and moral imbecility would ultimately win mankind to a philosophy of peace. Most of us now have little faith that the memory of such indict-ments will ever survive a fire in the crowd's blood or stimu-late intelligence in unintelligent political leaders. Peace, we think, is likely to come from more prosaic sources. It is more probable, for instance, that the increasing impossi-bility of modern war from the resource angle may prove an effective deterrent. And the geologist must help West-ern man to see the insanity of war in the light of his avail-able resources.

The biologist must play his part in the furtherance of this realistic pacifism. Only the biologist can tell us with authoritative accuracy whether, in modern wars, mankind loses its best and keeps its worst or keeps its best and loses its worst. If biological research reveals beyond question that war selects for slaughter our superior stocks and se-lects for survival our inferior stocks, it may be that a so-ciety which has declined to heed the hypotheses of the pacifist propagandist may listen to the factual proofs of the biologist. The active prosecution of further research in the biology of war and the active dissemination of its dependable conclusions must be an important part of the campaign of a realistic pacifism. The attitude of Western man generally towards war might be profoundly changed if wide currency could be given to such knowledge as we have or can arrive at of the effect of war upon the biological future of the West.

We know what war does to the armies that fill the trenches and fly the sky, or at least we think we do. Do we know as accurately as we should what war does to the civil populations alike of the belligerent and of the neutral nations in a time of widespread war? We know that huge armaments mean high taxes. We know that high taxes mean high living costs. Do we know as accurately as we should what high living costs do to the marriage and birth rates of our superior stocks? When expensive peace-time military establishments are maintained, do we know as accurately as we should what effect delayed marriage among those in service is likely to have upon the biological future of the West? Do we know as accurately as we should what relation exists between the birth-rate and the death-rate on the various biological levels, from bad stock to good stock, in war time? Do we know whether or not the injuries, disease, malnutrition, and nervous shocks that come with war directly affect the germ plasm and thus register their results in future generations? If the mechanism of heredity is such that the germ plasm cannot be thus directly affected, do we know whether, how, and to what extent the injuries, disease, malnutrition, and nervous shocks of war time indirectly affect future generations? Do we know whether or not a people recovers from the broad biological impact of war? If a people does recover, do we know how long statesmanship must allow for recovery from a war like the World War? Do we have accurate insight into the factors that hinder and the factors that hasten recovery?

I am not asking whether the biologist knows these things. I am asking whether we—the Western masses who follow reluctantly, it may be, but resistlessly the lead of the war makers—know them. In the first instance, only the biologist knows or is on his way to find the answers to these questions. And it is among his basic social obligations to see to it that mankind is made to see the full biological implications of war as it is fought in an age of science. This is his part in the promotion of a realistic pacifism.

I need not go further down the gallery of officers and soldiers in this non-military war to end war. I have spoken of the respective rôles of business man, geologist, and biologist only to illustrate the highly specialized division of labor that must mark its prosecution. Realistic pacifism will bear but little resemblance to romantic pacifism. Many of its most effective promoters will be so busy removing the causes of war that they will have little time to spend in conventional peace movements.

I do not, let me make clear, predict that these seven seminal ideas will surely fertilize the public policy of the Western future. I do not say that Western man *will* repent the sins of his political nationalisms and do penance in the perfection of a cultural nationalism. I do not say that Western man *will* prove sensible enough or statesmanlike enough to bow to the inevitable internationalism of Western economic relations. I do not say that Western man *will* rationalize his politics. I do not say that Western man *will* bring a new mass-consciousness to the making of industrial policy quickly enough and fully enough to forestall a sweeping renunciation of Western capitalism. I do not say that Western man *will* find in his religion the dynamic for an ethical reconstruction of his socio-economic order. I do not say that Western man *will* consciously prosecute the quest of biological enrichment for the race. I do not say that Western man *will* set out with relentless realism to remove the causes of war. I say only that, in my judgment, Western man *must* bring these seven ideas to dominance in Western affairs if his social order is to have a stable and significant future.

Western man must shake himself out of the despairing mood into which the prophets of doom have plunged him, and pull himself together for a new venture in social creation and social control. He must renounce his cynicisms and come with courage and confidence to the enterprise of building a stabler and more meaningful civilization out of the raw materials that modern research and modern experience have piled about him. This is not to suggest that he give himself up to the bland idiocy of a blind optimism. He must not attempt to dodge the facts of disintegration that face him at every turn, but he must not allow the difficulties of his time to dampen his social initiative. Courage is indispensable in the captaincy of a civilization. The capacity to face necessity and duty unafraid is the mark of a healthy mind. Western man quite properly prides himself upon the fact that he has emancipated himself from many of the credulities of earlier and less exacting eras. There is nothing but good to be said for this modern determination to look life in the face and to see it for what it is. It has never paid to traffic in self-delusion. The debunker is a social servant we can ill afford to exile. But even a good thing can be used to bad ends, and, it has been said, the corruption of the best is the worst corruption. Western man must beware lest debunking ends in a devitalizing of his courage.

Henri Frédéric Amiel, who spent his life dissecting and debunking his own moods, cries out in his *Journal,* "What a strange creature I am! If I were charged with the education of some one, I should seek what was best everywhere and in everything. But for myself I no longer have the taste to reprimand and direct. I merely examine myself and state my preference. Psychology has replaced morality. That is the effect of this flaccid existence that dispenses with adventures and duties, with work and purpose. I no longer know courage save by name, and hope save by hearsay." This comes uncomfortably near to an accurate etching of the contemporary mood of Western man. He tends to spend more time analyzing his plight than he spends harnessing his potentialities. The current juncture in the political, social, and economic affairs of the West calls for men in whom courage is not bankrupt. We do not want to fool ourselves about ourselves and our society, as some generations have done, but we must not allow the laudable venture of debunking to keep us on the side-lines of the life of our time. Our place is in the arena!

Manifestly the West is in a phase of unprecedented insecurity. International insecurity! Nations do not feel secure. Armaments are mounting as nations cock a skeptical eye at the prospects of war and peace. Such safeguards as we have presumed to set up against war seem none too convincing to the controlling leaderships of the several nations. Industrial insecurity! Industries do not feel secure. The sudden swooping down of depression in a period of prosperity that seemed secure to the masses and to many of the leaders of the masses has, for the moment, unnerved many industrial leaders. One senses, in talks with these leaders, something of the mood that must have fallen upon primitive men when earthquake and famine came upon them unawares. Business cycles! Technological unemployment! Surpluses that defy control! These and allied factors in the current industrial scene leave many in a mood of bewilderment. Individual insecurity! Individuals do not feel secure. There has been, for the generation now in early maturity, a vast unsettlement of mind and spirit. Many find themselves adrift from old moorings. The catch-words that once caressed their ears with assurance of unchanging values have gone stale. Science has shaken their youthful faith in the old slogans of politics, of economics, of religion, of education.

I have not attempted to minimize the danger to Western civilization that lurks in this insecurity. But it is important for Western man, as he seeks to muster and to maintain courage in the face of his social uncertainty, to remember that there may be tonic as well as tragedy in insecurity. Insecurity challenges as well as chastises men. The great advances of the race biologically have come out of phases of insecurity, when wits had to win their way in an unfriendly environment, when strength had to be summoned to meet a sustained medley of menaces, when men had to struggle to survive. Western man may make this as true socially as it has been biologically. If he brings realism to his handling of the raw materials of renewal that are available, this phase of unprecedented insecurity, as it tries his mettle, may bring new safeguards that shall give us just the amount of security that is good for the souls of men and the societies of nations. We should not want a security that did not itself have to be continuously rewon. It is not good to loll too long in the sun, despite the health-inducing powers of sunshine, for the tang of chill days challenges to action as sedative warmth can never do.

# V

# Educating for Social Mastery

THERE stands on my desk a bronze hand-bell which my father rang before country school houses in Missouri for forty years without missing a term. The black enamel of its handle is worn through where his fingers gripped it. Its resonant ring is still clarion as callers now and then swing its clapper while they question into its history. I thought, as I watched it this late August morning, that it looked a bit resentful over its present rôle as a paperweight. It looked a little like an old engineer, who had once piloted the transcontinental express, forced to spend his last years as gate-keeper at a crossing. I think the premonitory stirrings of the oncoming school year were fingering the atoms of the old bell and awakening its bronze memory of earlier decades when, as summer slipped into autumn, it got ready to ring the youth of the Missouri countryside to its books.

It has been out of active service for a good stretch of years. Until a little while ago, it had lain hidden in the obscurity of a summer-kitchen loft surrounded by discarded books, prints, and a medley of what-nots. It belongs to a generation that accepted its educational system with an ever so slightly critical spirit, to a generation that, by and large, looked up to the schoolmaster as the missioner of a sacrosanct enterprise. It stands on my desk with a dignity and with an assurance that indicate its aloofness from the acid questioning to which everything educational is to-day subjected. As it rang the youth of a simpler time from playground to class-room, it called them in serene confidence that it was the symbol of an education that was fitting them to create, comprehend, and control their civilization.

The era it recalls seems Arcadian in contrast to the current era when education is everywhere met by a tenacious and turbulent skepticism of its social effectiveness. I do not, let me hasten to make clear, deplore this skepticism. It must, I think, be sharpened rather than suppressed. The educational system suffers much criticism that is beside the point. Men whose interests are manifestly endangered by the liberation and discipline of intelligence bombard the schools whenever an honest scholar expresses an incisive judgment on a current issue. Politicians pounce upon the schools whenever their large budgets seem to offer a seductive political target. And peddlers of panaceas denounce the schools whenever they decline to become headquarters for this or that transient hysteria. But all this is quite apart from the deeper and more searching skepticism that Western education faces.

I am convinced that, unless Western man effects a radical reorientation of the program and processes of his education, the seven concepts I have suggested—cultural nationalism, economic internationalism, rationalized politics, mass-conscious industrialism, socialized religion, biological enrichment, and realistic pacifism—will stand a discouragingly slight chance of coming to ascendancy quickly enough to check the decline of the West and give stability and significance to its social order.

The political dilemmas and the economic disruption that beset the life alike of Europe and of the United States cannot be explained by any uncontrollable factors in the natural environment or by any shortage of material essentials in the economic life of the West, as I shall argue in detail in later discussion of the industrial phase of the Western problem. Even drought-stricken areas have their sky-lines fretted with elevators jammed with futile surpluses and warehouses bursting with supplies that mock the bread-lines of the unemployed. Nature has not failed us, nor has the industrial system fallen down on its job of quantitative production. It is obviously and solely a break-down in social management from which the West is suffering.

And, although it pains me as a schoolman to admit it, I cannot but believe that Western education must share the blame for this break-down of political, social, and economic leadership. We are reaping the Dead Sea fruits of an era of over-specialization in Western education. And these fruits are now painfully evident in a generation of leaders whose fingers have all proved thumbs in the moulding of those general policies of political, social, and economic organization which, in the end, make or break the separate enterprises of men. Western education has been superbly successful in training Western man for the technical execution of his separate enterprises. It has tragically failed to fit him for realistic statesmanship in the ground-plan and governance of his social order.

It is, I think, urgently important that Western man inquire, without permitting his inquiry to be lost in irrelevant details, into the cause of this social inadequacy of his education. He will find at the end of his inquiry, I confidently predict, that the temper and technique of specialization, which has made his civilization, has unmade the education to which he has looked to make him master of his civilization. I want, as a contribution to this inquiry, briefly to trace the rise and the implications of specialism in education, and to suggest the critically important relation that a de-specialization of education bears to any soundly conceived attempt that Western man may make to renew and to stabilize his social order.

There was a long run of centuries, reaching from early antiquity well into the Middle Ages, when man was neither beneficiary of the virtues nor victim of the blights of specialism. In all that time, a really first-class mind might tackle, without presumption, the learning of all the essen-

tial knowledge then existent in the fields we have come to
know as science, philosophy, and the arts. The principles
and the productions in these fields were not so bewilder-
ingly many as to baffle man in an attempt to master them.
It was possible for education to be encyclopedic in such
a world. It was possible for educators to integrate the
total knowledge of the time and to relate it directly to those
problems in which the survival and significance of the
social order were involved. Whether the educators of
the time did all this is quite beside the point I am interested
to indicate. It was possible.

A little later the stage-setting of education was disturbingly altered. The intellectual revival animating and accompanying the Renaissance, and the birth of modern
science that came in its wake, transformed the erstwhile
simplicity of knowledge into a complexity that has increasingly defied man's efforts to fit its parts into an intelligible
pattern. The serpent of specialization entered the Eden of
manageable knowledge. And everywhere the old omnibus
categories of knowledge were broken down into a larger
and larger number of smaller and smaller divisions. Philosophy, once the canopy that covered the total enterprise
of intellectual inquiry, breaks down into moral philosophy,
on the one hand, and natural philosophy, on the other.
Natural philosophy, in turn, breaks down into biological
science, on the one hand, and physical science on the other.
Physical science, again, breaks down into physics and chemistry. And these two basic sciences of physics and chemistry, in the processes of investigation and application,
divide and subdivide to make still other special sciences.
And, finally, each of the special sciences tends to become
a league of still minuter specializations. The once seemingly homogeneous empire of knowledge is sundered by
the self-determination of its several interests into a myriad
of minor duchies.

Without this intensive specialization the amazing advance of modern science would have been impossible. We

could not if we would, and we would not if we could, wipe from the record the rise and results of specialization in man's quest for new knowledge. But, as tool or technique, specialization has its limitations, and when it is forced to function beyond these limitations its use results, at best, in diminishing returns and, at worst, in downright hurt. Both of these outcomes are now recognizable in Western life. On the most active sectors of the research front, a purely single-track specialization to-day tends to produce diminishing returns, while, in determining the program and directing the processes of education, the dominance of the specialist-mind has worked downright hurt.

In saying that single-track specialization reaches the point of diminishing returns in research, I am but calling attention to the obvious fact that the walls between the sciences are breaking down, as the most productive researches of our time are seen to proceed on the borderlines between two or more sciences. None of the sciences, save in terms of the most pedestrian research, can operate within the sealed frontiers of its special field. Geology is dependent alike upon the materials and upon the methods of physics, chemistry, and biology. Radioactivity is forever flitting back and forth across the dividing line between chemistry and physics. Science grows increasingly hyphenate. Realizing that biology is chemistry as well as biology, we create a bio-chemistry. Realizing that geology is physics as well as geology, we create a geo-physics. And so on through a long list of newly recognized relationships in the enterprise of research and interpretation. The twilight zones between the sciences take on increasing importance.

In short, at the beginning of the age of specialization, the scientists went scurrying off to their severely separate provinces to dig for new knowledge, but, with the digging done, they find that, if science is to make genuine headway in man's age-old effort to penetrate the mystery and to perfect the mastery of life, they must come back together, pool their partial insights, and see to it that no intellectual provincialism of separate specialisms prevents a productive relating of their separate factual achievements one to the other. Specialization is a spade. Its function ends with digging. It has little to bring to the enterprise of evaluating and bringing into creative relationship the facts it unearths.

This recognition of the limited function of specialization in research has come about naturally and without resistance from scientists. The chemist does not feel that his sacred rights are threatened when he sees a section of the old wall between chemistry and physics crumble. The geologist does not feel that, in order to save his professional pride, he must sneak secretively through the back doors of biology, physics, and chemistry when he needs to borrow their materials or their methods. Unfortunately for Western man, this realistic attitude towards the restricted rôle of specialization does not prevail in the field of education as it prevails in the field of research. The field of research is being skilfully plowed by specialization, but, if I may shift and mix my metaphors, the field of education is being smothered by a rank overgrowth of specialization gone to seed.

The unpardonable sin of Western leadership, the wages of which may yet be the death of Western civilization, was committed when Western education was permitted to become a series of relatively unrelated specialisms, instead of its being made to center around or, at least, come to climax in a coherently planned attack upon the problem of creating, comprehending, and controlling the civilization in which Western man must live his life and pursue his varied enterprises. It is beside the point to try to fix the blame for this social sterilization that has fallen upon Western education. No one either desired it or designed it. It has come as the inevitable end-result of an all-Western abdication of educational leadership in the face of the ever more bewildering complexity and mass of modern knowledge thrown up by the spade of specialization. It is important that Western man analyze this abdication, come to see clearly what it has meant to the program and processes of his education, and relate its results in the minds of Western leaders to the political distraction, economic disruption, and social dishevelment that to-day plague Western life.

In the long run of centuries before the rise of modern science, knowledge increased so slowly that the masters of education could keep the materials of education easily in hand. In most instances, they could go leisurely about the business of digesting, interpreting, and relating to previous knowledge a fresh accession of information and insight. They were not harassed by a sense of hurry lest a new discovery might a day later upset their ordered scheme of instruction. Only occasionally did they have to make any major change in the map of human knowledge they had confidently drawn. But with the rise of modern science the masters of education lost this sense of mastery of the materials of education.

The invigorating winds of a new spirit of inquiry began to blow across the world. Men, animated by the itch to know, began hunting, blasting, boring, probing, boiling, cooking, and dissecting. The great adventure of modern science was on! Research began to throw up, at a disconcerting rate, all sorts of new facts and new knowledge. These new facts and this new knowledge were thrown on the study tables of the educators. Before long it became apparent that the new knowledge was coming faster than the educators could fit it intelligently into any formula of education. And there happened in the field of education what I saw happen in a Missouri hayfield many years ago. Six of us were putting up hay on Cal Shinn's farm. Among the six was a swashbuckling braggart who offered to bet five dollars that he could stack all the hay that the other five of us could pitch to him. We took the bet, pro-rating it at a dollar apiece, laid the base for a stack, and began pitching in earnest. The betting braggart managed to keep his head above hay for a while, but before long he was up to his neck in hay he could not handle. He managed to extricate himself from the mass of unstackable hay, slid off the stack, stuck his pitchfork in the ground, and said, "Damn it, stack it yourself!" In like manner, overwhelmed by new knowledge that the researchers were pitching to them faster than they could manage it, the educators slid off the stack and, turning to immature students, said, with the profanity deleted, "Stack it yourselves!" It was thus that the elective system was born.

I do not want to divert this discussion of the social function of education in the existing leaderless confusion of the West to a rehearsal of the warfare of theory that has been waged over a single educational device. I speak here of the elective system only because its pandemic sweep through Western education signalized what I have, with considered accuracy, I think, described as an all-Western abdication of educational leadership in the face of new knowledge accumulating at a speed that outstripped the possibility of prompt correlation at the time. The elective system was the result of educational drift rather than the product of educational design. The fact that its promotion was couched in terms of a positive educational theory does not do away with the fact that it was, in essence, a rationalization of the helplessness that educators felt in the presence of a mounting mass of new knowledge they could not readily assimilate. In the elective system, the educational leadership of the West executed a strategic retreat from the old integrations of knowledge, which were confessedly obsolete, and evaded the obvious challenge to a new integration of the educational process, which was and is imperative if Western man is to comprehend and control his increasingly intricate and interdependent civilization.

The key to an understanding of the relative impotence of Western education to prevent the social insecurity that has come like a murrain to afflict Western civilization lies, I think, in the fact that, with the onset of modern research, the educators adopted as the major method of *handling* knowledge the method that was *producing* knowledge, namely, specialization. The legitimate sovereignty of specialization in the explorative enterprise of research is unquestioned, but the extension of its sovereignty to the program and processes of education has prevented rather than produced the kind of discipline and direction the Western mind must have if it is to give stability and significance to its social order in the midst of modern complexity.

Under the mandate of specialization, the average college of the West, to take but one important unit of the educational system, is but a loose federation of specialized enterprises. The college is a kind of holding-ground where a diverse company of professional scholars drop anchor as each pursues his particular specialism. The biologist is busy teaching biology. The psychologist is busy teaching psychology. The chemist is busy teaching chemistry. The physicist is busy teaching physics. The economist is busy teaching economics. The political scientist is busy teaching political science. And it is assumed that, from the separate pursuit of these separate subjects, the student will somehow achieve enough of an integrated insight into the nature and needs of his social order to fit him either for wise leadership or wise followership in the design of those general political, social, and economic policies which, as I have said, in the end, make or break the separate enterprises of men, as failure in the field of general social management has to-day left a technically expert West floundering in political and economic blind alleys.

It is true, of course, that these separate scholars, in discussing the materials and diagnosing the problems of their special fields, turn their attention at times to the social matrix in which their separate subject-matters are set, but this concern with the nature and needs of the social order is incidental to the system under which these separate studies are prosecuted. Any deliberately planned attempt to comprehend the social order as a whole is itself looked upon as a specialism to be farmed out to the social scientists as a distinct breed separate from and suspected by the physical scientists. In practical operation, the pursuit of essentially incoördinated specialisms, which may or may not be orientated to the current social scene, depending upon the mind and mood of scholars sovereign in their separate fields, is both the *terminus a quo* and the *terminus ad quem* of college teaching in general throughout the West.

And we have produced what we have thus been organized educationally to produce, namely, a generation of specialists. The vast crowd of customers who enter and leave the colleges of the West without becoming good specialists nevertheless bear the mark of the system in their minds. They are partialists who are powerless to play a constructive rôle in the analysis and adjustment of a social order whose current instability is to be found at the point of the relationships of its parts. With a mind moulded by specialized instruction, Western man everywhere displays an increasing reluctance to wrestle with difficult problems as a whole. He dismembers his difficulties and sends their separate parts to the appropriate specialists. And then, when his social order faces a general crisis, as now, he finds the specialists unwilling, even in consultation, to assume responsibility for general conclusions.

It is important that Western man realize that a causal relation exists between the specialization of his education and the incapacity he has lately displayed in dealing with the general policies of his civilization. But he must scan with a skeptical eye the reforms that promise to rectify the miseducation that has made him a muddler in the fields of social creation and social control while making him an expert in the technical execution of limited enterprises. In particular, he will do well to go slowly with educational reforms that seek to sweep all of modern knowledge into

a new synthesis, with the intention of serving its essence
to him in pemmican form within the time-limit of two or
four college years. Tentative and provisional resyntheses
of knowledge are necessary if the thought of successive
generations is to have veracious backgrounds, but such
syntheses cannot be encompassed in a single college generation, save in the most touch-and-go fashion. And Western
man stands to gain nothing by exchanging accurate specialized knowledge for superficial general knowledge. It is
an authentic integration of the educational process, not an
artificial synthesis of knowledge, that promises most to
Western man in his task of rethinking and renewing his
civilization.

And the beginning of this integration of education must
be Western man's realization that specialization has given
him an educational system organized, in the main, to train
professional scholars rather than to educate men for the
creation, comprehension, and control of their social order.
The training of professional scholars is a crucially important matter for which a rational society will always
make adequate provision, but, in basic method and objective, it is an enterprise quite distinct from educating men
for leadership and followership in the making and mastering of their social order. The underlying pattern of the
Western educational system, with its endless and exclusive
separatisms of subject-matter and its insistence upon the
sanctity of sequence in the study of these separate subject-
matters, is a pattern dictated solely by the division of labor
that necessarily accompanies the research activity of professional scholars. It is a pattern that fosters scholarship
but frustrates education. And little headway can be made
in equipping the educational system of the West for its
social function until its ground-plan reflects a recognition
of the deep-going difference between scholarship and
education.

Scholarship is the quest of scientific knowledge. Education is the quest of social understanding. The scholar is a

man at home in his warren of scientific facts. The educated
man is a man at home in his world of social forces. The
scholar may be an educated man and the educated man
may be a scholar but the two are not of necessity identical.
The progress of science depends upon the scholar. The
progress of society depends upon the educated man. The
production of scholars and the production of educated men
are essentially distinct enterprises. The modern West is
seeking to execute these essentially distinct enterprises in
the same institutions, in terms of the same curricula, and
under leadership of the same faculties. It cannot, in my
judgment be done.

As long as these distinct and, at many points, conflicting
enterprises are tacitly assumed to be identical, and are
forcibly united in the single programs of single institutions,
both will suffer. The men concerned most with an education aimed at an understanding of contemporary civilization and the fitting of men to cope with its complexity will
find their crusades for change check-mated by the men concerned most with scholarship. And not without reason on
the part of the professional scholars. For the full adaptation of a college, let us say, to the purpose of education,
as I have here defined it, would play havoc with the pattern
of exclusive specialisms essential in the enterprise of
scholarship. Which is but saying, the other way around,
that the concurrent or successive study of separate subject-
matters which is the procedure of scholarship, does not and
cannot produce the education without which Western man
will continue to bring a baffled futility to a civilization the
parts of which he has created but the relationships of which
he cannot control.

The distinction I have drawn between scholarship and
education is not, of course, a new distinction. It has existed
from the beginning of organized knowledge and organized
society. But never before in Western history has it been
so critically necessary to make it and to fashion our educational system in terms of it. When the scale of Western

enterprise was small, when the inter-relationships of the Western social order were simple, and when the tempo of Western life was slow, fairly well-informed men of ordinary good sense could keep the ship of Western civilization on even keel. To-day, however, the scale of Western enterprise is so vast, the inter-relationships of the Western social order so complex, and the tempo of Western life so swift that, unless Western man brings something more than technical skill and specialized knowledge to its navigation, this ship of Western civilization, already listing dangerously, may conceivably flounder and go down.

Western man must send his critical intelligence, like a refiner's fire, through his educational system, which has come to its present form less by statesmanlike design than by accident, accretion, and accommodation. He must deliberately refashion the institutional system through which he to-day seeks to serve the dual purpose of scholarship and education. At the outset of this refashioning, as fundamental to all the further reforms he may effect, he must definitely separate the enterprise of scholarship and the enterprise of education far enough to prevent each from hamstringing the other as now. And, in this segregation of functions, he must richly and realistically provide alike for the promotion of scholarship and the prosecution of education.

He must, I think, provide for the promotion of scholarship and the training of professional scholars in research institutes severely segregate in organization and objective. These institutes may or may not be on the campus and under the control of universities, but, wherever located and under whatever administration, they must be absolved from all responsibility for educating students, in the sense of education as I have here defined it. This is not to say that the mature scholars in these institutes will be robbed of the stimulus that undoubtedly comes to the scholar's research from his being surrounded by eager young minds bent upon learning the meaning and methodology of productive scholarship. For these institutes will exist for the training of professional scholars as well as for the promotion of productive scholarship.

Let me speculate briefly upon the probable character of these institutes. To them will be admitted only those young men and young women who show aptness for and a determination to become practitioners of productive scholarship. And, once admitted, they will find themselves in a master-apprentice relationship. For these institutes will differ widely from existing graduate schools, whose programs and processes are still distressingly undergraduate in content and execution. The young scholars in these institutes will not be enrolled in classes or expected to take courses essentially informational in character. They will instead serve as secretaries, assistants, gatherers of data in the field, and collaborating investigators to the mature scholars who form the permanent staffs of these institutes. It will be assumed that prospective scholars, with the capacity requisite for admission to these institutes, will be able, with the informal and incidental counsel of their older colleagues, themselves to ferret out and to formulate the background-materials for their respective fields of scholarship. The thundering horde of students who now seek graduate work primarily to secure a degree that shall serve as an academic labor union card or character reference will find no place in these institutes.

The Samurai of scholarship who man these institutes will not be cut wholly off from contact with the educational system of the West. They will, from time to time, lay aside their laboratory aprons and halt their socio-economic investigations for a swing around the circle of the educational institutions. In this occasionally played rôle of peripatetic scholar, they will report their latest findings, suggest to the teachers the possible implications they see in these findings, secure from the teachers a sense of the new questions that are arising out of the attempts of the educators to help Western man create, comprehend, and control his social

environment, and give to the students of these institutions
first-hand contact with the men who are pioneering on the
frontiers of knowledge. Fresh from their laboratories and
study chambers, innocent of any responsibility for formal
instruction, and free to deal only with the special issue that
animates and absorbs their minds at the moment, these
visiting scholars will be a constant source of refreshment
to the educational institutions. This coöperation of the
enterprise of scholarship with the enterprise of education
will be socially fruitful. The existing coalescence of the
enterprise of scholarship with the enterprise of education
is socially fatal.

With the interests of productive scholarship supported
and safeguarded better, in these special institutes, than
they are now in institutions that hamper the productive
scholar with the distracting and uncongenial duties of
formal instruction, the way will be clear for concentrating
the energy and equipment of our vast system of schools
upon the socially imperative task of educating Western man
for what I have called, with the insistent repetition of a
refrain, the creation, comprehension, and control of his
social order. This is the objective in terms of which the
educational process must be integrated. We cannot integrate the totality of modern knowledge which grows with
mercurial swiftness. If, in the larger processes of building
and buttressing a civilization, the microscopic mind is
inadequate, the encyclopedic mind is, we must admit, impossible. We can, however, integrate our educational
process in terms of a coherently planned attempt to understand and undergird the civilization that determines the
destiny of our lives and our enterprises.

This integration will involve a fundamental revolution,
alike in the content of curriculum and in the method of
teaching, all the way from kindergarten to college. It will
mean taking the current scene as the subject of our study.
It will mean a smashing of the excessive departmentalism
that has marked a school system the ground-plan of which

has been adapted to the professional convenience of scholars rather than to the social objectives of education. It will mean a deliberate attempt to stimulate in students that sense of social responsibility which, if it is to be more than a merely amiable intent, must be grounded in social understanding. It will mean turning our schools into seedbeds for social statesmanship.

The concentration of education upon the triple objective of social creation, social comprehension, and social control, which this integration will involve, will not narrow its program to the fields now segregated as the social sciences. In its quest of a science of social forces, the new education must socialize all the scientific forces. It must levy upon the riches of all fields of research for aid in the attempt to make and to master a social order that will be at once historically stable and humanly significant. In its processes all sciences will be social sciences, for, unlike the professional scholar, the professional educator must approach the separate fields of inquiry and information, not in terms of their unique natures, but in terms of the light they may throw upon the common problem of social comprehension and the techniques they may contribute to the common enterprise of social creation and social control.

Two basic objections will inevitably be lodged against this suggestion of segregating the enterprise of scholarship in special institutes and of concentrating the program and processes of education upon the creation, comprehension, and control of the social order, if I leave unqualified the stark severity I have given it: (1) it will be said that any such segregation of the organized enterprise of productive scholarship will leave the educational institutions of the West denuded of intellectually alive teachers and in the hands of routineers content to rehash the decadent and dead formulas at whose foundations the productive scholar is forever blasting, and (2) that any such concentration of the organized enterprise of education upon the meaning and mastery of contemporary civilization will inevitably leave out many things of cultural and personal import that must obviously be included in a valid education. Both of these assumptions are, I am sure, unwarranted. And I want to consider them briefly in turn.

Let me consider, first, the contention that, with productive scholarship promoted separately in special institutes, the teachers of the educational institutions, not being professional scholars, in the specialized research sense in which this term is currently understood, would not keep intellectually alive. If the education I project were to be but a method for merchandising departmentally the knowledge discovered in the research institutes, I should agree wholly with this contention. We could not expect the renewal of Western civilization to be greatly helped or hastened by mere rewrite men. But all this is leagues away from the teaching problem that would be presented by an education deliberately concentrated upon a coöperative search by teachers and students for insight into the triple task of creating, comprehending, and controlling a valid social order.

The teachers in an educational system thus radically redirected could not be mere automats of knowledge pouring out sealed packets of information when tuition fees were dropped into the slot. The very nature of their enterprise would demand that they be scholars, no less than the men who would man the research institutes, but scholars of a different sort. They would be forced into research, no less real than the research of the specialized scholar, but research of a different sort. The whole enterprise of their teaching would be a research, but, unlike the researches of the specialized scholars, it would be a research in social values and social relationships. Under the existing régime of departmentalized instruction, the contention is sound that the well-springs of intellectual aliveness tend to go dry in the teacher who does not concern himself with productive research in his special field. I am not questioning the validity of research as a vitalizer of teaching. I am suggesting only that the research of the educator must have an objective different from the objective towards which the research of the specialized scholar drives. The objective of the specialized scholar must be the extension and verification of knowledge. The objective of the educator must be the enrichment and validation of the social order. Education, as I have here defined it, does not imply unscholarly teachers. It does imply philosophical scholars, to whom we must look for the enrichment of understanding, in contrast to technical scholars, to whom we must look for the extension of knowledge. And I cannot but believe that the enterprise of trying to understand the interplay of contemporary social forces and to fit men to play a productive rôle in their direction is quite as invigorating intellectually as research in ways and means of unlocking and harnessing to human use the inherent energy of the atom.

Let me consider, now, the contention that, with the educational system dedicated to the enterprise of fitting men to create, comprehend, and control a humanly significant social order, many things of cultural and personal import would be left out of education. This contention is born, I am sure, of a narrow notion of what the social venture of a civilization involves. Education must obviously play for the increase, the enrichment, and the moral integration of the life and personality of the individual. Significant civilizations cannot be built around sleazy individuals. There is much that cries aloud to be done if we are to transform our schools into better instruments for making men at home in the life of their time, if we are to save for men the values of specialization while saving them from the vices of specialization, if we are to enable men to understand situations outside their specialisms as well as subject-matters inside their specialisms. This will involve, I think, the development of a new form of education that shall be largely a guided practice in the difficult art of understanding complex social situations. It is this that I have had in mind as I have suggested an educational pro-

gram brought to focus in a coherently planned attack upon
the problem of creating, comprehending, and controlling
the social order of the West.  I am quite aware, however,
that, if education is to play its full part in the renewal and
reconstruction of the Western social order, it must concern itself with more than the stiffening and steering of the
intellect, as it wrestles with public issues, basic as this is.
It is the business of education to train the total human being
for effective participation in the civilization of his time.
And this means more than to train men to reason accurately
about the affairs of their generation, for we are motivated
by many things other than pure reason.

The things we want, the things we are afraid of, the
persons we love, the standards that prevail in our set, the
desire to stand in with our crowd or to break into the crowd
on the next avenue, the subtle sovereignty of fashion, the
hunger for prestige, the hypnotic lure of custom, these and
a hundred and one other things, quite as much as reason,
motivate and modify our behavior.  If we are guided by
our emotions as well as by our reason, a valid education
must deal with the nurture and discipline of our emotions.
We now know that our digestion, our blood pressure, our
pituitary and thyroid glands, and a long medley of like
physical factors work side by side with reason in dictating
our conduct.  If our bodies as well as our brains determine
our character and direct our conduct, a valid education
must deal with these physical determinants.  We now know
that a suppressed ambition may be as troublesome as a
septic adenoid, an inferiority complex as dangerous as an
infection center.  A valid education must, therefore, dip
down into the subconscious mind as well as deal with the
surface mind.

A valid education must get in many of its best licks in
the pre-school years and in the early years of tutelage.  It
must deal with what I may loosely call the emotional as
well as the intellectual side of men's lives.  It must be an
education of the character as well as an education of the

intellect. It must help men to act creatively as well as understand clearly when they find themselves in the complex social situations with which the modern West abounds. It must, as forecast by the Deweys, the Russells, and their colleagues in educational modernism, be an education that shall help men to safeguard and to sustain that rich physical vitality which gives tone and tang to living; an education that shall free men from fear, at least of the irrational sort, and develop in them the priceless virtue of courage; an education that shall stimulate and discipline in men a sympathy that shall be at once sensitive and sensible; an education that shall nurse and nurture the urge to create until it dominates the more easily followed urge to destroy; an education that shall give men a realistic sense of justice instead of a romantic notion of unselfishness that is more preached than practiced; an education that shall rescue sex from sentimentality and sniggering and bring it into the sunlight of sincerity and sense.

All these things that make for the expansion and enrichment of the life of the individual must be part of the purpose of the education that is to fit men to play a productive rôle in the renewal and reconstruction of the Western social order. But with the vastness of scale, complexity of relationships, and swiftness of change that mark the affairs of our time, the most richly developed individual life may find itself victimized and vanquished by the sort of political, social, and economic débâcle that has lately befallen the Western world. Deliberate provision must obviously be made for helping Western man to understand, better than he has understood, the forces that make or break the successful functioning of his civilization. This is why I insist that, with due regard for matters of more strictly cultural and personal import, and with adequate provision for the preliminary stages of specialized study essential to later professional training or later entry into the higher vocationalism of productive scholarship, the core of the enterprise of education must, if I may again repeat, be concerned with the triple problem of social creation, social comprehension, and social control. And the imposition of this coherent purpose upon the now incoördinate medley of enterprises that center in our schools will, I am convinced, give new meaning and new momentum even to the more personal and technical ventures in study.

The chance of survival for the Western social order will, in my judgment, be slight unless an education, integrated in terms of this triple objective, is created to serve alongside the existing and evolving agencies of specialized scholarship. Western man's instinct for survival must before long begin to give him a sense of the social support he might find in a revised education. The danger is that he will turn to indoctrination through instruction rather than to integration through education. In an essentially headless and disintegrate West, a vast population like the Russians, let us say, converting their school system into an agency of insistent indoctrination for a special gospel of social organization, might well prove invincible, if the rest of the West should cling conservatively to a system of specialized training uncorrected by an integrated education of its peoples. Western man is approaching the necessity of choice between dogmatic indoctrination through instruction and dynamic integration through education. His destiny may be dictated by the choice he makes.

# VI

## The Social Dynamism of Religion

A HAUNTING sense of uncertainty invades my mind as I
consider what I have written respecting a New Renaissance, a reluctant fear that I have sketched a fair promise
that may never materialize in fruitful performance. Despite the adequacy of its raw materials of renewal, despite
the insight and art with which the Diderots and D'Alem-
berts of the time may assemble these raw materials, and
despite the vantage-ground from which their social utilization may be advocated, Western civilization may yet go
to a rendezvous with death. And for this reason: the
genius of the social engineers may draft plan and prospectus
of renewal, at once scientific and statesmanlike, but the
brightest dreams of scientists and statesmen may be still-
born if the diagram lacks a dynamic.

It may be that the West must experience a New Reformation before it can realize a New Renaissance. The
formula of intensive scientific investigation plus intelligent
self-interest, which has underlain my forecast of a new and
needed statesmanship, is, I think, sound as a diagram of
procedure for the stabilization and enrichment of the
Western future, but social formulas of this sort are not
self-operative. Western man must seek and find the dynamic that will drive him into the sustained prosecution of
this enterprise of renewal and reconstruction. The motivation that gives momentum to vast processes of social development is a matter that, despite its centrality, does not
loom as large as it must in the councils of the political,
social, and economic planners. Intensive scientific investigation in the hands of intelligent self-interest can go far

towards building an urbane and useful social order, but self-interest, however significant the materials at its disposal, has never alone created a civilization that has been at once spiritually satisfying and socially durable. Beyond its legitimate concern with solvency and success, a people must be dominated by certain great binding beliefs that hold it together in a sense of dedication to objectives with greater richness and reach than the material advantage of the lone individual or the limited group, if it is to prepare the soil for a flowering-time of the human spirit and direct its civilization into a great and glowing period.

Intelligent self-interest, with its ethics of prudence, can, as I have said, produce a very comfortable sort of civilization. It can produce a civilization in which power and privilege will consider it good business to yield enough now and then to prevent restlessness from bursting into revolution. But this is not enough to insure a stable and significant future for the peoples of the West. I am convinced that any renewal of Western civilization that is to mean more than a mere reëstablishment of the old order of things under new names must be, in the deepest sense of the word, a religious movement. It must deal with the roots of life. It will not be enough merely to polish and to pack into new and fancy containers the fruits of life. Anything less will be only an adventure in what Mazzini called "the petty skirmishes for interests and rights."

Mazzini was seeking to recruit Young Italy for a crusade that would bring to the Italy of his time unity, independence, and something akin to the renaissance of social realism of which the West now stands in serious need. Recounting various unsuccessful manoeuvers towards the rescue and renewal of Italian integrity, Mazzini said to his followers, "We fell as a political party, we must rise as a religious party." Mazzini was not proposing a guerilla warfare between heretics and ecclesiastics. He was telling Young Italy that until then it had made the mistake of trusting to a social diagram without a spiritual dynamic.

"For us," said Mazzini, in a moving discussion of *Interests and Principles* which he addressed to the Italy of 1836, "we maintain that there has never been a single great revolution that has not had its source outside material interests. We know of riots, of popular insurrections, but of none that has been crowned with success, or transformed into a revolution. Every revolution is the work of a principle which has been accepted as a basis of faith. . . . It always fulfils itself in the name of a principle, that is to say, of a great truth, which, being recognised and approved by the majority of the inhabitants of a country, constitutes a common belief, and sets before the masses a new aim. . . . It reorganises everything on a new basis; it gathers and harmonises round the new principle all the elements and forces of the country; it gives a unity of direction towards the new aim to all those tendencies which before were scattered in the pursuit of different aims. . . . If a revolution did not imply a general reorganisation by virtue of a social principle . . . if it did not secure a moral unity . . . we should believe it our duty to oppose the revolutionary movement with all our power. . . . Everything depends on the presence or absence of a principle of reconstruction. . . . Wherever, in fact, individual rights are exercised without the influence of some great thought that is common to all; wherever individual interests are not harmonised by some organisation which is directed by a positive ruling principle, and by the consciousness of a common aim . . . every interest naturally conflicts with an opposing interest. . . . A social sphere must have its center. . . . The true instrument of the progress of the peoples is to be sought in the moral factor."

When I speak of the necessity of a spiritual dynamic back of our social diagram, I mean this factor that Mazzini pleaded with Young Italy not to ignore, an integrating factor at the center of the social sphere of the West. But why did Mazzini, why do I, refer to this invigorating and integrating factor as religious? I want, if I can, to make clear both what I mean and what I do not mean when I suggest that the social renewal of the West must be, at heart, a religious movement.

I am aware that some of the most distinguished minds of the West are convinced that its social renewal depends upon the repression rather than the release of the religious impulse. "Of all requisites for the regeneration of society," says Bertrand Russell, "the decay of religion seems to me to have the best chance of being realized." In so far as Mr. Russell has in mind the perversion of the religious impulse, intelligence must endorse his skepticism of its social significance. In asserting the indispensability of a spiritual dynamic for the social renewal of the West, I am by no means contending that religion is automatically and inevitably a social good.

Under the alleged mandate of their religion, men have practiced human sacrifice, slain babies on the red altars of superstition, gorged themselves at cannibal feasts, wallowed in sensual revels they deemed pleasing to their gods, given rein to their hatred of men of other races and other religions, surrendered their minds to anarchic hysteria, and gone the way of bigots, their brains aflame with fanaticism and their hands filled with fagots. Religion has been, throughout history, alternately a ladder to hell and a rope to the stars. Men have burned the prophets of righteousness and blinded the light of intelligence in the name of religion. It has now lifted and now lowered the human spirit. Religion has touched whole civilizations with nobility and given radiance to otherwise bleak eras, but it has also been the spawning-ground for dark purposes and sinister passions.

But the long historic abuse of religion does not invalidate the authentic religious impulse as an invigorating and integrating factor in the social renewal of the West. And the most telling argument I know for the religious impulse as a dynamic for civilization lies unconfessed between the lines of two of Bertrand Russell's incisive dissertations

on the ingredients and implications of the good life in his
*What I Believe* and in his *Education and the Good Life.*
"The good life," says Mr. Russell, "is one inspired by love
and guided by knowledge. . . . Neither love without
knowledge, nor knowledge without love can produce a
good life. In the Middle Ages, when pestilence appeared
in a country, holy men advised the population to assemble
in churches and pray for deliverance; the result was that
the infection spread with extraordinary rapidity among
the crowded mass of supplicants. This was an example of
love without knowledge. The late war afforded an example
of knowledge without love. . . . Although both love and
knowledge are necessary, love is in a sense more fundamental, since it will lead intelligent people to seek knowledge, in order to find out how to benefit those whom they
love."

That both love and knowledge are essential alike to the
life of a complete individual and to the social order of a
creative civilization is obvious even without the convincing
clarity of Mr. Russell's dialectic. Either is manifestly but
a half-key to a life of durable satisfactions or to a régime
of social significance. Love without knowledge may let the
baby die because it does not know enough to send for the
doctor. Knowledge without love may let the baby die because it does not care enough to send for the doctor. But,
in considering the problem of a dynamic for civilization,
we are concerned with a love more sweepingly social than
the love born of and bounded by the limited intimacies of
the family. Mr. Russell is thinking of a force beyond the
personalized loyalties of the fireside or the professional-
ized loyalties of the philanthropist. He is thinking of a
love dominant enough and dynamic enough to lead civilized
men to put the whole of human wisdom into the high enterprise of human welfare.

In discussing the varied aspects of this larger love, profound enough to provoke a scientific humanism, Mr. Russell suggests that we must develop a sympathy that will

reach beyond persons intimately related to us by family or
by friendship and be marked by a rich capacity for ready
response to situations not immediately under our noses.
The kind of love which, in partnership with scientific
knowledge, is capable of producing the good life for men
and for civilizations must, as Mr. Russell sees it, feel
sympathy even when the persons in question are not objects
of special affection, and be moved to action even when the
situation in question is not sensibly present but is merely
known to exist and to call for creative and chivalric consideration.

The very advance of scientific knowledge has made
socially imperative the development of this larger love
expressing itself in a long-distance sensitiveness and sympathy. "Science has greatly increased our power of affecting the lives of distant peoples," as Mr. Russell rightly
observes, "without increasing our sympathy for them."
Whether we of the West shall be able to achieve complete
control and creative use of the new powers arising from
modern knowledge may well depend upon our ability to
increase, in the political, social, and economic life of the
West, the number of strategic men who actually feel a
kinship with humanity, men who can feel the tug of famine
in China as keenly as they might feel the cry of hunger
from a brother's child, men who can feel the tragedy of
starved minds in the hinterland of their own state as poign-
antly as they might feel the pathos of the idiot-chatter
of an abnormal offspring, men who can be stirred by an
annual report of industrial accidents, deaths from cancer,
or the spiritual slavery of illiteracy as they might be stirred
by the story of a brutal murder by gangsters on the next
street-corner, men to whom evidence of stupidity in church
or state or blundering economic leadership is as compelling
a cry for help as the ravage of a plague. The captaincy of
Western affairs calls for men who, as Mr. Russell phrases
it, can actually "be moved emotionally by statistics."

It has been my good fortune to have intimate professional *camaraderie* with three men who have possessed this rare genius for abstract sympathy: John R. Commons, Edward Alsworth Ross, and Edward A. Filene. These three men, in their respective rôles of economist, sociologist, and business man, demonstrate three things: (1) that the synthesis of love and knowledge suggested by Mr. Russell is possible; (2) that a delicate sensitiveness to the physical and psychological needs of mankind, and an insistence upon the humanization of knowledge and power, are not inconsistent with sound scholarship or successful business; and (3) that sensitiveness and sympathy, whose other name is love, invest a personality with social effectiveness and make it a radiating center of spiritual influence in secular affairs.

This spirit I conceive to be essential if the renewal and reconstruction of the Western social order is to be more than the literary prophecy of soothsaying publicists. It is this spirit alone that can touch the realities of science with the radiance of a valid humanism. But whence shall come the force to generate this spirit and give it ascendancy in the life of the West? What shall be the point of departure from which we set out to make this spirit the *Zeitgeist* that shall color and control the minds and movements at least of the strategic leaders in church and state and school and factory throughout the West?

Mr. Russell pins his hope for the development of this spirit of sensitiveness or sympathy or love to a new education. I have already indicated that I think the development of a radically redirected education is of crucial importance to any Western quest of social realism that is to rescue Western affairs from the tragedy of drift and renew them in the triumph of social mastery. I do not believe, however, that the future of the West lies as exclusively upon the laps of the educators as Mr. Russell seems to imply. I cannot share the confidence of the social analysts who think that education is likely to provide the compelling impulse that will prompt a whole generation consciously to embark upon the noble enterprise of social renaissance through scientific humanism. And my skepticism of the adequacy of education as a social dynamic rests mainly upon two grounds: (1) the habitually tardy response of institutionalism to social change, and (2) the rarity with which the education of the school-room alone has ever produced social passion and scientific precision as cross-fertilizing factors in the minds of men. Let me examine these two contentions as they are reflected in contemporary Western education.

Educators have twitted the theologians for tardiness in revamping their doctrines in the light of the findings of modern science, but candor compels the confession that pedagogy has been about as leaden-footed as theology in following the lead of new knowledge. Educators have been about as slow in adjusting their programs and procedures to the results of modern research in psychology and biology, let us say, as the theologians have been in adjusting their cosmogonies to the results of modern research in geology, astronomy, physics, and correlate sciences. The most revolutionary knowledge of the nature and needs of human beings has been unearthed by modern research in psychology and biology, but, by and large, educators have looked upon modern psychology and modern biology as offering new materials to be taught in these fields rather than new points of view from which to teach in all fields. The universities have impounded this new knowledge in their departments of psychology and biology, taught it there with infinite care, but have not let it loose as the reorganizing force it might be throughout their educational processes. Honest efforts have been made to apply this new knowledge to the programs and processes of the earlier school years, but the colleges and universities of the West are, in the main, pursuing their traditional purposes and procedures as if the study of the mind and body of mankind had not moved an inch in two hundred years. Here and there cloistered and insulated experimentations go on, but no widely fostered reconsideration of the whole educational process in the light of our new knowledge of the nature of mind and of man.

If but a single university, anywhere in the Western world, should reconsider and redirect its total educational enterprise in terms of the new knowledge it is already teaching in its varied and virtually insulated departments, it would become the nursery of a new type of man, a man better fitted than we to wrestle with the issues of social reconstruction. To bring about this reconsideration and redirection, from kindergarten to university, is one of the major tasks involved in the renewal of the West. But the response of institutionalized education to social change and expanding knowledge is distressingly tardy. Educators have been slow to adjust themselves to the nature and needs of the new society their own investigations have created. H. G. Wells has described the social crisis of our time as "a race between education and catastrophe." If the future of Western civilization were wholly dependent upon the outcome of a race in which these alone were the runners, my guess would be that catastrophe would win, for I do not believe that the existing education of our schools has it in it to salvage a civilization, and, in view of the accelerated tempo of history, the race with catastrophe might be ended before the reform of education could be effected. Educators, in the main, are willing to be radical about everybody's methods but their own. It may be the fate of the makers of the new education to die as a generation of transition and to serve as fertilizing material for a harvest they themselves will never reap.

And education, as we know it and as it is likely to remain for many moons, save in scattered areas of exceptional enlightenment, to a regrettable extent produces men who are at once eager in the scientific discovery of truth and indifferent to the social application of the truth they discover. All too often the knowledge they unearth lies dead in their hands, at best a neutral factor in the life of their time, at worst a force twisted to anti-social uses. The existing education of the West seems not to generate in men that dynamism which brings knowledge to incandescence, flings its light along new trails, and by its warmth draws the age along after it.

"Those who like existing evils," says Mr. Russell, "are fond of asserting that human nature cannot be changed. . . . If they mean, as they usually do, that there is no way of producing an adult population whose behaviour will be radically different from that of existing populations, they are flying in the face of all modern psychology. . . . If existing knowledge were used and tested methods applied, we could, in a generation, produce a population almost wholly free from disease, malevolence, and stupidity. . . . In one generation, if we chose, we could bring the millennium. But none of this can come about without love. The knowledge exists; lack of love prevents it from being applied."

I do not venture dogmatically to assert that it will prove impossible to produce this dynamizing love on a large scale through a new education. He would be foolhardy, indeed, who would seek to set limits to the possible achievements of human intelligence. I quite agree, in fact, with the contention that Mr. Russell here makes. But I do feel justified in doubting that, in the crucial quarter-century that lies ahead, any educational program or process the West is likely to devise and widely adopt will provide a dynamic sufficiently sweeping in its effect to prompt a whole generation consciously to set about the task of revitalizing its civilization by the synthesis and social application of its best knowledge. This dynamic will be found, in my judgment, only in some fresh manifestation of the religious impulse.

I hasten to say that I am not referring to the religious impulse in the exclusive sense of any single organized religion, but as one of the universal, if intermittently operative, urges of the human spirit, manifesting itself now in this religion, now in that religion, and again outside the formulas of any recognized religion. It is not my purpose to undertake an exhaustive philosophical inquiry into the nature, the use, and the perversion of the religious impulse as it has variously manifested itself in the historic process. I want to consider but one of its offices, the particular office through which it does most towards creating that "love" which "knowledge" needs to transmute it into the scientific humanism of the good life for men and for civilizations.

The religious impulse differs from the purely intellectual impulse in its greater readiness to face discouraging dilemmas with courageous and contagious assumptions. If you want to love the human race, it has been cynically said, don't expect too much of it. But an age of social creativeness has never flowered from the stalk of cynicism. There has been a kind of mad Quixotism about those rare men and rare movements that have lifted whole eras into a fresh excellence of aspiration and action. Here and there in history, plodding pioneers of the mind have worked away, with relentless realism, in almost complete unawareness of the social scene, and have at last unearthed a fact or evolved an idea that has slowly and subtly changed the current of the world's thought. But the men who have pulled an age together, made it aware of the human implications of its knowledge, given it fresh direction, and infused its masses with a high-hearted social impulse have usually been men who have achieved the impossible by attempting the absurd, or what looked absurd to the coldly calculating. A kind of knight-errantry of the heart has given drive to their solid purposes.

I am not at all sure that the results of the intellectual process ever really dominate the mind of an age until some impulse other than reason touches them with light and invests them with warmth. Even at this late date, it is only a small minority of the Western masses that is directly or consciously concerned with the issues raised by modern science. It is almost impossible for men professionally absorbed in intellectual pursuits to realize the glacial slowness with which intellectual concepts move through the minds of vast populations. The majority of men throughout the Western world are living their lives and thinking about themselves and their universe as if Darwin had never given us a new biology or Copernicus a new astronomy. The great basic ideas of modern science are still the stock-in-trade of the limited few.

Men will not chart their direction or keep their bearings accurately save by a rigidly realistic rationalism, but they may never set bravely out for far goals unless some ultra-rational impulse moves them. I do not mean by this that civilized advance depends upon the abdication of the rational and the ascendancy of the romantic. Men must stand sternly on guard against the temptation to make the irrational a city of refuge from the drastic demands of the rational, a temptation that is always present in a phase of baffling complexity and blinding uncertainty such as Western man is now passing through. I mean only that, in my judgment, the secret springs of social creativeness lie, in the main, outside the realm of the rational, and that the rational reaches its highest effectiveness when illumined and warmed by ultra-rational impulses. The line that separates the ultra-rational as a drug and the ultra-rational as a dynamic is admittedly a thin line, but the ultra-rational is, nevertheless, I am convinced, a vital factor in the prompting of socially creative movements. The moment of analysis must be kept sacred to the rational, but the moment of action may hinge upon ultra-rational initiatives.

Walter Rathenau, one time directing genius of the *Allgemeine Deutsche Elektrizitäts Gesellschaft,* able business and astute social analyst, dealt with the problem of a social dynamic in his *Von Kommenden Dingen,* widely read by the Germany of the later war days, and afterward published in England and the United States as *In Days to Come.* "To seek goals implies faith," he said. "True faith springs from the poietic energy of the heart, from the imaginative power of love. It creates an emotional mood whereby events are determined. . . . We must never forget that it is feeling which initiates the movement of institutions; reluctantly, and yet obediently at last, the world movement is guided by the sentiment, as the hands of the watch obey the impulsion of the spring. The wheel-work is driven by the sentiment, not conversely; and no premature moving on of the hands can influence the machinery. . . . The ultimate principle is to feel aware of aims which are not derived from research and study, but which arise in the mind from a consciously or unconsciously intuited outlook on the universe. . . . The sphere of action is far more closely akin to the sphere of artistic creation than it is to the sphere of learning."

I am aware that we must assess with the utmost critical care the post-war mood of sensitive Germans, like Rathenau, for in Germany, as in ancient Israel, political and social disaster drove men from concern with social objectivism to the compensations of a spiritual subjectivism. But the Rathenau philosophy of the social dynamic seems to me to derive from a sounder source than the wistfulness of a beaten people. Rathenau saw, as many modern intellectuals do not see, the inadequacy of either sheer reason or sheer sentiment as the directing force of an age, and sought to save them from a sterile separateness, to bring about a cross-fertilization of intellect and spirit. In short, Rathenau recognized the crucial rôle of the religious impulse, in the sense I use the term, in Western man's currently imperative attempt to make his scientific knowledge, his economic power, and his social institutions servant instead of sovereign to his spirit. And we may concur with Rathenau in this without going all the way with him in what seemed at times his near-repudiation of the intellect.

I shall not quarrel with any one who may care to challenge my identification of the religious impulse with the faith, the poietic energy of the heart, the imaginative power of love, the emotional mood, the feeling, the sentiment, or the awareness of aims not derived from research and study to which Rathenau refers. If any one cares to call the social dynamic I am suggesting by some other name than the religious impulse, I have no objection. I am saying only that, in my judgment, there is not likely to arise out of our laboratories, industrial council rooms, and political headquarters, as a by-product of the rational analyses that may there be made, an impulse adequate to prompt the Western peoples to any sweeping synthesis and social application of the new ideas, new idealisms, and new spiritual values that, by and large, lie mute and socially inoperative in the mass of new knowledge that modern research and modern experience have produced. All of the requisite raw materials are at hand for a scientific humanism that would invigorate, integrate, and invest with fresh significance the life of the West, but the West lacks a leadership that sees these raw materials for what they are. They are unused by the cynics to whom an unimaginative rationalism has made progress seem impossible. They are ignored by the sentimentalists to whom an irrational optimism has made progress seem inevitable. The West must find and follow some leadership that is more courageous than the rationalist and more intelligent than the romanticist. And I think it is to the religious impulse, as I have here defined it, that we must look for this element of socially creative courage.

The problem of the stabilization and enrichment of the Western social order, as I see it, comes down to this: can we develop a leadership that will combine the realism of pure science with a readiness in the field of applied science to act upon some courageous assumptions respecting the possibility of a scientifically planned and controlled civilization, the potential capacity of mankind to respond to the call of intelligence made intelligible, and the feasibility of building a socially secure world in terms of the intrinsic and inviolable right of all races and all classes to respect for their human dignity and reënforcement in their social development. The cold calculations of reason will not, in my judgment, generate in men the courage to act upon such assumptions. For, frankly, the facts seem against them. Wide knowledge of the historic process and intimate acquaintance with contemporary affairs are powerful incentives to cynicism and fatal acquiescence in social drift. If one listens only to the ruthless reportings of reason, it is difficult not to look upon the life of man as "a brief and transitory episode in the life of one of the meaner planets." The "love" that Mr. Russell premises as the indispensable accompaniment of "knowledge" in the quest of the good life for men and for civilizations will hardly be born of a rational wrestling with facts. It must, I think, spring from the loins of some ultra-rational faith that dares to face the challenge of man and civilization with courageous hypotheses that may seem to fly in the face of the common sense and critical science of the time, but which, in Frederick Albert Lange's illuminant phrase, by demanding the impossible will unhinge the reality.

Again and again in history, faith-born hypotheses have created in men and in peoples the very qualities they assumed when the facts seemed to deny them. Courage has created that which it dared to assume. The leadership of the West needs what Eça de Queiros has called "that audacious courage of affirmation, which creates, in the midst of universal illusion, the sciences and the religions." I am not suggesting that the future of the West can be assured by the creative power of fictionalism, as fictionalism is understood in Vaihinger's *Die Philosophie des Als Ob,* but by the creative power of courageous hypotheses, not by the assumption of impossible truths deliberately used as a tonic to spur us to action, but by the assumption of truths that imagination, which Wordsworth defined as reason in its most exalted mood, sees as possible, when reason in its less adventurous mood does not see them at all. James Branch Cabell pertinently suggests that

". . . man alone of animals can, actually, acquire a trait by assuming, in defiance of reason, that he already possesses it . . . for man alone of animals plays the ape to his dreams." It is in the effective synthesis of the power of imagination and the process of investigation that great civilizations are born.

The greatest scientists, in the limited tasks of the laboratory, have exemplified this combination of the exalted mood of imagination and the exacting mood of investigation. Leonardo da Vinci, Faraday, Kepler, Einstein, to pick at random from a crowded gallery! What is the postulational method which, in the hands of a Planck remakes the world of physics, but this synthesis of imagination and investigation in which an improvised faith evokes the research or action that brings factual proof and fruitful results? In the social dynamic I project, I am, therefore, suggesting nothing that does not find its prototype in the processes that mark the scientific mind at its productive best. An imagination, innocent of social passion and indifferent to social purpose, may produce hypotheses that prod the scholar to the productive prosecution of the limited tasks of scientific research, but, in the larger tasks of social reconstruction, the drive towards sustained action in terms of courageous hypotheses respecting man and society seems peculiarly a fruit of the religious impulse, when this impulse is unperverted by doctrine-obsessed minds or prestige-hungry institutions.

In every time of grand-scale readjustment, new raw materials for social enrichment and spiritual enripenment are unearthed. It has been the tragic fate of Western civilization, in one period of readjustment after another, to follow a leadership that failed to appreciate and to apply these raw materials in the historic opportunity that the moment of confusion and change presented. The Renaissance was such a time. The Reformation was such a time. The Industrial Revolution was such a time. And, dramatically so, the World War was such a time. Never

were there as many people fumbling for fresh insight into
man, into society, and into the universe. And never was
less advantage taken of the spiritual opportunity presented
by a social crisis. The late C. E. Montague, in a volume of
post-war essays called *Disenchantment,* with exquisite
lucidity of perception and phrase, has left us an unforget-
table picture of the lost opportunity that the war brought
to the socio-spiritual leadership of the West, a picture that
brings to climax the contention I am here making.

"If you want to catch the Thames gudgeon," he said,
"you first comb the river's bed hard with a long rake. In
the turbid waters thus caused the creatures will be on the
feed, and if you know how to fish you may get a great take.
For our professional fishers of men in the army the war did
the raking gratis. The men came into their hands at the
time of most drastic experience in most of the men's lives,
immersed in a new and strange life of sensations at once
simple and intense, shaken roughly out of the world of
mechanical habit which at most times puts a kind of bar
between one's mind and truth, living always among swiftly
dying friends and knowing their own death at any time to
be as probable as any one's. To get rid of your phlegm,
it was said, is to be a philosopher. It is also to be a saint,
at least in the rough; you have broken the frozen ground;
you can grow anything now; you can see the greatest things
in the very smallest, so that sunrise on Inverness Copse is
the morning of the first day and a spoonful of rum and a
biscuit a sacrament."

Elsewhere in this essay on the sheep that were not fed,
Mr. Montague told at length of typical conversations from
trench and camp in which the most poignant hungers came
up out of their "twilight lairs" in the souls of men who were
searching for some key of meaning to a universe over which
the war had thrown the shadow of a great question.

"Thus would these inexpert people hang unconsciously
about the uncrossed threshold of religion," he said. "With
minds which had recovered in some degree the penetrative

simplicity of a child's, they disinterred this or that unidentified bone of the buried God from under the monumental piles of débris which the learned, the cunning, and the proud priests and kings, churches and chapels, had heaped up over the ideas of perfect love, of faith that would leave all to follow that love, and of the faithful spirit's release from mean fears of extinction. In talk they could bring each other up to the point of feeling that little rifts had opened here and there in the screens which are hung round the life of man on earth, and that they had peeped through into some large outer world that was strange only because they were used to a small and dim one. They were prepared and expectant. If any official religion could ever refine the gold out of all that rich alluvial drift of 'obstinate questionings of sense and outward things,' now was its time. No figure of speech, among all these that I have mixed, can give the measure of the greatness of that opportunity."

As Mr. Montague suggested, these "clumsy fumblings of uninstructed people among things of the spirit might, one imagines, be just such stuff as a skilled teacher and leader in this field might have delighted to come upon and to inspirit and marshal." But the opportunity went begging! The peoples of the West were caught in a crescendo of hatred, Western civilization, in many of its peace settlements and post-war policies, fell victim to a resurgence of jungle ethics, while the war proved but a prelude in general to a phase of unprecedented moral confusion and social irresponsibility.

I have given at length Mr. Montague's matchless and moving portrayal of the opportunity the impact of war upon the souls of men gave to spiritual leadership because I think it offers a fruitful analogy of the opportunity the impact of science and industry upon the moods and fortunes of men is now presenting to the political, social, and economic leaderships of the West. Science, like war, is making necessary an extensive readjustment of Western man to his intellectual and moral heritage. The explosive power of new ideas and the distant rumble of new doubts are stirring men to their depths, as the roar and destruction of war stirred men to their depths, giving short shrift to many library-made dogmas, and raising a thousand and one baffling questions about the purpose and procedure of a universe that no longer seems the simple and manageable universe it seemed to the fathers. The economic depression, political distraction, and social dishevelment which now harass the West and hover over every current consideration are immersing men in a new and strange life of experiences that are intense if not simple, breaking the frozen ground of men's traditional complacencies, and shaking men roughly out of the world of mechanical loyalties that so often shut the mind to the visitation of truth, and blind the eye to the vision of more humanly significant modes of organization and action.

However forced the use of the term may seem to some, Western science and Western industry need just now, above all else, a spiritual leadership that can awaken the spirit of social meaning that sleeps in the body of modern scientific facts and adjust to social purpose the processes of the machine economy of the modern West. I mean by this that the stabilization and enrichment of the Western social order will, in my judgment, depend upon the leadership of men in whom there is the requisite spiritual sensitiveness, love, sympathy, emotion, intuitive genius, imagination—call it what you will—to invest their scientifically disciplined intellects and inform their administrative actions with that clairvoyant penetration into the social significance of knowledge and the social function of human institutions which, in eras of reassessment and reconstruction, distinguishes the seer from the mere scholar and man of action. The careers of such men are invariably motivated and given momentum by the religious impulse, although, in many instances, the impulse is not so recognized by the religionists.

It is the leadership of such men and the response they might evoke from the Western masses, in their confused quest of a more secure and more significant economy, that I have in mind when I suggest that the social diagram of a New Renaissance needs the spiritual dynamic of a New Reformation. The issue here is something quite apart from the Catholic-Protestant schism with which the term Reformation is associated. I have approached the problem of spiritual leadership, not in terms of a concern with institutionalized religion, but in terms of a search for sources of power and strategies of progress for the Western future. The New Reformation towards which my contention points can function in the minds of men and in the movements of society quite above the metaphysical battles of the multitudinous theologies. The votaries of all the varied religions of earth may be at home in its ranks, for it will not be concerned with how they state the nature of their gods, but with how they see and serve the needs of men.

The New Reformation will be indistinguishable from the New Renaissance and the New Industrial Revolution, if the West is fortunate enough to bring these three ventures to fruition. It will be but the breath of life and the sense of social valuation that animates and gives human point to the secular life of the time. This will mark a departure from the historic antecedents of these movements of renewal and reconstruction. "Probably the heaviest weight in the scale against the Reformation was the Renaissance," says Preserved Smith, in his *The Age of the Reformation*. "The goods they offered were not the same, not even similar, but the appeal of each was of such a nature that few minds could be the whole-hearted devotees of both. The new learning and the beauties of Italian art and literature sapped away the interest of just those intelligent classes whose support was needed to make the triumph of the Reformation complete." The Dolet and the Rabelais, the Ronsard and the Montaigne of the New Renaissance will not hold thus aloof from the sweetening and socializing influence the New Reformation will bring to bear upon the science, the culture, and the economic enterprise of the time. The New Reformation and the New Renaissance will synthesize rather than sunder the spiritual and the secular.

The New Reformation will be none the less a revival of religion because it will lack the ear-marks of a religious revival with the implications this term has come to carry. It will not be likely to express itself in hectic mass meetings with vast choirs and vigorous exhorters. Many of its most striking episodes are likely to take place, neither in the stone aisles of cathedrals nor in the sawdust trails of evangelistic sheds, but in laboratories, in schools, in factories, in the council chambers of the directors of finance, and in political headquarters. The Martin Luther of the New Reformation may not appear in cassock and surplice; he may be a statesman, a captain of industry, an educator, a publicist. The New Reformation will not be born of an attempt to thrill the world with any new doctrine. It will represent rather a subtle recovery of the lost sense of the spirituality of secular affairs. It may not be recognized as one coherent movement by the men who live through it or by the men who lead it. It may come upon us silently, like a thief in the night, and it may arise from a hundred different sources in a hundred different forms.

While the New Reformation, unlike the antecedent Reformation of the sixteenth century, will not express itself obviously through churches, organized religion may play a productive rôle in its advancement. In the chapters immediately to follow, I present two case studies of contributions organized religion may make towards the renewal and stabilization of the West: (1) a study of the contribution that Western Christianity has to make in the critical matter of the conflict or collaboration of races, and (2) a study of the part the churches of the West may play in that non-military war to end war to which I have made earlier reference. It will be in the spirit and sense of social values that Western man brings to the handling of these and allied problems of political, social, and economic import that the New Reformation will find failure or fulfilment.

# VII

# Racialism and the Nazarene

THE renewal of the West may meet shipwreck on the rock of racialism. The color line that darkly divides Occident from Orient may be the battle-line on which the destiny of Western culture will be determined. By the grace of swift transportation and near-instantaneous communication, the races of the world rub elbows, but their spirits are poles apart. The psychological unification of the world has not kept pace with its physical unification. And, as a result, world politics becomes increasingly the politics of biology. The men of the sixteenth century fought about religion. The men of the nineteenth century fought about nationalism. The men of the century ahead may wage their greatest fight around the issue of racialism. The West may face ruin instead of renaissance if its leadership proves incapable of effecting an amicable collaboration of races in the common enterprise of civilization.

I am suspicious of the too greatly simplified determinisms of history that color so much of the consideration now being given to the probable future of Western civilization. There is no economic determinism of history, no climatic determinism of history, no racial determinism of history. But the existing intensity of race consciousness and the post-war instability of equilibrium between the white and colored worlds are very stubborn factors that must be reckoned with in the renewal and stabilization of the West. From whence shall come the initiation of a healing leadership in this vexed and vexing field of passions and contacts? The racial egotist and the economic exploiter have aggravated rather than assuaged the racial enmities that threaten the West. Statesmanship has been strangely sterile before the riddle of racial relations. Can religion help Western man to capture and to control this wild horse of racialism?

Such sinister adventures in racialism as the Ku Klux Klan, fostered in the early post-war years by the lunatic fringe of Western Protestantism, effectively dramatize the problem that racialism puts to religious leadership. Roman Catholicism in its cathedrals and Islam in its mosques have come nearer to eliminating distinctions of race and class than Protestantism has, in sections where such secular differentiations prevail with an air of finality, but I do not mean to imply that the intelligent majority of Protestantism is in any way responsible for such fantastic racial crusades as the Ku Klux Klan, or that Ku Kluxism is inherently a phase of Protestant psychology. I am myself, by temperament and by training, a Protestant, jealous of such perversions of its spirit. But since Ku Kluxism is a vivid expression of the cult of racialism, and since its promoters sought to steal the livery of Protestantism in which to garb its purpose, Ku Kluxism affords a good background against which to throw a discussion of the contribution Western Christianity may make towards a Western technique for administering racial relations.

The Ku Klux Klan, as a feared and fast-growing organization, has happily waned, but any one who knows hinterland as well as metropolis knows that the Ku Klux mind is far from dead. It may change the fashion of its hood and the form of its ritual, but this mind, sinister offspring of prejudice and passion, is likely to remain for many moons a factor in the racial politics of the West, so that, even as a passing organization, the Ku Klux Klan remains an instructive symbol of the psychology of racialism.

I do not want to over-simplify what is manifestly a complex phenomenon. The Ku Klux mind cannot be explained in a sentence. When the Ku Klux Klan was in the ascendant, there were as many explanations of it as there were communities in which it functioned. Here it was anti-Catholic. There it was anti-Jew. Yonder it was anti-Negro. Here it was an attempt to find in a gaudy ritual a sense of adventure denied by a drab environment. There it was an honest, if unintelligent, effort on the part of congenital uplifters to preserve law and order by lawless means. Yonder it was the serio-comic pranks of folk who felt inferior in reality, but superior in regalia. The Ku Klux mind, like the Ku Klux Klan it fostered, is the child of a medley of motives. In its most characteristic American expression, however, it represents an attempt to unite in one crusade Protestant Christianity and the Cult of Racialism, welding the two together in the fires of fanaticism.

I can understand racial fanaticism by itself. I can understand religious fanaticism by itself. I could even understand a fusion of the two, if the religion in question were a primitive religion with a tribal god. I confess, however, that I am at a loss to understand the recurrent attempts to drive Christianity and Nordicism abreast. For whatever Christianity may or may not have become, it was, in its spiritual and philosophical initiative, trans-racial. One of the distinctive contributions Jesus made to the spiritual future of mankind lay in the fact that, in the higher realms of the spirit, he wiped out the frontiers that divide races. And, in order to do this, he had to pay the price of becoming a renegade to the orthodox patriotism and to the politico-theological self-consciousness of his countrymen, for to the Jews of his time the Kingdom of God meant a religious monopoly, with Judaism as the only stock-holder. In the Jews of his time racialism and religion met and merged. It is one of the pretty ironies of history that the Ku Klux mind should copy the Jews it hates by attempting to create, as they created, a religio-racialism, and doing it in the name of a Jew who denounced it. For the Nazarene prophet flatly denied the Jewish claim to special privilege. He said he had never found among Jews such faith as he found in a certain Roman captain. He ventured the prophecy that heathen would come from the ends of the earth and sit down with the Hebrew patriarchs, while their own sons would find themselves in the discard. He did the impolitic thing of setting up a Samaritan as a model of chivalric ethics he did not find in Hebrew priest and Levite. We may be sure that all this was rather bitter medicine for the one hundred per cent Hebrews of the time. It was very much as if a California senator should open his campaign for reëlection with an apostrophe to the superiority of the Japanese immigrant over the native Nordic, or as if a Georgia congressman should set out to translate the assumed political equality of the Negro into an actual social equality.

With one magnificent gesture Jesus internationalized what had been until then a racial religion. One might imagine, therefore, that Jesus would be the last figure in history any one would think of relating, even indirectly, to a movement inspired by race consciousness and inspiring race discrimination. I find it difficult to believe that Jesus, the Jew, flouted his own race in order to flatter the Nordics. Although my own ancestry was white, Protestant, and Nordic, I cannot quite concur in the attempt to convert Jesus into a mere press agent for the Pilgrim fathers. Unless I have completely misread both the literature of Christianity and the literature of racialism, the inclusive humanism of Jesus and the exclusive tribalism of the racialist have nothing in common. They are at eternal variance. Christianity and racialism cannot be brought into a legitimate union.

We must beware of falling into the easy error of assuming that by seeing and stating the intrinsic incongruity of such religio-racialisms as Ku Kluxism we have either relieved or removed the race tensions that vex the Western social order. We must face the fact of a race problem that cannot be theorized out of existence. It may well become the overshadowing political problem of the century

ahead. If the varied races with which the leadership of the
West must reckon cannot find ways and means of decently
harmonious collaboration, Western civilization may enter
its night ahead of the Spenglerian schedule. The different
races must somehow learn to live together in a common
harmony or they will die together in the common horror
of a color war. We must beware also of falling into the
error of assuming that we can resolve the danger of race
hatred by the simple device of calling it un-Christian.
There is a vast amount of race hatred in the world, and it
cannot be exorcised by pious and abstract exhortations
about brotherhood.

Has Christianity any distinctive contribution to make
towards a constructive handling of racial relations? I think
it has. But if its adherents are to make this contribution
available to the leadership of the West, they must not
assume that it consists in substituting for the swashbuckling of the racialist the sentimentality of the romancer.
Not a little of religious discussion of the race problem
amounts to just that. The superficial religionist is too
likely to assume that we must choose between the point of
view of the extreme racialist who would grade the peoples
of the world in a changeless hierarchy, with the races
at the top forever sticking out their tongues at the races
at the bottom, and the point of view of the extreme
sentimentalist who, in the name of a theoretical brotherhood, would legislate a universal policy of unrestricted
migration and encourage the indiscriminate intermarriage
of the races. The followers of the Nazarene must not shut
themselves up to a choice between these two points of view,
both of which, it seems to me, are intellectually irresponsible and socially sinister.

There are, as I see it, two major questions involved in
the politics of race: (1) a question of scientific fact, and
(2) a question of social procedure. If we are to think
realistically about the relation of Christianity to the riddle
of racial relations, we must keep the distinction between

these two questions clearly and constantly in mind. Let me
state this distinction as clearly as I can.

*First,* there is a question of scientific fact. What are the
facts about the varied races that inhabit or impinge upon
the Western world? Are some races inherently superior
and other races inherently inferior? Are such gradations,
if they exist, fixed and final? Or is racial character among
the varied peoples of earth in the flux of evolution? If
some races are inherently and irrevocably superior, and
other races inherently and irrevocably inferior, have our
researches been extensive enough or critical enough to
enable us to say with scientific accuracy which are which?
What happens when diverse racial stocks intermarry?
What are the biological results of race mixture? What are
the social and political by-products of mongrelism?

*Second,* there is a question of social procedure. What
are we to do with the facts about race character and race
mixture after we find them? In what temper and with what
technique are we to relate them to national policies and to
world politics? Is it possible to maintain a temper and to
make use of a technique in handling race facts, whatever
they finally turn out to be, that will diminish rather than
increase the tension of races and the threat of an ultimate
color war?

On the first of these questions, the question of scientific
fact, Christianity has absolutely nothing to offer. Jesus
was not a biologist, and he did not anticipate the researches
of modern anthropology. If we want to know the facts
about race character and race mixture, we must go to the
laboratory, not to the cathedral. Christianity is not a
substitute for research. The New Testament is neither a
biological text-book nor a manual of anthropology. The
Christian and the atheist are alike dependent upon the
scientist for information in these matters. Whatever contribution Christianity has to make towards resolving the
racial dilemmas of the West must be made in the light of
the facts about race character and race mixture that the

investigations of biologist, psychologist, and anthropologist may unearth from year to year. Unless we are to assume that we are living in a capricious universe that we cannot trust to act the same on two successive days, even God cannot be superior to a fact.

It is only on the second of these questions, the question of social procedure, that Christianity has something to offer. Christianity cannot help us to find the facts about race character and race mixture, but it can help us to face the facts in a temper and with a technique that will help rather than hinder the development of a creatively harmonious world order. The thing Christianity has to contribute towards the administration of racial relations is not information, but a point of view. It can help us to use the facts about race wisely after we discover them.

The church of the future will but perpetuate the current futility of religion as a mediative factor in racial relations if, in its approach to the race tensions of the West, it ignores this distinction between Christianity's relation to the question of scientific fact and its relation to the question of social procedure. We must not read a biological content into the few remarks about race we find in the New Testament. Neither the racial egotist nor the sentimental internationalist is justified in turning the New Testament into an arsenal of proof-texts for his biological prejudices. When Paul stood in the center of the Areopagus and said to the men of Athens, "God . . . hath made of one blood all nations of men," he did not, I am sure, intend his statement to be taken as a biological pronouncement. He was not offering an anthropological thesis. In that memorable address, he was not dealing with the facts of biology, but with the politics of the spirit. He was saying only that, in the social and spiritual enterprises of mankind, neither caste nor race should be a primary consideration. This Pauline assertion of the one-blood-ness of all races was not a statement of scientific fact, but a suggestion of social procedure and spiritual relationship. There is nothing to indicate that Jesus foresaw the modern race problem or sought to suggest to the future any detailed scheme for the handling of racial relations. It is as fruitless to look to the New Testament for a detailed program for racial collaboration as to expect to find in its pages a specimen draft of a five-hour-day law or an engineering plan for disposal of the sewage of Chicago. The sole contribution Christianity has to make towards a Western transformation of race conflict into race collaboration lies, as I have said, in the point of view it may enable us to bring to the facts that research reveals respecting race character and race mixture.

Christianity offers to the statesmanship of the West a definite and distinctive world-view or, to use the richer German word for which we have no precise equivalent, a definite and distinctive *Weltanschauung*. This particular world-view can, I think, help Western man to use the facts of race in a temper and with a technique that will, as far as may be humanly possible, enable the Western world to realize a growing race harmony instead of a growing race hatred. Lugging the issue of a *Weltanschauung* into the welter of racial dilemmas that harass the West may seem a bit far fetched, but I suspect that the futile and fumbling approach Western civilization is making to such crucial issues as the race problem is due, in no small measure, to the fact that, for some time, neither its leaders nor its masses have recognized or resorted to the invigorating and integrating power of a dominant and worthy world-view. A civilization cannot long survive the absence of a richly conceived theory of the universe as the soil from which its day-to-day policies and actions may draw sustaining power.

"The greatest of all the spirit's tasks," says Albert Schweitzer, in his *The Decay and the Restoration of Civilization*, "is to produce a theory of the universe, for in such a theory all the ideas, convictions, and activities of an age have their roots, and it is only when we have arrived at one which is compatible with civilization that we are capable of holding the ideas and convictions which are the conditions of civilization in general. What is meant by a theory of the universe? It is the content of the thoughts of society and the individuals which compose it about the nature and object of the world in which they live, and the position and the destiny of mankind and of individual men within it. What significance have the society in which I live and I myself in the world? What do we want to do in the world, what do we hope to get from it, and what is our duty to it? The answer given by the majority to these fundamental questions about existence decides what the spirit is in which they and their age live."

Western affairs are not, at the moment, animated by any fructifying world-view. Throughout the West, leaders and led alike are blown hither and yon by the night-winds of anarchic and aimless activity. Patchwork philosophy stands behind Western policies, and patchwork statesmanship behind Western procedures. The renewal of the West requires the widespread achievement, first by the leaders and then by the led, of a worthy *Weltanschauung,* a vision of the social whole of civilization and a sense of social values, that will save the statesmanship of the West from meeting its significant difficulties, as the race problem, with shabby opportunisms and selfish obsessions.

I do not mean to imply that Western Christianity offers an intellectual and social finality that will relieve Western man of the necessity of using the utmost intelligence he can muster in the management of the racial relations with which he must deal. I mean only that the Christian *Weltanschauung* can contribute to a Western *Weltanschauung* elements that will help Western leadership to meet, with healing and harmonizing procedures, the dilemmas that arise out of the contacts of diverse races. By the Christian *Weltanschauung,* I hasten to say, I do not mean the world-view that has sometimes seemed to dominate the directing forces of institutionalized Christianity, but the world-

view that animated the provocative and prophetic career of
Jesus of Nazareth. I mention but two aspects of the world-
view implicit in the pronouncements and practices of the
Nazarene: (1) its contention that moral values rather
than material advantages should be supreme in private lives
and in public affairs, and (2) its insistence upon reverence
for personality and recognition of the primacy of the
individual human being. I cannot but believe that these
two elements, missing from the point of view that animates
the Cult of Racialism, must enter into the point of view
from which Western man uses the facts about race character and race mixture, whatever these facts may finally
prove to be.

These two contentions of Jesus seem to me to suggest a
specific and hopeful approach to the dilemma of racial
relations. Before defining this approach in detail, however, I want to set down five observations respecting the
present state of our knowledge regarding race character
and race mixture, for whatever contribution the religious
leadership of the West may make to the handling of the
racial dilemma must be made in the light of the facts as
they are known at the time.

*First,* our researches in race character have been neither
extensive enough nor critical enough to justify cocksureness
regarding either the inherent equality or the inherent inequality of human races. Research has revealed basic differences of specialized efficiency between races. The
researches of Davenport and Steggerda, for example,
indicate that the black man is superior to the white man in
matters of pitch, tone, intensity, rhythm, and kindred factors that affect musical ability, while the white man is superior to the black man in matters of sound judgment and
successful adjustment to varying conditions and demands
of environment. The study of special efficiencies and special inefficiencies has thrown up illuminating results. The
data available to the geneticist point convincingly to characteristic differences in mentality between races. But the

special efficiencies and special inefficiencies in which these
differences express themselves do not necessarily prove a
general and immutable superiority or inferiority. Efficiencies and inefficiencies must be valuated in terms of their
purpose. Definitive judgment on the general superiority
or inferiority of races must await further observation and
further experimentation. Only the charlatans speak with
an air of authority in this field. Realistic biologists and
responsible anthropologists profess no more than tentative theses respecting race character. They know that
they do not know enough yet to speak with scientific certainty. The literature of the racial swashbuckler and the
literature of the racial sentimentalist are alike the product
not of ripe scholarship, but of green scholarship. It is only
the occasional journalistic biologist who stoops to give
to the Ku Klux mind a pseudo-intellectual window dressing.

*Second,* the extreme racialists profess to present a dependable ethnography and a scientifically sound ethnology.
It is the business of ethnography to describe and to clas-
sify the races of mankind. It is the business of ethnology
to examine with scrupulous care the mental and physical
differences of mankind, to investigate the organic laws
upon which these differences depend, and to garner from
these investigations principles of human guidance that man
may use in the administration of social and international
relations. The weakness of the ethnography and ethnology of the extreme racialists lies, it seems to me, in the
fact that they have recklessly applied to whole races what
modern biological research has found out about individual
human beings. They leap the chasm between individual
and race with an alacrity the responsible scholars alike of
biology and of anthropology refuse to imitate. The renewal of Western civilization may well be found in the
social implications of biology, but the ruin of Western
civilization may be accomplished by the propagandist-
prostitution of ethnology in the hands of pseudo-scientific
Jeremiahs who ignorantly or intentionally confuse the

biology of the individual with the biology of the race. The extreme racialists seem to me to be basing their case on a perversion of biology in the form of a political ethnology which is not a science, but merely the sales-talk of impassioned dons nursing a thesis.

*Third,* neither our accumulated knowledge nor the existing techniques of research enable us accurately to disentangle the factors of physical heredity, social heritage, cultural impact, climatic influence, and other factors that may conspire to determine the status, the characteristics, and the civilized accomplishments of races. Until our research techniques have been developed for a more effective disentangling of these factors, there can be no scientific justification of a new Calvinism of ethnology that predestines to permanent inferiority racial groups whose present inferiority might be mitigated by a shifting of the factors that affect them.

*Fourth,* research in the biological results of race mixture has not reached the point where any sweeping and simplified yes-or-no judgment on the intermarriage of races is scientifically justified. I do not suggest that we are in dark ignorance of the meaning of mongrelism. We have learned much. The biologist has assembled an imposing mass of illuminating data on the results of race mixture. And the patient perfection of his knowledge of the genetic system has put him in a better position than ever before to know how to go about the investigation of the problem and the interpretation of his results. I have gone with some care through the major documents that research has produced on the results of race mixture, and have read rather widely in the more popular literature of the field. Much of this literature has been itself dictated by racial prejudice. Much of it signally fails to segregate for separate valuation the biological and the social factors that interlock in the problem of intermarriage. And the responsibly scientific research reports do not throw up a clear yes-or-no verdict. Here, given a certain set of biological factors and certain favoring circumstances, potentially good results may be forecast. There, given another set of biological factors and certain hampering circumstances, measurably certain bad results may be forecast. Any general conclusion that race mixture is either fruitful or fatal must await more complete knowledge, if, indeed, such sweeping judgment will ever prove justifiable. With the present status of our knowledge, however, we have ample justification for going slow in the matter of intermarriage of diverse racial stocks. It is a safe working policy to assume, pending further knowledge, that a race that is, for its purposes, superior at the moment has little to gain and may have much to lose by crossing with a race that is, for these purposes, inferior at the moment. And this policy may be pursued without indulging in any dogmatic verdicts of permanent and inherent superiority or inferiority. There are enough considerations of social adjustment to counsel caution in the indiscriminate crossbreeding of diverse races. "The argument from ignorance should not be used to defend race crossing because we cannot prove that it is bad," as S. J. Holmes suggests, "it should be used rather to counsel caution because we do not know that it is not bad."

*Fifth,* the extreme racialists rarely subject the qualities of their own race to the same critical assessment to which they subject the qualities of the races they dub inferior. The Nordic apologists are a case in point. I cannot think that the qualities usually ascribed to the Nordics in the polemics of Nordicism necessarily prove their intrinsic superiority and their superlative worth in modern civilization. It is said that the Nordics are the world's premier executives. But there is something less than universal agreement that the executive temperament is the finest flowering of the human spirit. It is said that the Nordics are the world's premier politicians. But we may be passing out of the age of politics into a period in which the management of our common life will be functionally decentral-

ized. It is said that the Nordics are the world's premier
industrialists. But the Western industrial system they have
created has to-day back-fired on them and totters in what
should be, on every count, its hour of triumph. It is said
that the Nordics are the world's premier commercialists.
But the major assets of a civilization are not found in its
daybooks and ledgers. It is said that the Nordics are the
world's premier inventors. But the inventive genius of a
people may prove its undoing if it permits too many of the
fruits of its inventive genius to be put to the use of mutual
slaughter in modern warfare. It is said that the Nordics
are the world's premier fighting breed. But, since modern
war has become a dysgenic agent, killing off the best rather
than the worst, will the civilization of the future spring
from a warrior breed? The extreme racialists are biological fundamentalists who decline to subject their own
racial characteristics to critical and comprehensive judgment. They hunt for facts to fit their fanaticisms.

In view of the fact that our knowledge respecting race
character and race mixture is admittedly inadequate, and
in view of the fact that the extreme racialists resort so
shamelessly to wishful thinking respecting the races they
praise and the races they pillory, Western man should see
the futility alike of uncritical sentimentality and of irritat-
ing dogmatism in his consideration of the dilemma of race.
Modern science, especially modern biology, has come that
the peoples of the earth might have life and that they
might have it more abundantly. But even biology can
realize its deepest mission only in the hands of a spirit in
which humanism and science meet in living synthesis, a
spirit immune alike to selfishness and to sentimentality.
It is at this point that religion may prove an untapped resource of policy for Western statesmanship in its handling of racial relations.

Does the Christian *Weltanschauung,* with its contention
of the supremacy of moral values over material advantages in private lives and in public affairs, and its insistence

upon reverence for personality and recognition of the
primacy of the individual human being, make for the sort
of scientific humanism that can use the facts of race character and race mixture more wisely than the racialists are
using them? I think so. Let me suggest the way in which
I think that a leadership animated by these two contentions will approach the dilemma of racial relations that now
disturbs the Western mind.

The modern world is so interdependent that no race
can isolate itself and live in a belligerently exclusive attitude towards the rest of the world. The soul of a people
will shrivel if it must live in a stockade surrounded by
enemies. It may exist. It cannot live. And yet this is the
inevitable end towards which the theories of the extreme
racialists lead. Western civilization is doomed if we pick
out some one racial group, say the Nordics, label them the
élite, and segregate them behind a wall of literal or figurative bayonets. For, even if investigation shall finally prove
that some races are inherently and irrevocably superior and
other races inherently and irrevocably inferior, the inferior
races will always have *their* élite, and this élite few will not
allow their race to be trampled upon either by the platoons
or by the propaganda of the superior races without resistance. The fevered flaunting of the dogma of racial
superiority and racial inferiority can have no other end
than a staggering from one blood-letting to another until
civilization itself goes down in a red sunset.

The extreme racialists sedulously set the stage for the
defeat of their own avowed purpose. They plead for the
segregated breeding of superior folk whose backs will be
broad enough to bear the burdens and whose minds will be
rich enough to develop the values of a valid civilization.
But they make their plea with a self-satisfied swagger that,
sooner or later, must lead to war, and war has become an
indisputably dysgenic agent. Modern war selects the best
for slaughter rather than for survival. If the campaign of
the Nordic apologists succeeds, the result cannot be other

than a huddling together of the Nordics for a war of defence against the rest of the races. The Nordics will have to breed for warriors. And war is hardly a womb from which a meaningful civilization may be expected. Convinced that their call is but for a rallying of biological aristocrats, the Nordics may, as they stumble into war, discover that, when they paged the aristocrat, the ape answered the call.

The *Weltanschauung* of the Nazarene suggests a different mission for modern biology, a mission conceived in terms of the supremacy of moral values and the primacy of the individual human being. And loyalty to these two contentions does not require a sentimental dodging of the facts of race character and race mixture. Civilization will advance at the rate we are able, in all races throughout the world, to breed away from the inferior and towards the superior. Modern science does not direct modern statesmanship to plunge the races of earth into a warfare of words about their relative superiority or inferiority. Modern science suggests rather that modern statesmanship bring together the superiors of all races in a vast international conspiracy to breed their respective races to a higher level of biological worth and cultural attainment. I do not mean an international venture in race mixture, but an international program of race improvement to be prosecuted within each of the races of earth.

Modern science has put into our hands enough knowledge to enable us to breed whole races to higher and higher biological levels. Civilization to date has largely set aside natural selection which roughly and wastefully weeded out the fools and the weaklings, but civilization has not yet substituted, to any adequate degree, rational selection for the natural selection it has set aside. This is the next step. And it is a step that can be taken in one race as well as in another. The goal of the racialist is a superior race. The goal of the biologist is a superlative humanity. In this the humanistic aim of the Nazarene and the scientific aim of the biologist meet in agreement. Why not, then, instead of pitting the assumed superiority of one race against the assumed inferiority of another race, pit the actual superiority within each race against the actual inferiority within its own ranks? This is the social procedure that seems to me to grow naturally out of the contentions of Jesus respecting the supremacy of moral values and the primacy of the individual human being. It is a procedure that is spiritually chivalric, scientifically sound, and socially workable.

I do not know an intelligent racialist, even of the more extreme Nordic persuasion, who does not respect and cannot work congenially with a superior individual from any of the allegedly inferior races. This fact has, I think, a wider implication. I suspect that the superior Nordic, instead of making common cause with the fools and weaklings and dunderheads of his own racial household against, say, the Orientals, would do better to make common cause with the superior Oriental against the fools and weaklings and dunderheads in both racial households. From such chivalric procedure I suspect that the Nordic might reap more solid advantage than from any clash of color in which he might swing a successful sword. If a biologic conspiracy of the superiors among, say, the American and the Japanese peoples should succeed in improving the human quality of both peoples, the average American might find himself no longer threatened by the willingness of the average Japanese to submit to a low standard of living, thus creating a kind of economic competition the average American cannot easily meet. The nationalistic perversion of biology may yet involve the Western world in a color war. The only dependable antidote to this perversion is the sustained collaboration of the biologically élite of all nations in a common effort realistically to utilize modern biological knowledge for the improvement of all races. It may be that the last word has not been said on heredity, but we know enough about its mechanisms and laws to enable us to improve the quality of any race, provided there is a leadership that refuses to bury its biology in its laboratories.

It is, I think, along some such lines that religious leadership might play a productive rôle in reducing the race tensions that harass the West. We know, at least, that Western Christianity, save in frank treason to its patron prophet, cannot be the spiritual sponsor of a Nordic cult that persists in playing the rôle of a blowing Babbitt of the races, forever posturing before a mirror, stroking his blond hair, and patting his ruddy cheeks in a self-satisfied racial ecstasy. The most sinister by-product of the Cult of Racialism is the creeping paralysis of complacency that it induces in its devotees. The assertive white man of the West may yet have to pay for the smugness of his self-appointed racial press agents. The future may enforce a reassessment of the braggadocio and bluster of the man of action. We may, as some wag put it, be facing a *Gogetterdämmerung,* the twilight of the man of action for action's sake. The white man of the West can learn much from the colored man of the East about the spirit of life. The colored man of the East can learn much from the white man of the West about the organization of life. If inter-learning and collaboration between the races of the West and the races of the East shall prove impossible, the East may go to slow death by superstition, the West to quick death by suicide.

The challenge that racialism throws to Western man is thus a double challenge: (1) a challenge to the negative enterprise of preventing a race conflict that would endanger Western civilization, and (2) a challenge to the positive enterprise of promoting a race collaboration that shall enrich Western civilization. For both of these enterprises I have tried to suggest that the *Weltanschauung* of Jesus, save when manhandled and misinterpreted by church or state, offers a fruitful point of departure.

# VIII

# The Church and War

ONLY as the church stands above the battle of the state can it exert its maximum influence in the battles of the social order. The New Reformation, if its radiant realism comes to cleanse and to clarify the social judgments of the West, will be shot through with the implications of this paradox. Certainly the religion of Jesus cannot, without treason to its essential genius, resort to the technique of accommodation and compromise without which the state, as an organization of interlaced interests, could not survive.

At no point does this paradox come more vividly to life than in a consideration of the church and war. This question has hovered in the ante-room and haunted the councils of every national religious assembly that has met in the post-war years. And, despite the hours of debate spent upon it and the barrels of printer's ink spilled upon it, it remains a question that the church, except in some of its minor and much abused sects, has failed to face save with sentiment during peace time and surrender during war time. I am aware of the sweeping renunciations of war that have been registered in numerous official manifestoes of the church and in the personal pronouncements of some of its most distinguished servants since the war, but we cannot know the depth or dependability of these renunciations, despite their sincerity, for it is easy to be brave when the battle-line is leagues away. Renunciations have been announced before, only to be adjourned when war has set the nation's brain on fire.

It may be that the church, as an organization with a thousand and one entangling alliances with the *status quo,* will never be able frankly to face such controversial issues and still maintain itself as one of the respectable institutions of society. Some of its most sincere servants have reluctantly reached this conclusion. "Lovers of peace have not much to hope for from organized religion," says Dean Inge, in his *Outspoken Essays,* with his refreshing habit of speaking honestly in an age of evasion. "Institutional religion does not represent the Gospel of Christ, but the opinions of a mass of nominal Christians. It cannot be expected to do much more than look after its own interests and reflect the moral ideas of its supporters. The real Gospel, if it were accepted, would pull up by the roots not only militarism but its analogue in civil life, the desire to exploit other people for private gain. But it is not accepted." This has been true throughout the history of the church. It may prove inevitable throughout the future of the church. It may be that we cannot organize the religion of Jesus without rendering it powerless to face such a living social issue as war.

The distinguished Dean of London's historic St. Paul's recognizes that the religion of Jesus is incompatible with many of the aims and methods of the political and economic systems of the modern West, but realizes the extraordinary difficulty the church encounters in acting officially in contravention of these aims and methods. There is much in the historic record, which need not detain us here, to indicate that Jesus was keenly aware of the tendency of organization to dampen the gossamer wings of the spirit, to dilute truth, and to delimit freedom through endless compromises in the interest of prestige and power. And contemporary affairs compel us to acknowledge the almost insurmountable difficulty of organizing the religion of Jesus without enfeebling its appeal through caution and compromise with the life around it.

The religion of Jesus as a free-lance adventure is one

thing; the religion of Jesus incorporated in a church is quite another matter. When we incorporate a prophetic and free-lance religion in highly organized institutions concerned with lands and buildings and budgets and staffs and memberships, we inevitably entangle it with the aims and methods of the political and economic systems under which these institutions function. Lands and buildings and budgets must be protected! A membership of many minds must be conciliated and kept coalescent! Institutional prestige must be looked after! Or so we think. A free-lance prophet can ignore the life around him. He is not hampered by an over-supply of baggage. Neither rearing a family nor running for office, he can, if need be, fly in the face of the majority and starve for his principles. A free-lance prophet can understand the occasional necessity of a man's losing his life in order to save it, but this is dark and difficult counsel for any institution to take to heart. There is always the temptation to do the thing that will keep the institution a prosperous going concern, even if the price of its maintenance be temporary treason to its dominant objective.

This is the dilemma that makes it difficult for the institutions of Western Christianity to manifest and to maintain under stress any attitude towards war that runs seriously counter to the majority opinion of the time. Can they take an attitude towards war consistent with the religion of Jesus and still maintain themselves as institutions dependent for support upon the rank and file of business men, bankers, industrialists, engineers, editors, educators, and other laymen whose incomes might be jeopardized by participation in an attitude towards war not shared by the political and economic systems of which they are the salaried servants or material beneficiaries?

Despite these bread-and-butter considerations that meet us at every turn of the road, the religion of Jesus either has or has not a distinctive word to say on war. If it has, the church must say this distinctive word without equivocation, or frankly join the business men, the labor leaders, and the politicians in the half-measures with which they timidly chide and shyly combat the war makers. Otherwise the subtle acid of insincerity will eat away the power of the church to move men's minds on other issues. Mankind cannot permanently respect an institution that pretends to reform society and in practice but reflects it. The essential genius of the religion of Jesus cannot be captured in any single social, economic, or political platform, but the church, as a moral force in modern affairs, is doomed if it keeps discreetly silent or contents itself with amiable generalities on such living moral issues as war. I cannot rid myself of the conviction that anything less than a clean and courageous cutting loose from the whole war business will mean, at best, but slow suicide for the church. The church cannot, as it did in the World War, make its God the ally alike of Pershing and of Hindenburg and bring Him back unsullied for worship in peace time. Clergymen cannot convert themselves into hysterical press agents of the war gods whenever the bugle blows and expect men to take them seriously as authentic representatives of Jesus of Nazareth the day after the armistice.

This conviction is not dependent upon our identifying the religion of Jesus with the doctrine of non-resistance. I am not greatly interested in involved dialectics on the question of whether Jesus was an uncompromising opponent of the use of force, or whether he himself lapsed now and then in language and in action from the philosophy of non-resistance. It is enough to determine whether war hastens or hinders the supremacy of spiritual values in human affairs. If evidence is clear that war, in every circumstance and regardless of its professed purpose, stands stubbornly across the path to the spiritual objectives of the religion of Jesus, then the church cannot consistently do other than maintain a continuous boycott of all wars, whether Jesus was a non-resistant or not.

The church has always justified the passion of its war

activities by the piety of its war aims. What must be the impartial verdict of history upon these justifications? We forget so easily! During the World War, accredited religious leadership predicted, with contagious confidence, that the war would bring a vast spiritual uplift to Western civilization. We were told that the war was a refining fire that was burning the dross from the lives of men and of institutions, and that men would emerge from the war with a new and more spiritual conception of the state and of public affairs. Where are these dreams of regeneration now? Can any competent observer contend that a single nation on earth reaped a single lasting spiritual benefit from the war?

We have turned our backs upon most of the things by which we sought to give spiritual sanction to the war. Having stilled our consciences with the thought that we went to war to save the souls of men, we have since trimmed our mission down to the smaller project of saving our own skins. This is the end of a war which the churches, in the main, felt justified in blessing! The church of the future must be less gullible. It must set its face against the unconscious hypocrisies with which it has heretofore masqueraded its war-time inconsistencies. If it surrenders to war psychology, it must do it in an honestly confessed apostasy to its spiritual objectives. From the beginning of time, war never has stimulated, and to the end of time, war never will stimulate spirituality in anybody or anything. War is the utter negation of all that the religion of Jesus stands for. If the church of the future is to be more than an exhorting ambulance driver in world affairs, it must choose now between Jesus and the jingoes.

It is so easy for the church to say that it will not bless any war, and then attach the weasel phrase "except wars of defence and wars waged in a righteous cause." As if any nation ever admitted that it fought a war that was not in self-defence or in a righteous cause! In all the nations involved in the World War, the church obediently fol-

lowed the lead of the state and press-agented the war aims
of the rival powers. The church in America supported the
war aims of the American state. The church in Germany
supported the war aims of the German state. And so on
through the roll of the belligerent powers. With but few
minor exceptions, the church everywhere tended to adjourn
its gospel for the duration of the war, to surrender its
spirit to the sordid and shabby epidemic of hate, and to
cry lustily with the pack. An aviator, flying over the lines
on Sunday morning, might have seen the ironic spectacle
of German Christians praying to the Christian God for
victory over American arms, and American Christians
praying to the Christian God for victory over German
arms. Thus can the churches confront their God with a
dilemma when they become but an annex to the state. A
handful of really conscientious objectors huddled in
Leavenworth prison gives more courageous and consistent
testimony to the spiritual essence of the religion of Jesus
than the whole church can give when it surrenders to the
war mind of the moment, ties itself to the cart-tail of the
state, and is content to preach to wounded soldiers in hos-
pitals a brotherhood in death that its nationalistic perversion has denied to them in life. The church of the future
must realize that even a war waged for a righteous cause
is a spiritually destructive process.

In considering the problem of its attitude towards war,
the church faces three possible decisions that follow
naturally from three differing conceptions of the nature
of religion and the function of the church: (1) it can
follow a policy of aloofness; (2) it can follow a policy of
compromise; or (3) it can follow a policy of renunciation.
Let me define these three possible decisions and the divergent philosophies underlying them.

*First,* the church can assume that its function is to cultivate the inner spiritual life of individual men and women
as best it can in an imperfect world, ignoring the moral
issues involved in the organized operation of the politi-

cal, social, and economic systems of the time, and limiting
its protest to lamentation when secular leadership plays
havoc with the lives of its members. It can accept the contention of Harnack that the immediate objective of Jesus
was not social reform but spiritual regeneration. It can
assume that such influence as it may exert upon public
affairs should come as the result of a subtle alteration in
the valuations of the worldling. So assuming, the church
will concern itself directly with the minds of men, and only
indirectly with the mechanisms of society. It will tend to
tolerate undesirable political, social, and economic practices in the here and now in anticipation of an all-sufficient
hereafter, as a man might be indifferent to the leaking roof
and sagging floor of his hunting shack in the woods if he
were looking forward to leaving for his real home in the
morning. Animated by such a philosophy of its function,
the church will take no decisive or distinctive attitude
towards war. Holding itself thus aloof from active antagonism to secular decisions of the state that contravene
its spiritual aims, its members will be under powerful social
pressure to acquiesce in these decisions.

*Second,* the church can frankly admit that it does not
represent the unalloyed religion of Jesus but, as Dean
Inge suggests, the opinions of a mass of nominal Christians, and that it cannot, without destroying itself as a
going concern, do more than reflect the moral ideas of its
supporters, particularly in times of crisis when tense dogmatisms of spirit dominate them. It can candidly confess
itself to be the product of a compromise between the purity
of its founder's convictions and the pressures towards social
conformity its members bring to bear upon it. It can set
as its objective the doing of as much good as it can by
effecting the best compromise it can between the spirit of
Jesus and the spirit of the age. Acting upon this assumption, the church will not hold wholly aloof from such secular problems as war, but it will take no attitude towards
war more decisive or distinctive than the general run of

its members will normally take through their chambers of commerce, their labor unions, and their political parties.

*Third,* the church can run the risk of losing its life as a popularly supported institution by attempting to apply, with uncompromising realism, the test of spiritual values to the public affairs of the time. It can assume that it is obligated to exalt the things that hasten and to exorcise the things than hinder the supremacy of spiritual values in human affairs. So assuming, it will concern itself with the moral issues involved in the policies and procedures of the current social order. And, in view of the complexity and interdependence of the modern social order, the church can so conceive its function in complete loyalty to the objectives of Jesus, even if the critics be right who contend that, in the simpler society of his time, Jesus was essentially an internalist. Acting upon this assumption, the church will, if it follows the logic of its assumption, refuse to sanction, bless, or take part in any war.

I shall not attempt to conceal my conviction that this is the attitude the church should assume. The church, as an institution representing the religion of Jesus, cannot, in my judgment, survive many more surrenders to war psychology. I am quite aware that, if the church should, without qualification or quibbling, consistently decline to sanction or to take part in any war, many of its semi-Christian laymen might withdraw from its association. The question the church must face is this: Might it not well afford to suffer desertion from its ranks, depletion of its treasury, and retrenchment of many of its elaborate but hardly exigent enterprises, if necessary, in order to free itself for the taking of a courageous step that would morally electrify the world? The church has not always enjoyed its greatest moral power in the periods of its greatest material prosperity. The church is not an end in itself. It is but a means to an end. The men who lead it must not allow the care of its machinery to steal away their strength from the prosecution of its deepest mission, a fundamental aspect of which is the spiritual validation of the social order, an end that will, in my judgment, remain unattainable as long as the church, save in its peace-time rhetoric, stands as the tacit apologist of such moral travesties as war. It is better for the church to remain silent on the subject of war until it is ready to speak with sweeping courage and to act with the contagious power of a great renunciation.

I do not suggest that the church should demand that its members become devotees of the doctrine of non-resistance. I suggest only that the church, as an institution, refuse to give its official sanction to any war, that it refuse to bless the flags or the fanaticisms that foment the moods of war in the minds of men, that it refuse to lend its pulpits or its ministry to any war service other than acts of mercy to enemy and ally alike, leaving its individual members free to follow their own consciences. Anything less will, it seems to me, leave the church confessedly an institution of social compromise, preaching a high-minded ethics whenever it can do so without running counter to the dominant mood of the state. I doubt that, as an individual, I should be equal to the challenge of non-resistance in the face of invasion or attack. But I am a father! And, with that utter illogicality which is sometimes deeper than logic, I should like to see the church take heroic measures against those perverted notions of nationalism and patriotism that will, unless checked, revised, and spiritualized, almost certainly claim my son as a victim. If, in suggesting that the church boycott war, I am not suggesting that the church demand adherence to the doctrine of non-resistance as requisite to membership in its communion, neither am I suggesting that the American state, let us say, should adopt a pacifist policy of non-resistance, sink its navy, disband its army, dismantle its aircraft, and become a martyr nation if attacked. Let me try to interpret the seeming illogicality and to clarify the seeming contradiction of this position by putting it concretely.

If I were a bishop, priest, or pastor, I should refuse to take part in any war, save in acts of mercy to enemy and ally alike, unless I first unfrocked myself. If I could prevent it, I should not allow my church officially to take part in any war, save in acts of mercy to enemy and ally alike. If it did, I should withdraw from any position of leadership in it. If I were the responsible head of the state, I should see to it, if I could, that its army, its navy, its air force, and the supporting industrial arrangements were adequately organized for the defence of the nation against attack. But, even as the responsible head of the state, I should want the church to hold to its official boycott of war.

I should take this seemingly illogical and contradictory position for two reasons: (1) I should have no fear that the state would lack soldiers in the event of wanton attack. The world is facile enough in surrender to war cries. The task of this generation is not to cultivate a willingness to fight, but rather to build restraining walls against the impulse to combat that has come so near to wrecking Western civilization; and (2) I should realize the virtual bankruptcy of politics in the prevention of war. Machinery of adjudication will never alone insure the abolition of war. I have made earlier reference to the importance of a realistic pacifism of social and economic engineering, that shall remove the foundations of war, to supplement a romantic pacifism of protest against and abstention from the fact of war, but the practical inadequacy of a pacifism of protest and abstention does not make it irrelevant in Western man's imperative venture in war prevention. Practical judgment moves, I think, to the conclusion that alongside projects of social and economic engineering, forces must be set in motion to change the mind of the world. As the responsible head of the state, I should realize that the state might suffer defeat in wars if its army and navy and air force were not kept in working order, but I should realize also that the state will ultimately go down unless war itself is conquered. And for this reason I should want

to see the church dramatically and uncompromisingly boycott war in the hope that it might effect a decisive and
definitive change in the mind of mankind respecting war.

The state is society's organ of compromise. Compromise
is not the business of such institutions as school or church.
Sound social strategy demands that such institutions stick
to the job of supplying the state with the raw materials of a
creative politics. The moment either school or church becomes concerned with the political task of compromise,
the intellectual and moral reservoirs of politics are drained.

The school, the church, and the state are engaged in a
common enterprise, the enterprise of achieving the good
life for citizen and for nation. I dislike to speak of education, religion, and politics as if they were three distinct
fields. In an ideal society they would be an indivisible unity.
Even in our imperfect society, if we isolate any one of them
from the other two, it is orphaned and ineffective. The
professor, the parson, and the politician are at work on
the same job, not on three different jobs. The unity of
purpose shared by these three cardinal institutions of society cannot, however, be best served by the standardizing
sovereignty of any one of them over the other two. Now
and then the professor, the parson, and the politician can
best collaborate by valiantly opposing one another. Issues
arise respecting which corrected vision and creative policy
can come only out of a clash between school and church
and state. But even in these hours of necessary opposition,
school and church and state are engaged in a common
enterprise. War seems to me clearly to be an issue that
thus presents to church and state the problem of collaboration through conflict.

The dilemma that war presents to religious leadership
and to political leadership is illustrative of innumerable
dilemmas that arise out of the relations of church and
state. We are citizens of a highly institutionalized society.
The spiritual ideals of the church may tell us one thing.
The political necessities of the state may force us to do the

opposite. Not within the lifetime of any of us now living will the church, when loyal to its ideals, and the state, when loyal to its necessities, be found in full accord on policy and action. Our lives will continue to be torn by their conflicting claims. Nothing is to be gained by forcing them into an artificial unity. Perhaps the best we can do is to play one against the other to the end that they may neutralize their alternate extremities of emphasis upon pure ideals and practical necessities, killing an evil and creating a good as they might not do in more intimate agreement. Church and state involve us in many contradictions of logic. We can at least try to evolve a workable logic of contradiction between them.

# IX

# The West Goes American

FOR the last dozen years I have spent every hour I dared
steal from my family and from my profession in an eager
search for an accurate understanding of the impact of
science and the machine upon American civilization. Insight into the living forces that are dictating the current
evolution of American civilization is an essential preliminary to responsible speculation on the future of the West,
for the forces that have dominated American civilization,
in particular, are the forces that promise to dominate Western civilization, in general. Here and there a sweat shop
tailor, maddened by the monotony of stitching the mil-
lionth trouser-seam, may throw his sewing machine
through the window. Hungry for a touch of romance we
cannot find in our rolling mills, we may crowd the book
stalls eager for the color and charm of idyllic tales of the
South Sea. But, as a people, we shall not renounce our
technological economy. America will not go native. The
West will go American.

Despite the emotional loyalties to older cultures that
dispute its advance, the Americanization of the world
swings along ever more swiftly with seven league boots.
This is not to say that Americans are the conscious pos-
sessors of a peculiar *Kultur* that they are seeking to uni-
versalize either by swaggering conquest or by subtle
contagion. We have our chauvinists who are not above
making a gospel of their bank accounts and their bluster.
We have our embryo imperialisms. And the devilment
they may do in the affairs alike of West and East cannot

be exorcised with pious phrases about pure intentions. But the obsessions of our professional patriots and the ambitions of our budding imperialists are not the forces making for the fast-moving Americanization of the world. The Americanization of the world is an impersonal process quite independent of any nationalistic urge. It is a process over which Americans are exercising little more conscious control than the Europeans and Asiatics who are beginning to feel the decisive tug of its current. The whole West is to-day facing Americanization simply because the twin forces that have sired the civilization of the United States, physical science and technological industry, are gathering greater and greater momentum in other and older civilizations.

Being a younger nation, carrying a lighter baggage of craft traditions and cultural fixations, we were more plastic than the older peoples when modern science and modern technology began to play upon the minds and movements of men. The old world was reluctant to consider science as other than the disinterested pursuit of knowledge for its own sake. The new world rapidly utilized the scientific method for elaborating new modes of behavior and new methods of production. The old world, enamored of the sure, if slender, independence of its peasant farmers, the artistry of its handicraftsmen, and the more ascetic aloofness of its scholars from the sweat and struggle of the world's work, has been slow to shift its civilization to a technological base. The new world, with a clean slate before it, swiftly embraced the outlook and objectives of a technological economy. And out of the unhampered marriage of physical science and technological industry was born the distinctively machine civilization of the United States. These same forces of science and technology that have been allowed freely to fashion the more plastic American clay are now clamoring to escape more fully than they have yet been allowed from the laboratories and industrial council rooms of the old world and to mold to the same pattern the more reluctant clays of Europe and Asia.

This contrast between the American readiness and the European reluctance to embrace a technological economy is not meant to imply that science and technology are strangers to the European mind or that the American mind has brought an intrinsically greater genius to matters scientific and technological. In many aspects of science, as science, and of technology, as technology, Europe is schoolmaster to America. This is obviously true, I think, in the matter of fundamental research. The allocation of the Nobel awards in the physical sciences from their establishment down to 1928, the latest date for which I have the complete tabulations readily at hand, is illuminating. Denmark, with some 3,000,000 inhabitants, had received four of these awards. Sweden, with some 6,000,000 inhabitants, had received five. Holland, with some 7,000,000 inhabitants, had received six. England, with some 35,000,-000 inhabitants, had received twelve. France, with some 40,000,000 inhabitants, had received eleven. Germany, with some 60,000,000 inhabitants, had received twenty-three. And the United States, with some 120,000,000 inhabitants, had received but five. Europe is manifestly here abreast and there ahead of America, not only in matters of pure science, but also in the experimental application of the findings of pure science.

All that this contrast between the American swiftness and the European slowness to shift from a pre-machine to a machine economy means is that there have been more traditional and environmental factors to resist the march of the machines in Europe than in America. The discovery and experimental application of the scientific and technological principles that have made the machine economy of the United States have not lagged in Europe. What has lagged has been the nation-wide and continent-wide adoption of these principles as a way of life, a way of economic life, for the peoples of the old world. And this lag is not to be explained in terms of intrinsic differences in the intellectual caliber and social perspective of the peoples of the old and new worlds. Its explanation rests, I think, upon more material factors.

The United States faced the machine age with a vast expanse of territory, destined to hold teeming millions of potential consumers of the machine's output, a territory that was politically unified and commercially unhampered by internal tariff barriers, a territory containing unusually varied sources of power, and richly stocked with raw resources to satisfy the voracious appetite of the machine. All of these environmental factors combined to foster the swift development of a machine economy in the United States. America must credit the speed of its industrialization, in no small measure, to the fact that it has been able to operate on a scale and with access to sources of power and materials not possible to any single nation in Europe. If Europe, at the dawn of the machine age, had been a political and ethnic unity, unhampered by racial frontiers and economic tariff walls, and the machine could have taken the whole of Europe as a free field of operation, the story might have been different.

The political fragmentation of Europe, as long as it persists, will definitely retard the development of the machine economy in the old world. Whether the spirit of political nationalism will be intensified or modulated in the Europe of the next half century is an important consideration in any speculation on the future of machine civilization in the West. The outlook is, I think, that the forces of the new machine age will, in the end, dominate the stubbornly surviving forces of the old age of politics. How long it will take to achieve this domination is highly speculative. The emotions of nationalism wear an air of the eternal. But everywhere throughout Europe the inherently trans-national interests of industry are straining against the inhibitions of nationalistic politics. While the political leaderships of Europe jealously guard the sacred

separateness of their respective national interests, the
industrial leaderships of Europe ignore frontiers, carry
on international conferences, and effect international com-
bines above the battle of politics, although, to date, political nationalism has persistently stepped into the picture
whenever these economic urges of the machine age have
threatened to cut too drastically into that national self-
sufficiency for which peoples are forever angling and never
attaining.

But, whatever the future of the machine may be in
Europe, the fact remains that the evolution of machine
civilization has run faster and reached farther in the United
States than in any other sector of the civilized world. We
cannot, therefore, avoid serving as a symbol alike of the
vices and of the virtues of machine civilization both to the
peoples that hate and to the peoples that hunger for this
social modernism of science and the machine. The attitude
we take towards the past and potential implications of the
machine order in American civilization becomes, by virtue
of this symbolic status that is inevitably ours, an important factor in the psychology of our world relations. As
smug beneficiaries of the output of our machines, going
about the world as uncritical press agents of prosperity
for its own sake, we have at times seemed to be little more
than an irritant in international intercourse. If, on the
other hand, we can be grateful for prosperity, when it
visits us, without being gullible about it, if we can achieve
a critical understanding of the long-time forces that will
determine our future after obviously temporary factors of
good fortune have run their course, and if, out of our first-
hand knowledge of its operation, we can contribute to
world opinion an objective interpretation of the newer
tendencies of our machine economy as they come into
play, we may bring genuine leadership to the West in its
problem of how best to adapt itself to the advancing
forces of science and technology.

It would be futile to deny that the development of a

machine economy may mean, for a time of transition, at
least the temporary loss of many precious values inherent
in a social order resting upon agriculture, handicraft, and
the disinherited pursuit of truth and beauty for their own
sakes. The American record would deny the denial. The
millions of Europeans and Asiatics who are spiritually
wedded to the ways of a pre-machine world know this.
And their rage rises as the shadow of an impending industrialization falls across their lives. They struggle to make
their rage articulate. They have seen science and technology, in the adolescent industrialism of America, result
in standards, processes, and a tempo of working and living
against which their spirits revolt. America becomes the
symbol of the fate they fear. And, since the human animal
finds it easier to swear at a people than to subject a process
to analysis and control, the pre-machine minds of the old
world cry out against "the Americanization of Europe."
This, more than the gaucherie of American tourists or the
insistence of American treasury officials, is the source of
the European "hatred" of Americans. It is not so much
that we are a menace to Europe as that we are a handy
metaphor for Europeans to use in protesting the march
of the machines.

Beyond the possibility of a chronic ineptness of economic
leadership that would render the whole economic enterprise of the West profitless and undependable, there is
nothing to indicate a halting of the march of the machines
across the Western and, ultimately, the Eastern world.
Science and technology relentlessly extend their sovereignty. We can neither plot our future nor plan its control
without full insight into the social implications, present and
potential, of a machine economy. And I do not know how
better to begin the quest of this insight than by listening
to the cry of the rebels against the machine age. Their
cries may be surcharged with emotion, and their eyes
blinded to the ultimate nature of a machine civilization
by its temporary and transitional aspects, but they may

in their passion point out certain unhappy results of a machine economy that more temperate and less sensitive observers might overlook, thus making our analysis of the immediate more searching. And they represent a form of social resistance to the advance of a technological order with which statesmanship will have to reckon for many moons.

In the course of a caustic analysis of Americanism, as the apotheosis of machine civilization, in *La Revue de Genève,* Fernand Baldensperger, a Frenchman of Alsatian stock, educated in Germany, and ardently French in spirit, addresses his European compatriots thus, "Let us thank the gods that we have not become entirely the slaves of the mechanical piano, of ready-made sauces put up in bottles like patent medicines, of automatic restaurants where you can select from a menu of three dozen dishes by dropping coins into that number of slots. Let us congratulate ourselves, for it is one of the guaranties of our civilization, that the farms of France are so small that our laborious peasants cannot afford to buy McCormick reapers. Let us felicitate ourselves that we still have good, old, sympathetic family physicians, whose familiarity with our personal history enables them to make instinctive diagnoses of our complaints, rather than a host of specialists armed with delicate devices for registering mechanically our pulse and listening to our lungs and heart. Let us still leave to our teachers the function of discovering the aptitudes and abilities of their pupils, instead of submitting the latter to carefully devised, inflexible tests supposed to group them mechanically and automatically into future industrial managers, horticultural specialists, and presidents of the republic. Let us still cherish pride in our skilful artisans whom no machine can rival in dyeing silk, weaving beautiful worsteds, dressing leather, or polishing to microscopic nicety the parts of an airplane motor. Let us thank the gods that we cannot be interrupted by the telephone when dining at a restaurant or sleeping in the

privacy of our home." This Alsatian Frenchman is typical
of the pre-machine mind that considers a technological
civilization inconsistent with the dignity, the independence,
and the qualitative labor and leisure of the human spirit.
"The man of Europe," he says, as if to shame by contrast
the mechanized millions of America, "is deeply concerned
in augmenting his leisure, affirming his dignity, and equal-
izing his opportunities. On the other hand, he instinctively
rebels against anything that unduly transforms his labor
into a simple mechanical activity. He does not fancy a type
of existence divided between intense production and complete idleness."

Let me call another witness in the case that the pre-
machine minds of Europe are conducting against Americanization as a symbol of the advance of machine civilization in the old world, a witness even more passionate and
pointed than M. Baldensperger in his indictment of American civilization. This second witness is Karel Capek. I
shall not soon forget the evening I watched this Czech
dramatist bring machine civilization to the bar of judgment in his *R. U. R.* I thought then that there was more
than a chemical trace of the crusader in M. Capek. The
voice of the impassioned evangelist spoke from the wings
that night warning us moderns against making mechanization the spiritual mistress of our existence. And M.
Capek's interest in the issues arising out of man's relation
to his machines did not die with the production of this
play. Later, in the columns of *The New York Times,* I
found him preaching a lay sermon against what seemed
to him the sterile ideals of a materialistic and mechanized
America. In the rôle of Samson he sought, in this sermon,
to push down what seemed to him the three pillars of
American society; (1) speed; (2) success; and (3) size.
We are, if this Czech contender is to be believed, a hasty
and hoggish lot. He sought to shame us by showing us the
picture of a Europe that is, or was, before it began to be
Americanized, creatively lazy, qualitatively successful, and

uninfected with the craze for quantity. Let me give the essence of his triple indictment.

*First,* M. Capek thinks that the American passion for speed, generated by our machine economy, is bound to produce a people spiritually out of breath. And, with the dramatist's habit of arguing in the concrete, he lauds a more leisurely way of life by recounting the story of the building of a little house in a Europe that is less surrendered to the machine age than we.

"I built myself a little house," he says, "small, yellow and white, like a hard-boiled egg. You have no notion how complicated such a thing is in Europe. Before my house was finished, we went through a strike of bricklayers, carpenters, cabinetmakers, parquet layers, and tilers. The building of the house proceeded as a two-year social struggle. As long as the work went on at all, the workmen had time enough between the laying of two bricks to chat a little, to drink beer, to expectorate, and to scratch their backs. For two years I went to see how my house was growing. It was a piece of my personal history. My relation to the house grew into an endless intimacy. In the course of these two years I learned a great many details about the labor and the life of bricklayers, cabinetmakers, canteen keepers, and other bearded, serious, and joking men. All this is walled in between the bricks and the beams of my house, and you can understand that after so many difficulties I cling to it with a certain wild patriotism and that I would not exchange it for any other.

"Now, you in America, you would perhaps build such a house in three days. You would come in your Ford cars with a finished steel construction, tighten some screws, pour several sacks of cement into it, jump into your Ford cars, and drive away to build somewhere else. It would be far cheaper and quicker; it would have all the technical and economic advantages; but I have a feeling that I should be less at home in my house if it had grown up with such unnatural speed."

M. Capek thinks the more leisurely and less efficient way he built his house was better for him and better for his workmen, but he tells the tale to point a moral in a wider field. "Europe," he reminds us, "was in very little haste when she made her cathedrals and her philosophic systems. . . . In old Europe we are astonished to note how little hurried those people were who left behind them great vestiges. . . . Europe wasted her time for many thousands of years; this is the source of her inexhaustibility and fertility." With sly irony, M. Capek speaks further of the "broad-minded laziness" that has fertilized the life of Europe with some of its richest values.

*Second,* M. Capek thinks that the American passion for success, intensified by our machine economy, is bound to produce a people insensitive to the more delicate as well as to the more daring values of life. He speaks of "a certain heroic tradition" fostered and followed by a Europe in which "people have been living and dying for faith, for truth, or for other somewhat irrational things, but never for success," at least not for the sort of success hawked in the American market-place by gaudy advertisements that stir the stevedore to dream of becoming a steel king. "Foolish Europe," he sighs, chiding us by indirection, "found time to interest herself in thousands of things other than successes, while all the successes, no matter how many there were in history, went to the devil. How many things would have been left undone if those who did them had been thinking of success!"

*Third,* M. Capek thinks that the American passion for quantity, inherent in the mass production of our machine economy, is bound to produce a people decreasingly concerned with quality. He lashes us with his critical cat-o'-nine-tails for our abject worship of bigness. "America corrupts us with her predilection for huge dimensions," he cries. "Europe will lose herself," he warns his compatriots, "as soon as she makes this fanaticism of dimension her own. Her measure is not quantity but quality."

The Baldenspergers and the Capeks are faithful examples of the romantic rebels against the machine age. We may set down their reactions as more a rebel yell than a reasoned indictment of machine civilization. Behind these romantic rebels, however, is a growing army of more realistic rebels against the machine age, careful critics who have descended to details in their indictment. I shall summarize the indictment drawn by these realistic rebels in the chapter to follow, but meanwhile M. Capek serves admirably as dramatizer of the fact that the future of Western civilization may well depend upon whether the technological economy of the United States can be made an instrument for the emancipation rather than the enslavement of the human spirit.

I agree, as most literate Americans agree, with many of M. Capek's observations, but I dissent heartily from the major conclusion that may be read between his lines, the conclusion that a machine economy is a dragon that must be slain if we are to save our souls. I refuse to bind myself so readily to the cart-tail of M. Capek's social fatalism. If we are to play St. George to the dragon of modern industrialism, it is the part of wisdom, I think, to try our hand at domesticating it before we consider destroying it.

The romantic rebels of the Baldensperger and Capek sort sting us into awareness of the fact that our machine economy must stand or fall by virtue of its success or failure in safeguarding the economic independence, augmenting the leisure, affirming the dignity, investing with charm the environment, and assuring tasks worthy of the talents of modern men. As pointers-out of the problem, they are valuable social servants, but their dependability as social analysts is, I think, open to question. They reach their judgment of what the spread of the machine order will mean for the future of Western civilization by comparing the ripe fruits of a mature European civilization with the raw fruits of an adolescent American civilization. And they leave out of their reckoning profoundly revolutionary forces of a scientific, technical, and administrative nature that are already well on their way towards making the machine industry of to-morrow radically different from the machine industry of yesterday, different in its economic results and in its social implications.

It may be that, in respect of art, of culture, and of seasoned statesmanship, more heads rise above the human plane of the masses and rise higher in Europe than in America, but in matters of material equipment, potential economic security, and educational privilege for the millions, the human plane is higher here than in Europe, and in time our quota of exceptions will fill up. We are a young society, as the historian reckons time, and criticism must not cast up the account prematurely.

It may be that in America just now the men of congenital superiority are not flocking into non-material fields in quest of careers. Industry and finance are attracting men who, in a more mature society, would be enriching the arts and extending the sweep of science. Men are becoming bankers and business men who, in an older social order, would be writing our books, painting our canvases, and capturing the consonance and dissonance of the universe in our music. Men are wrestling with the recalcitrant balance-sheets of mass production who, in an America come of age, would be dedicating their genius for social insight and invention to the modernization of our maladjusted political system, bringing the living power of prophecy to our religious perplexities, and playing Socrates in our universities where youth, wistful for all its wildness, waits to be led beyond a mood of neutrality and drift. In the machine civilization of the United States, the drift of distinguished ability into industry, commerce, and finance is decisive. But, aside from the God-driven geniuses, men of congenital superiority, under any sort of economy, rarely flock into non-material fields in quest of careers, save from a leisure class that has been matured by generations of fine heredity and favorable environment, freed by economic security from the urge to acquire, and enriched in outlook by long cultural traditions. Our leisure class is too young. Give it its *nouveau riche* adolescence and we may see.

And, more important still, we may, if we are but patient in our judgment, discover that a machine economy that has matured effects a profound transvaluation of values to the end that the material and the non-material are more intimately interlocked than in the pre-machine age. I suspect that, in a machine civilization come of age, men concerned to contribute to the non-material values of their time will not be interested, as heretofore, in retiring from business and entering a secular priesthood that sets itself apart from the world's work to manufacture a culture or to manifest a beauty that is but tacked, as a tinsel decoration, on an otherwise superficial or sordid social order. They will prefer to make the world's work itself the instrument of their priesthood.

I cannot agree that, even now, we worship at the shrine of material success with the single-mindedness of which M. Capek accuses us. I have no disposition to minimize the materialism of our adolescent business system. But I am less interested in indictments of our materialism than in finding clues to our future. And I do not know a people more pathetically reverential in the presence of brains and genuine achievement in non-material fields. The very weakness of our materially successful for "lion hunting" among authentic celebrities may well be a sort of shy confession of faith in things of the mind and of the spirit.

I confess I am a bit sick of the cultural snobbery of the professional European and of the flunkey-mindedness of many Americans in the presence of anything European. One can hardly go through a season in New York without growing tired of the sycophantic genuflections before mildewed lords and tarnished ladies just because they are European. But I have gone at length into M. Capek's jeremiad against American civilization, not as an illustration of the cultural snobbery of the professional European, but as an illustration of the superficiality and essential futility of the romantic rebellion against the machine age. We are wasting our time when we sigh wistfully for a leisurely and gossipy handicraft world in which workmen may, between the laying of two bricks, "chat a little, drink beer, expectorate, and scratch their backs." The machine is here to stay. M. Capek's Europe will build and buy more and more machines. The Europe of Shakespeare and Shelley, of Turner and Titian, of Beethoven and Bach, of Mont-Saint-Michel and Chartres is destined to be remade by physical science and technological industry. Neither poets nor premiers can successfully dispute the advancing sovereignty of these modernist forces. The West will go American. And when this is consummated, the pressure of a common problem may induce us to repent alike the snobbery of the professional European and the swagger of the professional American, and to pool our genius for the discovery of ways and means by which Western man may master his machines instead of being mastered by them.

# X

# Mystic and Muckraker View the Machine

MUST we of the West smash our machines in order to save our souls? The social mystics of the slower paced Orient are sure that we must. Every energy of the frail body and flaming spirit of Mahatma Gandhi, exemplar extraordinary of social mysticism, is invested in the attempt to convince the Western world that it must emancipate itself from the sovereignty of the machine if it would avert the downfall of its civilization. To him the application of machine power to production meant the entrance of the Serpent into the Eden of a handicraft world. To this wistful ascetic of India, the spinning wheel becomes a symbol of salvation from the moral devastation of the machine.

The Mahatma is a milder St. George challenging the dragon of Western industrialism. He is skeptical of attempts to domesticate it, for he thinks it inherently and incorrigibly anti-humanistic. His social pacifism prevents his advising its destruction by violence. He is content to advise his countrymen to hold aloof from its appeal, and, in a machineless India, to preserve unbroken the chalice of the spirit so that, when we Westerners return repentant from our sinful orgy of inhuman industrialism, we may find it there to drink from. He is convinced that we of the West will stand but slight chance of realizing either the spiritual invigoration of a New Reformation or the social enrichment of a New Renaissance unless we divest ourselves of our inheritances from the Industrial Revolution. For, in Gandhi's judgment, a machine economy will continue, in its maturity as in its adolescence, to mean the excessive centralization of production in great industrial cities where congestion breeds its ugly offspring and the human spirit bruises itself against an unfriendly environment, a narcotic monotony of factory routine that turns masters of tools into servants of machines, an over-speeding that leaves men spiritually spent, a mass production that puts quantity above quality, a standardization of processes and products that stamps its sterile sameness upon men's characters as well as upon their commodities, and a subtle conspiracy against beauty that makes ugliness and utility interchangeable terms.

This may seem, in the light of some of his utterances, an over-statement of the Mahatma's attitude towards the machine. "I would favor the use of the most elaborate machinery," he has said, "if thereby India's pauperism and resulting idleness could be avoided. I have suggested hand spinning as the only ready means of driving away penury and making famine of work and wealth impossible." And, again, I find him saying to his followers, "burn that wheel if you find a better substitute." This might suggest that Gandhi rebels against the machine economy only because he thinks it ill adapted to the immediate Indian situation. And I do not know that he would seriously suggest that the West dismantle its industrial establishment. There is a singularly practical intelligence hovering in the background of his startling renunciations of modernism. I doubt that Gandhi would, were he the executive head of the British or German governments, let us say, advise the wholesale renunciation of the machine order. But at most, I suspect, he would continue its operation in the spirit of making the best of a bad bargain. He might tolerate the machine, if it were already installed and the lives of his people inextricably entangled in its operation, but it is difficult to visualize Gandhi's looking upon the machine as a potential emancipator, even in the West. "Machinery has begun to desolate Europe," he says, in one of the Socratic dialogues in his now famous *Hind-Swaraj,* ". . . Machinery is the chief symbol of modern civilization; it represents a great sin. . . . I cannot recall a single good point in connection with machinery. . . . It is necessary to realize that machinery is bad."

We might dismiss all this as but the natural reaction of the mystical East if it came alone from Mahatma Gandhi, seated at his spinning wheel, but Gandhi and his fellow rebels against the machine age are winning converts in the West. Western muckrakers lock arms with Eastern mystics in protesting the march of the machines. Some of these Western converts belong to the romantic rebels who, like Karel Capek, stop with the shout of their rebel yell; others belong to the realistic rebels who base their rebellion, not upon their own temperamental affinity for a more gracious and leisurely civilization than science and technology have yet produced, but upon detailed studies of the operation of the machine order and its reflection in the fabric and feel of Western civilization. These new muckrakers are indicting the philosophy of our civilization as the old muckrakers indicted the practices of our business men and politicians.

I want now to examine with some care the picture of our machine civilization that these realistic rebels have painted. Save in dilettante drawing-rooms and in the studios of the literati, we have not really given these disbelievers in our machine economy their day in court. Certainly we did not in those drunken days before the market crash of 1929 came to shake us from our smugness. Stimulated to self-satisfaction by the wine of prosperity, we amusedly watched these queer intellectuals who wanted to poke about the foundations of our socio-economic order. As if anything could be wrong with a civilization that paid such excellent dividends! But these rebels now ask, with a new insistence, that we adjourn for a time our Babbittry and our back-patting and ponder some things we have been prone to leave in the vestibule of our pep meetings. And this, I think, we can afford to do. We may disagree, as I think we shall, with the remedies they prescribe and yet learn a lot from their diagnoses of the dilemmas with which the machine economy has confronted us.

I want first, by direct quotation, to sample the spirit that animates these Western critics of Western civilization, and then to summarize the indictment they have drawn. And, as illustrating the spirit of their inquiry, I take at random the following paragraphs from a paper that Nathaniel Peffer, a brilliant young American, wrote for me, when I was an editor.

"It is proper to question," said Mr. Peffer, "whether the Oriental at his harsh labor and in his primitive home and without organized amusements or modern improvements does not derive as full a satisfaction as the American shopkeeper and factory worker. If he works hard and long, his work is not deadening. He is a craftsman, not a tender of machines. He makes something in which he can express himself. He does not spend his life turning one screw a thousand times a day, always the same screw, the relation of which to the finished product he does not know or care to know. His pace is not forced by a thing of steel driven by a power he cannot see. He has a personal relation to his work, his fellow workers, and the product. He chats as he works, takes a cup of tea, stops to regard the passing excitement in the street, to greet a friend, or to reprimand his children, his workshop being also his home. If he has not so much leisure measured in hours, he has more leisureliness. . . . He smiles easily. He is not ridden by the childish ideal of efficiency. If he can play at his work, as Americans cannot, also he does not work at his play, as Americans do. . . . When you have seen one of his cities you have not seen them all; he does not model the street of his little hamlet in imitation of the metropolis. . . . He does not say the same, do the same, think the same, feel the same as every other human being in his land. He has not been regimented, and his life has not been standardized, stratified, dulled, and ironed out of every element of individuality until he is one pea in a huge, globular pod differing from the other peas in curvature, form, and external variations, but identical with them in flavor, taste, and texture. . . .

"The America of to-day—its monotony, tastelessness, vulgarity, and mob dictatorship—is not the product of a unique American race stock or race spirit. It is the product of the machine age, its inevitable product. America to-day is the England, France, and Italy of fifty years from to-day. It is what it is fifty years before them because it did not have to overcome the arresting power of a long tradition and implanted social forms. Here mechanization could establish itself unresisted, and America is the product, the inevitable product, of the machine age. You cannot have machinery without quantity production. You cannot have quantity production without standardization. You cannot have standardization of all material adjuncts of life without standardization of thought, opinion, conduct, and morals. When the first tie was laid for the first mile of the first railway, the road was started that ends in Rotary—on this or any other continent. The young gentlemen who assuage themselves in the Americanized Latin Quarter in Paris and write sadly, but mordantly, to the American liberal weeklies can still their vituperations or vilify the proper evil. What they fled from in Denver and Dubuque will be also in Paris, London, Florence, and Constantinople.

"For the material benefits brought to mankind through industrialism there have been compensating evils. Every material good has its price. The price may be too large for the good. It may not. . . . My own belief is that it is too large. If I were a Hindu, a Turk, an Egyptian, a Chinese, or a Siberian, I should inoculate my social system against industrialism as I should against the plague."

Here speaks the disillusioned Westerner!

This single sampling gives, as well as a more extensive

show of specimens could, a sense of the spirit animating the revolt of many Westerners against the machine economy of the West. That this spirit is more than mere temperamental dislike of the life of action becomes clear as we burrow into the bill of particulars with which these Western muckrakers support their protest against the modern industrial order. Perhaps the most comprehensive single presentation of this bill of particulars that the realistic rebels have drawn is found in the diagnostic chapters of R. Austin Freeman's *Social Decay and Regeneration,* in which are traced, with rare analytical skill, the social reactions of mechanism (1) on its own evolution; (2) on the human environment, the primary environment of natural conditions and resources and the secondary environment of social inventions and institutions; (3) on man collectively; and (4) on man individually. The framework of this Freeman study, simple in form and sweeping in scope, provides the formula I want to follow in attempting an interpretative condensation of the mass of anti-machine literature that the self-critical minds of the West have produced. Mr. Freeman completed his study in 1921. There have been extensive technological developments since then, but the social criticism to which these later developments have been subjected has not resulted in any major indictment of the machine economy that did not appear,, directly or indirectly, in Mr. Freeman's philosophical assessment of the social reactions of mechanism.

It is a bleak and barren picture that these realistic rebels have painted, but Western man stands to learn more about his machine civilization from its sincere critics than from its sycophantic press agents. I list the major charges they make without inquiring, for the moment, into their validity. I dispense with references to the sources of these contentions for all of them appear and reappear throughout the current literature of socio-economic criticism, and have thus become a kind of common property of the critical fraternity. Here, then, is the unrelieved indictment as the Western muckrakers of the machine economy draw it:

*First,* a machine economy is, by its very nature, uncontrollable by man. The machine is not a slave that man can make serve him at his will, but a tyrant that will, in the end, make man its slave. Man first looked upon machines as simply added tools with which he could supplement the power of his arms and the skill of his hands, and he thought, simple soul, that he would invent and use more machines only as fast as he found he could make his work easier and his life more liveable by using them. He soon found, however, that he did not have the power to dictate just how fast and how far machinery should be introduced into modern life, for machines, he found, have a way of calling still other machines into existence without regard to his desire for them or his facilities for their social assimilation and control. Man invented his ancient tools under the pressure of felt needs, but other pressures, less clearly related to his immediate welfare, are responsible for the rabbit-like rapidity with which his modern machines multiply to enforce kaleidoscopic changes in his manner of working and his mode of living.

It is sufficient to mention two of the pressures that make for the increase of modern machines, pressures that did not, in like manner, make for the increase of ancient tools: (1) Machines grow in number, not only because man needs a new kind of machine now and then, but as more or less inevitable by-products of advancing knowledge. Pure science ever presses for verification in tangible instruments that put its findings to the test of practical operation. The inventor does not sit with folded hands until some human need comes to him, like a cry out of the night, and then set feverishly at work to invent a new machine to answer the need. The inventor is colleague of the scientist, marching with him into the alluring unknown, checking and verifying the scientist's hypotheses and generalizations with instruments that test their truth.

And, in this association, the inventor is animated by the itch to invent, just as the scientist is animated by the itch to know, and the artist by the itch to create. As mechanical knowledge grows, inventors invent more machines, whether the relation of the new machines to human need is clear at the moment or not. And there is always somebody to see to it that man uses a machine after it has been invented. (2) Machines that produce power induce the invention of machines to consume power. The industrial system always persists until it finds ways to use the power it is able to produce. Thus every new machine, as if it were a human thing, is the prolific parent of still other machines. As a result of the spontaneous and forced fertility of invention, the world of machines as well as the world of men here and there faces the problem of overpopulation.

*Second,* a machine economy must, as the price of its efficiency, pay less and less attention to its men and more and more attention to its machines. This has nothing whatever to do with the goodness or badness of the captains of industry. The reason is technical. Machines must, if their maximum efficiency is to be realized, be substitutes for men rather than supplements to men. In a process of production executed with hand tools, it is possible to indulge in those pauses and variations of power and pressure, of tempo and treatment, which are inseparable from hand labor. But the moment any important part of a production process is committed to a machine, the necessity for committing the rest of the process to mechanical means becomes pressing. A machine can tolerate man as a collaborator only if he achieves the impossible by becoming himself as accurate and as automatic in the manner and speed of his movements as another machine, flawlessly synchronized with the first machine, would be. Otherwise the power of the first machine would be squandered and the uniform perfection of the product made speculative.

And so, a machine economy tends to forget its men in

an increasing absorption in its machines, not because the directors of machine industry are heartless, not because its operators are congenital materialists, but for the technical reason, inherent in the machine, that machine production can reach perfect efficiency only through perfect mechanization. Machine industry is thus under the technical imperative to move towards the progressive elimination of the human worker. And this relentless drive towards the complete mechanization of industry is a process over which man seems to have little more conscious control than he has over a glacial drift.

*Third,* a machine economy robs posterity of its capital by a rapid and reckless consumption of natural resources. Pre-machine man barely scratched the surface of the mineral resources of his environment. He did not build at such breakneck speed, and, whether he was building a peasant cottage or a baronial castle, he built for endurance, so that neither he nor his sons had to go soon again to forest or quarry. The once-for-allness of the structures he fashioned and of the objects of art and utility he fabricated greatly reduced the levy pre-machine man had to make upon the raw materials of his environment. He did not bring down about his ears a problem of resource depletion. His sons could expect as square a deal from nature as he had enjoyed. But the sons of the man of the machine age face a different fate. From the beginning, the machine has displayed an abnormal appetite for minerals and metals and woods and oils. The day the machine was born the raid on our resources began. And the rate at which the raid proceeds increases with the further evolution of the machine economy. In a year the man of the machine age spends natural resources that would have lasted pre-machine man for a century. A machine civilization depletes its heritage in the spendthrift spirit of the dissolute heir of an undeserved fortune. Pre-machine man showed wisdom and restraint in the way he used replaceable raw materials, and left largely untouched the irreplaceable resources with which nature had stocked his environment. The man of the machine age shows little wisdom and less restraint in the way he is using such replaceable resources as soil and forest, and, in seeming disregard of his descendants, is using up the irreplaceable resources of his environment with a speed that startles men who have expert insight into the limitations of these basic supplies.

Here the machine proves itself a trouble maker outside the walls of the factories that house it, for this rapid and reckless machine consumption of natural resources is raising all sorts of momentous questions in which the fate of Western civilization may well be locked. It is compelling statesmen to go into conference with geologists, physicists, chemists, and experts in correlate fields to determine just what the exhaustion of this or that basic resource in this or that area may involve by way of shifting the centers of military power, economic privilege, and political prestige, in necessitating new international alignments, and so on. And as long as the machine economy lasts there will be no let-up in this raid on natural resources and no lessening of the military, economic, and political complications it creates. Science and technology will go on discovering, digging, and depleting the capital of man's physical environment. The resistless march of the industrial system towards magnitude of operation will continue to make man insensitive to the possible famine of power and failure of basic materials that the present rate of resource consumption brings appreciably nearer each year.

*Fourth,* a machine economy destroys the natural beauty of the regions in which its industries operate and puts ugliness in its place. Our mining districts bear mute testimony to the seeming inability of a machine economy to prosecute an essential industry without vulgarizing its environment. In the less industrialized regions of the West, one may still ride through valleys where the countryside, as Spring begins to touch it with an exquisite green loveliness, seems a long ribbon of radiant beauty. But, if machine industry has reached the region at all, ride far enough and you will find the ribbon punctured here and there with patches of unredeemed ugliness. A mine mouth in a setting that is bleak and black and barren! A slattern cabin with a sloven and grassless yard! A weather-beaten wagon turned out to rust! The paintless and patternless outskirts of a factory town! Wherever machine man has touched this stretch of countryside, he will have made ugly what nature made beautiful.

The machine defiles even its own home. The graceless outlines, the drab walls, and the belching chimneys of its factories ignore even the most elementary æsthetic values as they range themselves along our streets and throw themselves against our sky-lines. And this will remain true as long as the machine dominates our civilization, for the machine will compel the concentration of production in great industrial centers, and these industrial centers will be designed to fit the requirements of the machines that produce in them rather than the needs of the men who live in them. Pre-machine man set consciously out to make beautiful the temples of his toil no less than the temples of his worship. Machine man struggles to make beautiful the places where his money is spent, but leaves bleak the places where his money is earned. Pre-machine man created the eloquent beauty of the little French villages that edge the roadway from Paris to Chartres. Machine man has created the American small town in which house after house is so ugly that accident might have been its architect. Pre-machine man in mediæval England built lime-kiln and smithy and malt-house with a touch of the appropriate and the æsthetic that still lure artist and architect. Machine man in modern America runs up galvanized iron shacks and calls them shops. Here and there power and wealth will house a great business beautifully, but the bulk of the work of the machine age is done in a barren and bedraggled setting.

*Fifth,* a machine economy robs the world of local color

and of local character and heads humanity straight for a sterile uniformity. The machines of transportation bear primary blame for this. The pre-machine community was of necessity self-contained and self-reliant. No railway train, no motor bus, no power-driven truck, no airplane existed to bring men and materials from afar to alienize its atmosphere and make it like a thousand other communities a thousand miles away. The color and the character of the pre-machine community were determined by local men and local materials.

The buildings that remain from the pre-machine age invariably reflect the geological character of the region. Pre-machine man had to build his structures from local materials. He was unable to bring heavy building materials from afar. Out of this dependence upon local materials, unique architectures arose, a result that makes a motor ride through rural England, the French countryside, or the Tyrol a bath in vibrant and varied beauty. But now, with our machines of transportation, we can bring our building materials from the ends of the earth, and as a result we begin to see a sickening sameness in new construction throughout the world. Pre-machine man was himself a closely tethered animal. He was, in the main, restricted to the radius of territory he could cover behind old Dobbin during daylight. This tyranny of distance threw men back upon themselves and their immediate neighbors and made for marked individuality. But this rich intensity of type has been undergoing dilution ever since man traded the old gray mare for a motorcycle. To-day the towns, the men, the clothes, the customs, and the ideas of the machine age tend to become everywhere alike.

This is not because modern man is inherently less gifted than mediæval man, or too lazy to like variety, but the result of the invention and use of machines that move men and materials over long distances in a short time. Theoretically, a modern community that can, thanks to its machines of transportation, levy upon the whole world for the building materials of its structures and the personnel of its institutions should bring greater and greater variety into its life. Practically, it becomes a colorless counterpart of ten thousand other communities.

*Sixth,* a machine economy decreases rather than increases man's freedom and control in matters of transportation. At first blush, this contention seems absurd. Has not the machine age enabled man to get about faster and to go farther than ever before in history! It has. But the major machines of transportation are no longer under the intimate control of individuals and local communities as were the older pre-machine means of transportation. And the major machines of modern transportation are incapable of as accurate adjustment to the needs of individuals and of communities as were the older pre-machine means. Pre-machine locomotion was controlled exclusively by the individual and adjusted exactly to the needs of the local community. The farmer on horseback or the tradesman in his cart went up byways and across fields at will wherever human needs and local interest called, but the Twentieth Century Limited cannot cut across fields and career up country roads to pick up a local passenger because life happens to hang upon his making an engagement, or because convenience or whim calls.

Pre-machine transportation was adapted to man. When machine transportation came along, man had to adapt himself to it. His convenience had to give way before the technical necessities of the construction and the operating schedules of the modern railway. Roadbeds are established where sound engineering suggests. Stations are located at stated and sufficiently separated intervals. Trains are run at certain times. Community after community may be passed by if the bulk of business originating in them does not justify the expense of maintaining stations. The machine dictates this program of stations and schedules, and man must fit himself to it. The physical necessities of construction and the economic necessities of operation compel the modern railway to concern itself with larger and larger areas. It cannot make the needs of the individual and of the small community its main consideration. Thus the machine age, as far as its great organized systems of transportation are concerned, gives man better facilities for going long distances, but it restricts his freedom in matters of transportation. He must move along the lines and at the times dictated by the systems.

Then, too, the control of these great established systems of transportation systems, like railways and steamship lines, has definitely slipped from the hands of the individual and of the local community. This loss of control means that, at any moment, these systems of machine transportation may seriously disrupt modern man's life and business without so much as asking his leave, either when governments control them or when organized labor sees fit to hamper or suspend their operation.

*Seventh,* a machine economy destroys the spirit of craftsmanship and organizes itself upon the basis of a handful of manufacturers directing a host of unskilled or semiskilled machine tenders. It wipes out the world of skilled craftsmen to whom industry was a medium of self-expression as well as a means of self-support. It compels man to become the slave of a system rather than the master of a shop. It renders impossible, by its competition, the extensive development of small industries in which men might use inexpensive tools and live independent lives.

A machine economy conspires against the spirit of workmanship that created the great cathedral at Chartres. The craftsmen who built Chartres were not in a hurry. They were not artisans under the lash of a contractor. They were artists under the lure of the creative spirit. They were singularly unworried by the wage problem. They worked, not so much for hire, as for holiness. They were not making beauty that they might make money. The stonecutter's chisel and the saint's rosary were alike instruments of devotion. Each blow for beauty was a blow for God. Before their sense of the divinity of their toil professional and social distinctions disappeared. The artisans performed their work as a religious observance. And the nobles, taking the place of their horses, hauled stones from the quarries for their cathedral to the magic rhythm of chanting priests and swinging censers. The whole world of pre-machine craftsmanship was moved by something of the sense that animated the builders of Chartres. The tapestry weavers! The potters! The makers of books! The wagonwrights! The ship-carvers! The shipwrights! The cabinetmakers! They were artists all. But the machine knows nothing of the spirit that hovered over Gobelin and Aubusson looms where priceless hangings were woven by craftsmen as poets weave sonnets from the strands of their imagination and insight. The machine knows only hurry mitigated by high wages and shoddy work done by sullen workmen.

*Eighth,* a machine economy makes commodities for sale rather than for use. Pre-machine methods of production and distribution were more elastic and more easily adaptable to the needs and tastes of the consumer than the methods of the machine age are. In the pre-machine age, the consumer told the producer what he wanted. In the machine age, the consumer must ask the producer what is being manufactured this season. In the pre-machine age, commodities were consciously adapted to the needs of the individual consumer. In the machine age, commodities are adapted to the technical necessities of the machine that makes them and to the economic necessities of the system that distributes them. In the pre-machine age, the number of commodities was relatively small, their character varied, their quality high. In the machine age, the number of commodities is large, their character tending towards uniformity rather than variety, their quality shoddy oftener than superior. In the pre-machine age, it was a matter of making commodities for consumers. In the machine age, it is a matter of finding consumers for commodities.

And, like the relentless mechanization that is running the skilled craftsman out of the factory, this policy of production for sale rather than for use is running the skilled shop-keeper out of the store. The pre-machine shop-keeper, who was an artist in the selection of goods intimately adapted to the needs and tastes of his immediate clientele, gives way to the mere salesman, who is an expert in getting rid of the flood of goods that flows from the machine. The store of the pre-machine age was dominated by the customer's need of services. The store of the machine age is dominated by the manufacturer's need of sales. The store becomes a mere adjunct to the factory. The colorful apothecary of the pre-machine age, to take a random instance, gives way to a clicking automat in the midst of the miscellany of a modern drug store.

*Ninth,* a machine economy finds its progress dogged by a problem of unemployment of its own making. In the pre-machine age, more work meant more workers. The aim of a machine economy is to do more work with fewer workers. Its major symbol is a machine with which one man can do the work it took ten men to do before, with the dream in the distance of a virtually manless factory. When the machine that can do the work it has before taken ten men to do appears, one may stay behind to tend the machine, but the other nine must look elsewhere for employment, and probably have a hard time finding it, unless leadership has looked ahead for them. Even before the onset of drastic depression, the machine was taking one hundred thousand workers off the payroll annually in the United States. Industries decrease the number of men employed while they increase the amount of business done. Thus the machine economy confronts its workers chronically with the situation that confronted the workers acutely when machinery was first introduced into production and the factory system founded.

It is assumed in some quarters that, in view of the rising importance of distribution in a machine economy, the bulk of the workers who lose their jobs to machines can be absorbed in the enterprises of distribution. Many of the workers who have been displaced by machines in the United States during the last decade have gone over from production either to the distribution or to the servicing of machines and other manufactured products, but to assume that distribution will offer a permanent city of refuge to the victims of the machine is short-sighted. For one thing, thousands of these displaced workers will not be adapted either by native capacity or by training for distribution. And, then, the increase in the cost of the average article from the time it leaves the producer until it reaches the consumer is so great that the retail world will be under an increasing pressure to reduce the costs of distribution. We may count upon it that the genius of the retail world will exhaust its ingenuity in finding ways and means to reduce rather than increase its personnel. The ratio of workers to work is destined to go progressively downward in distribution as in production.

This technological unemployment is not as concentrated or as dramatic as the unemployment that attended the beginning of the Industrial Revolution and the founding of the factory system, but, as far as individual workers are concerned, the new unemployment is just as serious as the old unemployment that led enraged workers to wreck the machines that had thrown them out of work.

*Tenth,* a machine economy breeds class antagonisms. The class cohesions and the class conflicts of the modern West are not due to the natural cussedness of man but to the natural character of the machine. In the pre-machine age, workers were, by and large, skilled, unorganized, and contented. In the machine age, workers are, by and large, unskilled, organized, and discontented. The hand workers were, in the main, contented because their work was a pleasant medium of self-expression, while the conditions under which they worked were fairly satisfactory and wholly under their control. The machine workers are, in the main, discontented because their work is not a pleasant medium of self-expression, but only an unpleasant means of self-support, while the conditions under which they work are relatively unsatisfactory and not at all under their control. These craft discontents with the character and conduct of machine employment have inspired class-conscious organizations of the workers. This class-conscious organizations of employees have called into being class-conscious organizations of employers. And periodically these rival organizations clear the deck for tests of strength. In the pre-machine age, men were members of society. In the machine age, men are members of an occupational group. And it tends more and more to be a group that will not hesitate to act against the general interests of society if the particular interests of the group are at stake. Class warfare is thus one by-product of a machine economy.

*Eleventh,* a machine economy degrades the taste of its people. The contagious vulgarity of the machine age not only despoils the countryside and defiles the factories in which it carries on its toil but desecrates the products it fashions. And the shoddy and ugly output of the machine carries on a constant education in bad taste. As we have mechanized the processes of production, we have run beauty out of business and compelled it to take refuge in the side streets of the world in the obscure shops of craftsmen who are wistful survivors of an age in which artisans aspired to be artists. Machine man haunts antique shops and pays absurd prices for ancient articles in a pathetic effort to prove that he can at least appreciate a beauty he is no longer capable of producing.

Nature seems to consider beauty worth something for its own sake. Only machine man seems to think that ugliness must accompany utility. Nature will lavish her genius upon an effort to make beautiful in form and radiant in color a common radish that grows underground and has only a brief fling in daylight before it is eaten. Pre-machine man seems to have caught some of this sense of the æsthetic from nature. He pursued his varied crafts in the conviction that the things he made might rightly have values beyond their market value. If machine man were playing God in the garden, he would probably think it an unjustified waste to squander so much artistry on a radish, feeling that so much effort for beauty should be saved for something at least as important as the Painted Desert, the Grand Canyon, or, better still, a summer sunset that could distribute its beauty to millions of consumers in one operation, thus economizing in overhead effort. It is in this spirit that machine man administers the basic process of production.

*Twelfth,* a machine economy encourages wastefulness in the rank and file of its people. It encourages wastefulness in two ways: (1) People do not respect the easily replaceable products of the machine as they respected the sound and durable output of the handicraftsman. The housewife does not mind breaking an earthen crock or jar. They are cheap. The Kentucky Colonel will waste a whole box of matches on one stubborn stogie. They are cheap. The housewife's crock and the Kentucky Colonel's matches are not, in themselves, important, but they are symbols of the attitude of the machine age towards its products. They are more than symbols; they are seeds of wasteful habits that grow until they hold sway over larger and more significant areas in the economic life of individual and of nation. (2) The machine economy, when it is equipped and geared for mass output, must have mass consumption to absorb its products, and it resorts to high-pressure salesmanship to foist them upon the people, whether they answer genuine needs or not, using the commercial seduction of annual models and a hundred allied devices to lure the people to buy when no valid necessity prompts them. When the machine is god, waste must be the religion of his worshipers.

*Thirteenth,* a machine economy creates bad citizens while it is creating bad commodities. Machine man notoriously lacks a sustained interest in the good management of his government. Little more than half of the qualified voters of the United States, for instance, take the trouble to cast their ballots in normal elections. Pre-machine man brought a sense of initiative and the saving grace of self-reliance to his work. He had to. There was no one to order and to organize his work for him. He was an independent individual with creative responsibility. Machine man has no such compulsion to initiative and self-reliance. His work is ordered and organized for him. He finds that too much initiative may interrupt the smooth and standardized routines of modern industry. And he finds but intermittent need for self-reliance. Every move is plotted for him. And, like pre-machine man, his work-shop is a school in which he forms the habits alike of thought and of action that he carries over into every other field. A machine economy cannot train men to dependence in their working hours and expect them to display in-dependence in their voting hours. We cannot enforce self-renunciation in industry and expect self-reliance in government. We cannot deify the boss in industry and dethrone the boss in politics. Subservient workers mean subservient voters. The machine in industry means the machine in politics.

*Fourteenth,* a machine economy transforms man from a self-helpful into a self-helpless creature. Machine man has standardized and mechanized so many things that pre-machine man had to initiate and improvise that he has become spectator instead of participator in the life of his time. Pre-machine man was a skilled craftsman. Machine man is an unskilled machine tender. Pre-machine man drew and painted. Machine man takes snapshots. Pre-machine man played the flute and the fiddle. Machine man listens to talking machines and turns on the radio. Pre-machine man wrote and acted folk plays. Machine man goes to the movies. He leads a pre-digested breakfast food life.

During office hours, machine man is singularly self-sufficient and readily resourceful. After office hours, he is pathetically dependent upon bought-and-paid-for amusement. He is helpless in the face of an idle hour. Diversion means to him a ticket to something, laughter a thing induced by a salaried clown, and music a seat at the opera. Machine man develops a grandstand mind. Pre-machine man won games. Machine man watches games. An American football game dramatizes the tendency of machine man to buy his pleasure instead of brewing it in his own brain and backing it with his own muscle. Seventy-two thousand Americans watching twenty-two husky youngsters play up and down the gridiron! Twenty-two playing to win! Seventy-two thousand paying to watch! This spectatorism spreads far beyond the realm of sports.

Machine man lacks self-reliance in his leisure because he does not practice self-reliance in his labor. Pre-machine man was a marvel of all-round self-helpfulness. Machine man is a marvel of self-helplessness. He is self-reliant only within the radius of his specialisms. A random dozen of pre-machine men could take adequate care of themselves if stranded on a deserted island. They could run up pretty creditable houses and improvise a pretty creditable civilization with rare readiness. What would be the fortune of a dozen machine men, so long dependent upon machinery that they had forgotten how to do the many things that pre-machine men had to do daily, if they were similarly stranded? Would the operative from a modern cotton mill be able to make cloth for the stranded company? Would the hand from a modern shoe factory be able to furnish the ship-wrecked dozen with shoes? Would the man who works in a modern factory that turns out machine-made pottery be able to turn out earthen bowls for the colony?

The machine economy has conspired to relieve us of the

necessity of working out our own salvation as individuals in the ordering of our work, the cultivation of our minds, and the amusement of our spirits. The diet of civilization has had a destructive influence on our teeth. By substituting the refined fare of civilized man for the rough fare of the savage, we have made things easier for our teeth, but we have induced their progressive deterioration in the process. In like manner, the machine economy is making things easier and easier for our minds. We began by making machines do our manual work for us. We are beginning to delegate much of our mental work to various mechanisms. Our brains may, as Dean Inge whimsically suggests, go the way of our teeth. Self-sufficiency is everywhere the price of survival. And the machine subtly robs man of his self-sufficiency. In many ways, machine man is coddled, where pre-machine man was challenged.

*Fifteenth,* a machine economy breeds the menace of the multi-millionaire. The machine compels the integration of industry. The intergration of industry throws money and might into the hands of the captains of industry. And the captains of industry, with the winning cards of power in their hands, tend to dictate the culture of the age. It is not alone an indirect influence that the captains of industry exert upon the cultural tone of the age through the influence their industries have upon the temper of their workmen and the tastes of their customers; the captains of industry affect the culture of the time directly through the power of patronage and purchase. They buy newspapers and bend them to their liking. They endow universities and do not hide their feelings about the temperament and talk of recalcitrant professors. They lay bags of gold upon the altar and subtly suggest that their salaried divines be discreet. They see to it, with an almost super-human impartiality, that competing political parties have fat campaign funds, and then practice polite blackmail on the successful party, asking patronage and plums of varied sorts. Having paid the piper, what more logical than that they should call the tune! In a thousand ways they stick their fingers in the pie of public opinion. And thus are the dangers of a machine economy doubly compounded!

*Sixteenth,* a machine economy, marked by the characteristics and making for the results here listed, puts even the material advantages it creates in constant jeopardy by the way in which it inevitably subjects men (1) to the treachery of economic insecurity, and (2) to the terrorizing tragedy of mechanized war. A machine economy makes, in many ways, for the atmosphere and the actuality of insecurity, which, in the end, offset its gains. It holds over the minds of men in mid-maturity the fear that the ruthless demand of the machine for vitality will throw them on the human scrap heap at an all too early age. It means an industrial system so interlocked and interdependent that a strike in a key industry, let us say, may at any time disrupt the whole social scheme of men's lives. It intensifies the hazard of accident. But, above all, it moves, with the inevitability of a Greek tragedy, towards a society-wide economic insecurity because machine production sooner or later results in over-production and the back-firing of the whole economic order. And, finally, a machine economy intensifies the pressures towards war, and, by its increasing perfection of the mechanisms of human slaughter, increases its peril alike to the citizen and to the social order. A machine economy must roam the world around in quest of raw materials, and in the roaming foments international dissension. And, when it has saturated its domestic markets, it must move heaven and earth to find foreign outlets for its over-production, even if this race for markets means war. The simpler human combat of the pre-machine age might conceivably be mitigated by codes to tone down its terrors, but warfare in the machine age shows an increasingly savage candor in its disregard of codes, and grows ever more ruthless and ruinous as its mechanization proceeds.

For our immediate purpose these sixteen counts may stand as constituting the indictment of a machine economy

# Mystic and Muckraker 315

as drawn by the realistic rebels. There are innumerable subsidiary counts that might be added, but they are, in the main, only elaborations or effects of these major charges. The sixteen charges I have here defined appear and re-appear, as I have said, throughout the anti-machine litera-ture of the West. The full indictment is rarely brought together by any single critic. Mr. Freeman's *Social Decay and Regeneration,* to which I have already referred, is an exception. All of the charges I have listed appear directly or by implication in the Freeman study, and with a richer attendance of detail than I have employed.

It will be seen that the realistic rebels share with the romantic rebels a nostalgia for the more leisurely life and the lovelier products of a handicraft economy. A strain of emotional resentment creeps into their analyses, and keeps them, at times, I think, from giving the devil of mechanism its due. But, for all that, the realistic rebels do descend to details and give us an indispensable, if at certain points exaggerated, picture of the profoundly revolution-ary effect the machine has had upon the life of Western man.

From their indictment we see that the social *milieu* of Western man is undergoing rapid and revolutionary trans-formation, with science and technology as the agents of its change. In America, at any rate, it is obvious that the rise of a machine economy has altered the stage-setting of every fundamental social enterprise—religion, educa-tion, literature, art, family life, agriculture, labor, business, industry, finance, and politics. The machine has so thor-oughly remade the *milieu* of the contemporary American that it is quite impossible for a man wisely and effect-ively to rear a family or run a government, practice a pro-fession or preach a gospel, conceive a philosophy or con-duct a business, unless he has caught something of the inner meaning of this machine economy, because, for good or for ill, the whole of life on this continent takes its cue from the machine. Machine industry is the living background of every American enterprise. It colors and controls both the way Americans live and the way they make their living. It dominates alike the business order and the social order.

An inquiry into the present tendencies and probable future of the machine order and its social implications is not, therefore, merely a pleasant pastime for professional observers in ivory towers remote from the rough-and-tumble of the day. It is an intensely practical project that men of affairs cannot ignore and still lay claim to practicality. This is not an inquiry we dare leave to the casual curiosity of occasional publicists who may happen to attack segments of it. Our lives and our enterprises are too intimately involved in its issues for that. Physical science and industrial technology have transformed the *milieu* of Western man. This new *milieu* is in turn transforming all of his basic social enterprises. Western man must either control this new *milieu* or capitulate to it. And, clearly, he will never control it unless he takes the trouble to comprehend it. Happily the realistic rebels against the machine age have done much of the preliminary spade-work for his adventure in understanding. Such seems to me to be, in stark outline, the problem confronting Western man.

In a sober analysis of the amazing intricacy of the reactions of mechanism upon man, his environment, and his enterprises, Western man finds a possible clue to the comprehension of his new *milieu* and the control of his future. This clue is to be found, I think, in the one thing that stands out most clearly in the sixteen-sided indictment of the machine economy I have here summarized. Its major evils are not, in the judgment of the realistic rebels, chargeable to the malevolence of the industrial captains, but have arisen as inevitable by-products of the use of machinery for large-scale production. The technology of industry rather than the treason of industrialists is, in their rebel reasoning, the main source of our troubles. If this contention is true, in essence if not in full exactness, it offers a fruitful point of departure for speculation on the probable future of the socio-economic order of the West.

I say this because, if it be true that machine industry has dehumanized the Western social order through the inexorable effects of its technical operations rather than through the intentional exploitations of treasonable operators, Western man is emancipated from complete dependence upon the unselfishness and social insight that may or may not mark the industrial captains of the generations ahead. He may shift his inquiry into the probable future of his civilization from the unpredictable field of personal forces to the more predictable field of impersonal forces. Assuming, for the purpose of his inquiry, the soundness of this rebel contention, he may state the problem of his social future in terms of two divergent hypotheses: (1) If the technical operations of machine industry are to be the same in the future as they have been in the past, and if the social reactions of these technical operations are to be the same, the outlook for Western civilization is dark, and we are sentenced either to resignation or to revolt; (2) if, on the other hand, the machine industry of the future is likely to undergo profoundly revolutionary technological changes that will alter its physical locations and its functional operations, there is the chance that its social reactions upon man, his environment, and his enterprises may frustrate rather than fulfil the prophecies of the rebels.

I am quite willing to venture the judgment that inquiry will verify the second of these hypotheses. For this reason I think it important to consider carefully whether machine industry, with its interlocking processes of production and distribution, is now undergoing changes that may make the machine economy of the future potentially the creator of humanistic values as the machine economy of the past has been the creator of many anti-humanistic effects. Have the rebels overlooked important emergent factors in the industrial system? Are processes of self-correction at work in the machine order of the West? In what respect will a machine economy come of age probably differ from an adolescent machine economy? And how may we expect this difference to affect the outlook for Western man? It is to these basic questions I want now to turn.

# XI

# Humanism through Technology

ONE would have to be strangely insensitive to human values to face without blinking the factual allegations in the indictment that the mystics and muckrakers have made of the machine economy that came from the loins of the Industrial Revolution following the introduction of machine power into industry. Many of the assumptions made by the muckrakers respecting the ultimate significance of the disarrangement of the craft traditions and cultural modes of the pre-machine world are, I think, open to question, but it is indisputable that the Industrial Revolution left a black trail of bad results.

When the mystics and the muckrakers confine themselves to an objective analysis of the social reactions and readjustments involved in shifting from the handicraft to the machine economy, and do not go on to color their findings with the subjective temper of their social defeatism, the major counts in their indictment, as I have summarized them, may, I think, be admitted without material reservation. But this indictment has to do with the past of the machine economy. What about its future? We are not naïve enough to expect the machine to turn messiah, but we should subject its potentialities to as careful assessment as we have subjected its past performances before we presume to pass definitive judgment upon its ultimate significance for man.

To begin with, I think we may safely assume that the machine economy of the West will continue for the lifetime of all of us now living, and probably far beyond the lifetime of our children and of our children's children, barring its breakdown from causes not inherent in it, but external to it, notably from failure in the fields of social and economic statesmanship. No revolutionary power, adequate for its overthrow, is at the moment organized against it. The two polar opposites of contemporary revolution—Bolshevism and Fascism—are alike bent upon the extension rather than the extinction of the machine economy.

If the technological order of the West is to continue, we must face the problem of living with our machines. It is futile to talk of running away from them. We may become rebels in theory; we cannot become renegades in fact. There are not enough islands to accommodate all of us as isolate Robinson Crusoes. At least the more romantic of the Western converts to the anti-machine mood of the Eastern mind are, as the late Walter Rathenau called them, Shepherds of Arcady. Face to face with the admittedly anti-humanistic functioning of much of our machine economy, they counsel nothing more constructive than a cowardly retreat into an Arcadian simplicity of life which none save a select few of the saints and seers of any generation will adopt. It is at least more sportsmanlike, I think, to buckle down to the business of trying to wrest health and happiness and to win security and serenity from our machine economy for the millions of men and women throughout the West who will not and cannot run away from the modernism of the machine age to the mediævalism of some private paradise.

Two major philosophies are battling for control of the future of Western civilization. One is the philosophy of the social mystic. The other is the philosophy of the engineer. If I may use terms with a confessed looseness in order to heighten the contrast I want to draw, the philosophy of the social mystic is symbolized by Mahatma Gandhi, and the philosophy of the engineer by Henry Ford. André Siegfried, in his *America Comes of Age,* recognized the tussle that is going on between these two philosophies when, after contending through more than three hundred and fifty pages that the machine economy of the United States is pitting the material against the mental, the mass against the man, he ended his singularly incisive study by saying, "So the discussion broadens until it becomes a dialogue, as it were, between Ford and Gandhi."

I am quite aware of the caustic criticisms that have lately been leveled against the practical operations of these two symbolic figures. I have listened to American observers, returning from India, describe the financing of the Gandhi movement as a glorified racket or squeeze. And I have gone ear-weary listening to indictments of the employment policies of the Ford industries. But, in terms of their announced philosophies, it is interesting to speculate on what might be said if the fair-skinned Henry Ford sat down to talk with the dark-skinned Mahatma Gandhi either in the nerve-racking roar of Ford's factory or under the sedative hum of Gandhi's spinning wheel. Let me try my hand at guessing the gist of their colloquy.

At first glance, Ford and Gandhi would seem poles apart. Gandhi is the uncompromising foe of the machine economy. Ford is its ardent apostle. Gandhi considers mechanization the mortal enemy of mankind. Ford considers it the mighty emancipator of mankind. To Gandhi, the machine is a tyrant to be dethroned. To Ford, it is a tool to be developed. Certainly, two such antithetic spirits could find little common ground from which to survey the Sphinx riddle of the Western future!

At second glance, however, Ford and Gandhi would seem in surprising agreement on the humanistic objectives of a sound work economy. Both agree that a defensible labor system must, directly or by indirection, augment the leisure, affirm the dignity, and assure the independence of the worker. Both agree that no system is sound that freezes the spirit of the worker with the fear of the insecurity of employment. Both agree that the worker should be given opportunity to express creatively the best he may have of knowledge, artistry, and insight, that the tasks of labor should be adapted to the talents of the laborer, although Ford's estimate of the eager capacity of the average worker to go beyond routine might be lower than the Mahatma's estimate. Both agree that the intrinsic quality of a product should be its chief credential and its most convincing appeal. Both agree that any system is subject to severe indictment that compels mankind to devote its major energies and most of its time to the primary task of providing itself with food, clothing, and shelter. Both agree that the Industrial Revolution left many social maladjustments in its wake. Both agree that the machine has been master of man, and that man must become master of the machine.

At third glance, Ford and Gandhi would be seen to part company as they began to discuss ways and means of achieving these humanistic objectives upon which they agree, Gandhi going the way of the social mystic, Ford going the way of the engineer. Gandhi would run away from the technologic age, smash the machines, go back to hand production, and simplify life generally. Ford would seek to bend the technologic age to human purpose, develop the machines to the limit, and try to emancipate the human spirit through mechanization rather than to emancipate it from mechanization. He would use the machines to gain higher wages, shorter hours, and greater economic security. Through an ever-increasing efficiency of production and distribution, he would strive so to lower prices that the conquest of the simple necessities of life might become, for the average man, a minor rather than a major concern. Ford and Gandhi agree that industry should be decentralized. Both would take industry back to the villages and coördinate it with farming, so that men could alternate between their industrial crafts and the cultivation of the soil, but Gandhi would do it by installing the ancient spinning wheel and hand-loom in the farmer's cottage, while Ford would do it by putting little factories on the rivers of the rural regions for the making of carburetor valves, generator cut-outs, and magneto parts for his cars.

As seen in their announced philosophies, Gandhi is not more keenly aware of the perils of the machine age than Ford is, but Ford, I think, is more keenly aware of the promise of the machine age than Gandhi is. In the preceding chapter, I presented sixteen observations on the past of our machine economy from the Gandhi point of view. In this chapter, I want to present certain counter-observations on the future of our machine economy from the Ford point of view. I do not mean, by this, to imply a wholesale commendation of Ford or a wholesale condemnation of Gandhi. In many ways the West needs the gadfly ministry of a Gandhi, and in many ways the theories and practices pursued in the Ford industries neither accurately represent the character of the majority of the machine industries of the West nor adequately reflect the ultimately possible humanism of a machine economy. I use the names of Gandhi and Ford to distinguish the divergent points of view I am discussing only because they happen to symbolize more vividly than any other names that intense belief and that intense disbelief in mechanization I am trying to compare and to evaluate.

I am by temperament and by training a democrat, with the democrat's distrust of concentrated power. Instinctively I belong with the rebels against the machine age rather than with its rooters. Gandhi's idyllic picture of the independent and pleasantly paced life of the handicraftsman warms my heart more than the gray silhouette of a Ford factory against a winter sky. I have no direct stake in the industrial system of my time. I am at most its beneficiary by indirection. If, therefore, I see certain beacon fires of hope for mankind shining through the smoke of its factories, it cannot justly be charged to wishful thinking or traced to a vested concern. I have a far greater temperamental affinity to Henry Thoreau than to Henry Ford, but I have a profound respect for facts, whether they affirm or annihilate my preconceptions, and the facts I have been forced to face, particularly during the last dozen years, have driven me to the conclusion that the machine economy of the West, doubted by Eastern mystics and derided by Western muckrakers, may be made humanity's most effective instrument of emancipation and enrichment, if socio-economic leadership does not, through muddling and mismanagement, permanently cancel, as it has periodically halted, the potential contribution of the machine to a man-centered civilization.

The Western industrialist may, in my judgment, write a new Magna Charta for mankind. This new Magna Charta, if it emerges from theory to exist in practice, will be largely an unintentional by-product of the Western industrialist's enterprise in invention and organization. He has not set consciously out to create a humane social order. He has, on the contrary, been all too often singularly unconcerned with the social implications of his practices. But in his very eagerness for excess profits he has, without conscious intent, elaborated a technique of social emancipation. The old Magna Charta, wrested from King John by the commoners, meant the conquest of despotism. The new Magna Charta, implicit in a socially minded management of a machine economy, will mean the conquest of drudgery. The old Magna Charta was won by the social insistence of great mobs. The new Magna Charta may be won by the social inventiveness of great manufacturers.

A great industrialist of the West has said that "hard labor is for machines, not for men." Here are eight short and simple words. There are no polished phrases in this sententious sentence. And yet, unless I am far afield in judgment, the germs of a new civilization are hidden in it. There are a hundred unwritten Iliads in it. There is the birthright of a new Shakespeare in it. It is the charter for new art galleries. It foreshadows a new birth and an undreamed extension of education. There is unreleased music in it. It prophesies for common men a leisure hitherto enjoyed only by the rich and the royal. It opens a road to freedom to Egyptian fellah, Chinese coolie, and Russian peasant, no less than to the American toiler. It is an emancipation proclamation for child laborers the earth around. It is a sort of secular *Let there be light* for a new kind of world.

All this sounds, I know, a bit lyrical in a book that seeks seriously to analyze our machine civilization, but I mean it as the soberest of sober sense. The flowerings of literature and art and music, of all the things that give grace and distinction to life, of all the more elusive social and spiritual values, for which the rebels against the machine age hunger, sink their roots in the soil of economics. I do not mean to say that wealth is the sure parent either of worthy art or of widespread happiness. My contention is simpler than that, and, I think, truer. It is that, while poverty has spurred many men to great art and to high achievement, drudgery has not such claims to enter. Poverty may prod men; drudgery poisons them. And the emancipation of mankind from drudgery can, as I see it, come only through a further and finer development of the much abused machine economy.

I am willing to grant to Mahatma Gandhi and to his Western converts that to date the machine economy has much to its discredit. It has too often subjected men to a new and more terrible drudgery of soul-killing speed of work. Its savings have not always been put to work for the improvement of its service. It has sometimes been guilty of the short-sighted policy of paying its men the least they would stand for and charging its customers the most they would stand for. It has admittedly made for the mushroom growth of congested industrial cities ill fitted to serve as homes for the human spirit. It has set going forces that have subtly disintegrated the spirit of craftsmanship. It has too often made monotony, routine, and haste the common lot of Western workmen. It has turned men's minds too often to quantity when it might have exalted quality. It has frowned upon variety and preached uniformity in the name of economy and in the interest of profit. It has exiled beauty and enthroned ugliness in the name of utility. It has all too often produced for sale rather than for use. And so on to the end of an indictment the facts compel us to admit.

But these must, I think, be judged as sins of a pioneer period. The machine economy of the West is a mere fledgling among the social schemes of history. It is less than two hundred years old. The more revolutionary effects of machine production upon the social order began to register well within the memory of men now living. Most of the sins of this pioneer period are, I think, destined to disappear as the machine economy reaches its maturity. Many of them are, in fact, disappearing, and disappearing more rapidly than the casual onlooker is likely to think. And they are disappearing, not because manufacturers have received a sudden baptism of brotherly love, but simply because it is becoming daily more evident that these sins are bad business and effective barriers to profit.

At the present juncture in Western affairs, the masses have more to hope for from great engineers, great inventors, and great industrial statesmen than from the social reformers who woo them with their panaceas. The soundest social progress of the next half-century, granted decently intelligent economic leadership, will come as a by-product of technical progress. The most potent social revolutionists of the next half-century are likely to be the more far-sighted of the great manufacturers, the more productive of the great inventors, and the more professionally unhampered of the great engineers.

That the true champions of the masses are the engineers

and inventors rather than the social reformers is brilliantly
argued by Count Richard Nicholas Coudenhove-Kalergi
in his *Apologie der Technik*. The real emancipations of
the last century and a half, as this singularly critical intelligence sees them, have not been the conscious achievements of social reform so much as the unconscious
by-products of technical advance. Societies for the prevention of cruelty to animals had done much to ameliorate the
lot of the horse, but it remained for the inventor of the
automobile really to emancipate the horse from undue toil
and unnecessary suffering. The galley slaves of the older
era were not freed by fervent abolitionists, but by the cool-
headed inventor of the marine engine. Socially minded
legislation has done much to make the life of the seamen
more livable, but the use of fuel oil represents a very real
emancipation from the inferno of the stoke-hole.

The engineer and the inventor, no less than the social
reformer, are engaged in a war of human liberation. They
may not be always aware of the war they are waging, but
they are waging it nevertheless, for the ultimate goal of
technical progress is to make available to the masses the
comforts and conveniences that are now the exclusive
privilege of the millionaires. In waging this war, however, the techniques of engineer and inventor differ from
the techniques of the social reformer. While the social
reformers are fighting wealth, the engineers and the inventors are fighting want. The engineers and the inventors,
like the social reformers, are working to make wealth,
power, leisure, beauty, and happiness the heritage of all,
but, while the social reformers are fighting the slave
drivers, the engineers and the inventors are fighting
slavery.

"A high standard of living," says Coudenhove-Kalergi,
concluding the argument I have here paraphrased, "is of
more real value than equality. It is better for all to be
prosperous and a few to be rich than for all to sink back
to a common level of poverty. Best of all, of course, would

be universal wealth. But that is an achievement for the future, and only technical progress can bring it about."

If I thought the pioneer sins of our machine economy were incurable, I should throw up the sponge, buy a spinning wheel, and join the Gandhis. If I thought these sins were curable, but that their cure could be effected only by reformers from the outside, I should be tempted, could I gain their consent, to bundle my wife and son into a seaworthy vessel and emigrate to some idyllic island in the South Sea, if any such island has escaped the ravages of the romancer, for the complexity of the machine economy is so great, the articulation of its varied forces and factors so delicate, that I doubt the capacity of the lay reformer to captain its regeneration. He might wreck it, but I doubt that he could reform it and keep it a going concern. At least I have no desire to live through the muddle of such experimentation. And, finally, if I thought these sins were curable by the industrialists themselves, but that hope of their cure within my lifetime depended upon the epidemic sweep of a new and unique unselfishness through the business ranks, I should quickly surrender my belief in the potential humanism of the machine economy.

I have tethered my hopes to a stronger stake. My hopes respecting the future of our machine economy rest neither upon outside reformers nor upon any internal reform of the human nature of business men, which, I suspect, has not changed materially since the aboriginal Indians passed their wampum from hand to hand. My hopes rest, rather, upon the belief that the steady advance of science and technology plus an increasingly intelligent search, upon the part of business men and industrialists, for the most efficient, most profitable, and most consistently dependable forms of organization, processes of production, and methods of distribution will correct most of the existing evils of the machine economy and make for a stable and significant socio-economic order.

I am not overlooking the fact that faulty economic policy

in the politico-business world generally can nullify even the most constructive results of a technical system of production and distribution. I shall discuss at length, in the succeeding chapter, the peculiar dependence of the machine order upon the economic order. I believe, however, that, as it becomes increasingly clear that flaws in the general economic policies of a people can bring to a standstill businesses and industries that are, in themselves, magnificently managed, the socio-economic outlook of business and industrial leadership will inevitably broaden, and that intelligently selfish interest will foster rather than fight sound social and economic policies. The argument of intelligent self-interest will acquire increasing validity as the machine economy matures. It was a doubtful doctrine before the later days of the machine economy, for the penalties of unintelligent self-interest were not so devastating as now. As heads of industries halted by the current depression can testify, the tone and temper and health of the socio-economic order in general is the soil in which the enterprises of the industrialists must grow, and upon the thinness or fertility of this soil the success or failure of their separate ventures depends. In the sensitively intricate technological economy we have elaborated, the dependence of the machine order upon the economic order is such that the industrialist must either turn statesman or go bankrupt. The pressures will be powerful upon him to turn statesman in the generation ahead.

I do not want to be understood as cavalierly ignoring the legitimate rôle of the lay reformer. In my anxiety for emphasis, I have drawn a rather severe antithesis between the politico-social reformers, on the one hand, and the engineers, inventors, and industrial captains, on the other. I mean only that the politico-social reformer cannot, in my judgment, alone correct the manifest maladjustments of the machine economy and make it a mainstay instead of a menace to a sound and satisfying social order. Reform is, in one important respect, like revolution. Revolution never quite succeeds in any sweeping sense until it captures the army. In like manner, political or social reform, to be realistically effective, must be the ally, not the antagonist, of technical advance and economic power. The paradox of progress in the machine age is that liberalism cannot succeed without the support of the conservatives. And, happily, circumstances are maturing, I think, under which economic power will realize that it is to its own best interest to have the forces of science and technology directed by principles that make for a humanistic social order.

As the complexity and interdependence of the machine economy increase, and as large-scale industry becomes further dependent upon the confidence and economic capacity of the masses, sound social policy will more and more prove the surest support of legitimate self-interest for the industrialist. This fact may result in a surprising shift in the relative positions of the reformers and the reactionaries. The army of reform has hitherto been recruited from men outside the ranks of industrial management and economic power, that is to say, from sideliners. The owners and operators of the industrial system have been an ultra-conservative force consistently resisting what has, again and again, later proved sound politico-social reform. These conservative captains of the machine order, like the liberals in opposition, acquired stereotyped dogmas and fell into the habit of standardized reactions to social criticism and social change. But it is a chastened industrial mind that faces the future! The impact of drastic depression has, in fact, broken down the socio-economic dogmatism of the conservative captains of Western industrialism more than it has shaken the inherited patter and patterns of politico-social liberalism. Much of contemporary liberalism still lingers in the latter half of the nineteenth century, speaking the language of a generation and an order of life that are gone forever, whether their having gone is a matter to mourn or to make merry over.

Every system, if it is to keep its controlling policies

progressively adjusted to its changing problems, must
maintain a searching and sustained self-criticism. Until
now Western industrialism has been something less than
self-critical. Fair weather makes for complacency. And
until lately the economic weather has been, for the most
part, fair for a good run of years. Foul weather makes for
self-criticism. In the case of Western industrialism, however, the minor squalls of foul weather that have come
with perplexing periodicity throughout the history of the
capitalistic industrialism of the West failed to induce
anything like an adequately self-critical mood. In earlier
phases of depression, the captains of Western industrialism
have uniformly declined to admit that any critical reconsideration of its basic policies and broad relationships
was called for. To jail its critics as "damned radicals" was
all too often industrialism's answer to criticism. Western
industrialism was the spoiled child of a cocksure capitalism.
To-day this cocksureness is gone! To-day, instead of send-
ing its critics to jail, industrialism is studying their criticisms. To-day intelligent industrialists are less concerned
to prosecute radicals than to prevent radicalism by removing incentives to it, admitting, with a candor unprecedented,
that the only sure prevention of radicalism lies in making
Western industrialism serve the masses better than any
alternative economy can serve them.

The West has moved definitely out of the age of a
small-scale-enterprise economy into the large-scale age of
a machine economy. This machine economy is a magnificent, but hitherto misdirected, social instrument. The
strength of Western industrialism has been its frank acceptance of the inevitability of the large-scaleness of the
machine age; its weakness has been its tardy recognition
of the fact that a machine economy cannot survive save
at the price of making the welfare of the consuming masses
its first concern. The strength of Western liberalism has
been its unwavering insistence that the industrial system
must serve humanistic ends; its weakness has been and is

that, at heart, it has never quite accepted the inevitability of the large-scaleness of the machine age. Liberalism still looks wistfully over its shoulder at the age of a small-scale-enterprise economy. Its effectiveness in the crucial quarter-century just ahead will depend upon its catching step with the forces of historic inevitability that make and move the machine age. Western industrialism and Western liberalism alike face a judgment day.

If Western industrialism, under the pressure of necessity, comes fully to realize that its survival depends upon its service to the masses, and sets consciously and comprehensively out to make available to them the wages, the hours, the prices, the leisure, the security, and the self-respect which alone can make them a consistently dependable market for its multitudinous goods and services, and if Western liberalism continues to buck the historic process by trying to legislate the West back into the small-scale-enterprise economy of the nineteenth century, then we may see, as I have suggested, a surprising shift in the relative positions of the reformers and the reactionaries. The erstwhile conservative captains of Western industrialism may become the most potent agents of mass-benefiting social change, with Western liberalism, sound in its humanistic emphasis, but obscurantist in its practical politics of socio-economic adjustment.

But I am getting ahead of my story. It is not the alteration of outlook that necessity is enforcing upon the more far-sighted owners and operators of Western industry I want mainly to consider here. I want rather to point out some of the ways in which the machine economy of the West is effecting and will effect a self-correction of the more seriously anti-humanistic results that have marked its pioneer phase, the correction coming as an incidental by-product of technical advance and a scientific search for the soundest and most profitable ways of doing business. I shall do little more than suggest a few illustrative tendencies, for, as I have said earlier, I am not attempting to write a comprehensive treatise on Western civilization, but to set down a secular confession of faith respecting certain social tendencies of the present and certain social techniques for the future, introducing only as much objective material as may be necessary to give body and point to my affirmations. I shall discuss six such tendencies and techniques now manifest.

Let me speak, first, of the technological forces making possible an extensive self-correction of the admittedly anti-humanistic results following the excessive centralization of industry involved in the establishment and evolution to date of the factory system. The politico-social reformers have sought to relieve or remove the bad social effects of industrial centralization through reform movements originating outside and opposed by the rank and file of the captains of Western industrialism. I do not minimize their devoted and determined efforts. They have written laudable factory legislation into our statutes. They have brought corporate self-protection to the factory worker through trade unionism. They have zoned cities as if to quarantine the industrial disease in segregated districts. They have put potted plants on the window ledges of work-shops. Seeing that the human spirit, either through lack of free energy or lack of free opportunity, was not kicking up its heels as it should in our industrial cities, they have organized recreation. The city planners have knocked at the doors of the captains of industry, asking them to make their factory sections high-lights instead of smudges in the municipal picture. Slum after slum has surrendered before the onslaught of the crusader. The reformers have purified and policed one unhappy spot after another. But the results of these political and social reform movements have been distressingly piecemeal and transient. Only at the price of eternal vigilance have the gains of reform movements been conserved and continued. And the reform passion itself has been pathologically periodic. It has risen and fallen. And, with the rapid growth of machine production, as fast as one spot has been made fair, another has been fouled by some new and brash industrial development.

It is important to inquire into the causes of this transiency of reform results. They have been transient, I suggest, because, during the pioneer phase of the machine economy, it has been technologically imperative that large-scale industry be highly centralized. There are human disadvantages inseparable from excessive industrial centralization, but, as long as it is technologically imperative that industry centralize, industry will centralize, and continue to create these human disadvantages faster than any outside reform agency can correct them. This fact has been increasingly evident during the last twenty-five years. And this has dampened the earlier optimism of the reformers. Seeing the fleeting character of so much of their reform, many critics of the Western industrial order have thrown up their hands, and turned either to a philosophy of social revolution, as in Russia, or to a philosophy of spiritual resistance, as in India. Disillusioned with the flare-and-fade results of their Fabian tactics, they have enlisted under Stalin's banner of assault or Gandhi's banner of abstention.

But, just as the missioners of social progress begin to despair of controlling the evils of industrial centralization, the makers of technical progress come within sight of a solution. Technical advance in the field of motive power promises to reduce, if not ultimately remove, the social blight of industrial centralization by making centralization unnecessary and unprofitable. We are to-day technologically in the twilight zone between an old machine industry that has rested on steam power and a new machine industry that will rest on electric power. And between the two there is this significant difference. In a machine industry resting on steam power, the worker must go to the power. In a machine industry resting on electric power, the power can be taken to the worker. We are witnessing the emancipation of the machine economy from slavery to stationary power into the freedom of transmissible power. An industrial system driven by stationary motive power must centralize. An industrial system with transmissible motive power at its disposal may decentralize. This single technological achievement of transmissible power is destined radically to transform the machine industry of the West, and profoundly to alter by indirection the character of the machine civilization which has drawn the fire of the mystic and the ire of the muckraker.

In an age of stationary power, industries locate their factories at the sources, or within easy and economic reach of the sources, of their motive power. In an age of transmissible power, industries will tend to locate their factories at the sources of their raw materials. Industries that use more sorts of raw materials than are available in any one place cannot, of course, go all the way with this tendency, but, with transmissible power, industries will operate as near as possible to the sources of their raw materials, establishing themselves in convenient regional locations where diverse raw materials involved in their operation can be readily assembled without shipping them across the continent or from the ends of the earth. For some time, there will be many gradations of decentralization, but decentralization will be the goal towards which Western industry will inevitably move.

With transmissible power at its disposal, Western industry will ultimately stop the manufacture of all parts of complicated machines in vast industrial centers, fabricating them instead in smaller factories located at the sources of the raw materials of the respective parts. For a transition period, the length of which will depend upon the tempo of technological progress, vast industrial centers may persist throughout the West as points at which parts, manufactured elsewhere, are assembled, and from which shipment is made to local markets. But ultimately these congested centers are likely to disappear even as points of assembly, for the practice of shipping parts to the very doorways of local markets will prove more profitable.

I do not mean that all industries will shift from steam to electricity as motive power, and that decentralization will get swiftly and sweepingly under way as technological progress in the field of electric power proceeds. There are many modifying factors in the situation. I need do no more than mention a few such factors to indicate the complexity of the problem and the limitations to which my generalization is subject.

Motive power and raw materials are not the only considerations that determine the location of industrial establishments. Accessibility to markets and to an adequate labor supply, among other things, must be taken into account. And for some time to come, if not, indeed, for all time to come, electricity may prove economically, if not technically, inapplicable to some industries. Electricity is, and may remain for an unpredictable future, more costly than coal in the smelting of ores for steel production, let us say, save under special circumstances, as in Norway, where there is an abundance of water power, a lack of coal supply, ample and easily available iron deposits. There seems little probability that the steel industry will decentralize within any reasonably near future. Other exceptions will appear on closer analysis.

The drift will undoubtedly be towards the decentralization of industry, but the shift from steam to electricity will be neither quick nor complete. We shall not retire some night citizens of the age of steam, and awaken the next morning citizens of the age of electricity. Steam and electricity will continue to interlock in the maturity of the machine economy. As in the case of the steel industry at Gary, great industries are to-day generating surplus electric power which, not needed in their own operation, is being distributed by the utility corporations. This is likely to increase rather than decrease among the great industries that do not follow the decentralizing trend. It may, indeed, increase to an extent that will make the matter of water power a less crucial issue than it is coming to seem in American politics. The air is filled with forecasts of the magic potentiality of water power as a source of electric energy. But there is, I suspect, only slight likelihood that water power will, for years to come, seriously compete with coal and oil in this respect. Half a century hence we shall, in all probability, find water power still a minor source of electric power, and steam-driven industry a major source.

If the production of surplus electric power by steam-driven industries increases with marked rapidity, the problem of the social control of public utilities will become a much broader and more complicated matter than it now appears to the political mind. For if the major part of a nation's supply of electric power is being generated as a by-product of industries, any scheme for the social control of the public utility corporations distributing the power will unavoidably involve a correlate control of the industries producing the power.

And, then, despite the anti-social effects of excessive industrial centralization, we may find a marked social resistance to decentralization. The steady migration of competence from country to city may mean more than a hunt for higher incomes. Maybe the superiority of small town and countryside as homes of the human spirit is half in the poet's eye. Maybe humanity, when faced with the possibility of getting away from congested cities, will rebel against a return to smaller centers. A social habit may be strong enough to set aside a technological force. When Charles Lamb was, for a time, exiled from the Fleet Street he loved, and sentenced to life in the country, he cried out, "Give me old London at fire and plague times rather than this healthy air, these tepid gales, these purposeless exercises." It may be that Western man has caught Lamb's love of the city. Ten thousand forces have been at work weaning him from village and farm and wedding him to the city, where genius congregates, where the conveniences of living are concentrated, where the fruits of the arts are garnered, where there is a sense of civilization stirring, where even the dullard catches some thrill from the throbbing life around him. What will happen when technological tendencies towards industrial decentralization meet cultural tendencies towards social centralization no one can now foretell with assured accuracy.

I do not presume to predict either the rapidity or the reach of the industrial decentralization made possible by the development of transmissible power. I merely record the fact that the emergence of electricity, natural and artificial gas, and other forms of transmissible power that may be discovered in the future, means the freeing of industry from the technical imperative to centralize. And as the technical imperative to centralize disappears, the economic imperative to centralize will disappear. The outlook is that, by the grace of transmissible power, we shall be able to carry on even our mass production operations more profitably in a decentralized than in a centralized industry by manufacturing parts in factories located at the sources of their raw materials and shipping the parts to the local market for assembly.

It has been assumed that we could not practice mass production without an intensive centralization of industry. From this assumption, many social reformers have argued that we could not remove the social disadvantages of centralization without renouncing mass production, and, knowing there is not the ghost of probability that we will renounce mass production and return to cottage industries, they have given up hope of correcting the evils of centralization save through a radical revolt against the machine economy itself. And, if the technical imperative to centralize should remain, and industrial decentralization be impossible save at the sweeping sacrifice of profits, it would be difficult to dodge the logic of their conclusion.

If I may summarize and generalize, through technologi-

cal developments in the generation, transmission, and sale
of electric power, and other forms of transmissible power,
the inventor, the engineer, and the industrial captain
promise to deal with the anti-humanistic results of centralization in a more radical fashion than is possible through
social reform measures. Social reform, through regulatory legislation, can do little more than ameliorate the ad-
verse effects of centralization. Technological reform,
through transmissible motive power, can remove the major
cause of centralization, and release rather than restrict the
energies of the machine economy in the process. When industry has been decentralized, the ugly social problems
created by industrial centralization must automatically
disappear. Thus the machine economy, in its maturity,
may cure the evils that the machine, in its adolescence,
created. Thus social progress may be realized as a by-
product of technical progress. Thus humanism may be
served by technology. On account of the modifying factors I have mentioned, and still others, an extensive decentralization of industry may be delayed or defeated. But,
if so, centralization and its attendant social disadvantages
cannot longer be charged to causes inherent in the machine
economy.

But there is more implied in this potential decentralization of industry than a negative atonement for the pioneer
sins of the machine economy. A decentralized industrialism would be found rich in unexploited positive advantages. It would, for instance, mean a wider geographical
spread of the economic advantages of mass production. In
the hands of a business and industrial leadership that will
exploit their full implications, mass production and mass
distribution may make possible four seemingly contradictory achievements at one and the same time: (1) higher
wages; (2) shorter hours; (3) lower prices; and (4)
larger total profits. These four factors, taken together,
form a more realistic foundation for social progress than
politico-social reform measures have ever been able to pro-

vide. Under a highly centralized mass production, however, the immediate personal benefits of three of these factors—higher wages, shorter hours, and larger total profits—come most richly to the great industrial centers. The factor of lower prices is not, of course, so confined. Under a widely decentralized mass production the immediate personal benefits of higher wages, shorter hours, and larger total profits would be spread throughout the nation. And, in so far as these benefits could be spread with fair uniformity throughout the nation, the national handicap of regional discontents would be materially minimized.

I do not want to make a greater claim for the social ministry of mass production and mass distribution than the facts warrant. Certainly to date the mass process has failed to father an economic millennium. The big business régime has not reduced the cost of living. It has raised the cost of living. For the average gainfully employed worker in the United States, in normal times, subsistence cost still tramples hard upon the heels of salary check. But this does not mean that the mass process has been tried and found wanting. It means only that its principle has not been applied comprehensively and administered comprehendingly. The fact is it is only here and there, in a few significantly managed industries, that the underlying philosophy of mass production and mass distribution is clearly understood and creatively applied. It is not accurate to assert that American industry is dominantly an industry of standardization, mass production, and mass distribution. It is a large-scale industry. But the few instances in which the full significance of standardization, mass production, and mass distribution has been worked out to date are little more than laboratory demonstrations of what these principles might mean to the nation as a whole, in reduced living costs and increased leisure, if they were comprehensively and comprehendingly applied to all phases of American industry which are properly subject to standardization, mass production, and mass distribution. By and large, the big business régime is, as yet, maladministering these processes. It is not malevolence but muddling that is responsible for this maladministration.

The wastes of mass selling are still largely absorbing the economies of mass production. Many American industries supposed to be practicing the principles of standardization, mass production, and mass distribution are in fact perverting them. Currently popular articles that promise quick profits are picked out for specialized manufacture, their basic materials are cheapened, their design stripped for economy rather than simplified for utility and beauty, factories geared for their fast production, and high-pressure sales campaigns put behind them. Their price is fixed as high as a sizeable traffic will bear. The wages of the workers who make them are kept as low as custom and trade union pressure will permit. And it is assumed that this is an authentic application of the mass process. This, however, is but a poor parody of its underlying principles.

Authentic mass production and mass distribution mean something quite different from this. The mass principle means specialization on articles that have the greatest possible value to the greatest number of people. Mass production, in the sense in which I use the term, does not follow the whims of the period or fall into step behind every will-o'-the-wisp of capricious fashion. It settles down to the business of meeting basic needs. And it centers its operation upon articles that answer measureably permanent needs and demands. It seeks the utmost simplicity of design consistent with utility and beauty. It declines to use other than durably excellent materials in manufacture. To these durably excellent materials it brings a high quality of workmanship. It strives to put such good materials and such good workmanship into its articles that their intrinsic quality will be their most cogent sales argument. It is unwilling to save money through shoddy production and waste money through sales pressure. It strives to put its price low that many may buy. It strives to put its wages high so that many may be able to buy.

It takes imagination, insight, and ingenuity on the part of the directing minds of a machine economy to see the logic and profit in the full sequence of principles that underlie standardization, mass production, and mass distribution. Short-sighted business leadership can go part of the way. Statesmanlike business leadership will go all of the way. When enough such leaders have demonstrated what authentic mass production and mass distribution mean, when the contagion of their success has caught widely on, and when transmissible power has spread the practice and the benefits of the mass process throughout the nation in a decentralized industrial régime, we of the West shall see how social progress can come as a by-product of technical progress.

I do not mean to say that the social advances I have suggested as being made possible by the technical development of transmissible power will come so automatically and inevitably that there will be no need of the directing hand of social statesmanship. If the transmissible power resources of the United States, during the next twenty-five years, become mere pawns in a game of financial manipulation, we shall miss many, if not most, of the rich social benefits that electric power can bring to American civilization, and we may find ourselves in the midst of a social revolt against the perversion of this significant social asset to purely financial ends. The generation, the sale, and the use of electric power represent a factor which, if wisely administered, can remake our machine civilization, redeeming it from many sins that have shamed it in the past. But we shall not see a wise administration of this new agency of social change unless the voice of the engineer and of the industrial captain dominate the voice of the financier alone in the development and control of power.

Another social advance that may be realized from the industrial decentralization made possible by technical advance is a functional correlation of industry and agriculture. It has been dinned into our ears that farm and factory must prosper together. This is an infectious slogan for political campaigns and commercial good-will tours into the hinterland, but farm and factory are not likely to prosper together until they work together. Agriculture, in its traditional enterprise, is functionally outside the formulas that foster prosperity in a machine economy. America will sink or swim according to its success or failure in making a go of its machine economy. One part of America, its agricultural part, is still outside the machine economy. This is not to say that agriculture does not use machinery. It does. As witness the vast mechanized industry of wheat-raising. But while farmers use machinery, agriculture as a national enterprise is neither organized nor operated in the spirit and by the formulas of the machine economy. Rural America is trying to lead a simple life in a complicated age, to hang onto hand production in a technological age, and to remain individualistic in a corporate age. And it is having a hard time to make ends meet. As I write, the part of America that has gone over bag and baggage to the machine economy, the industrial part, is not clipping coupons as it did in the dizzy days of our pathological prosperity. This does not, however, alter the fact that the failure or fortune of every phase of American life hinges upon its capacity to enter and to exert mastery over the processes of the machine economy. And, happily, technical advance is making it possible for the agricultural part of America to correlate with the industrial part of America and, with it, jointly to shoulder responsibility for converting technical progress into social progress. Permit me one illustration of this contention.

The agricultural regions of the United States are the source of many industrial raw materials, and increasingly so, as the industrial chemist annually finds new industrial uses for the main output and waste products of American farms. Corn, wheat, rye, flax, barley, cotton, wood, sawdust, cornstalks, straw, corncobs, cottonseed, husks, whey, and other designed and waste products of the farm are already being transformed by the industrial chemist into movie films, printer's ink, wallboard, dynamite, glue, floor covering, radio parts, substitutes for ivory, silk, leather, linen, marble, and so on through a long list of manufactured articles. The farmer of the pre-machine age fed the stomachs of the world only. The farmer of the machine age may feed the factories of the world as well. The farmer of the pre-machine age was a grower of foodstuffs only. The farmer of the machine age may be a producer of raw materials as well. The chemist, servant extraordinary of the machine economy, may, with his test tubes, lay the ghost of agricultural over-production by opening up to the farmer a whole new outlet for his products. This is a phase of development under the machine economy that may ameliorate the lot of the farmer quite apart from any decentralization of industry. If, in addition to this, transmissible power makes it possible ultimately to plant small factories throughout the agricultural regions of America, utilizing as raw materials much of the main output and most of the waste products of the American farm, we shall be able to absorb in these rural factories the present seasonal idleness of farm labor to an extent that will go far towards putting a sound economic foundation under agricultural regions without the succor of subsidy from the government, and, at the same time, introduce a new stabilizing factor into the industrial scene.

If Mahatma Gandhi had been listening to my contentions to this point, he might say, "Granted transmissible power may succeed in pushing the factory system out of the cities into the country, it will but spread the blight of standardization and factory routine over areas that have before been saved from it." This supposititious reaction of Gandhi raises the question of how much the current cry against standardization and routine is reality and how much rhetoric. I am by no means convinced that standard-

ization of production processes, with all the routine it implies, is the unmixed evil its critics assert. There is a case
for, as well as against, standardization.

I am quite aware of the deadening effect the monotonous
repetition of a specialized operation may have upon the
worker. It is true that the man who makes one-forty-
second of a watch may, unless he calls upon counteracting
factors, become one-forty-second of a watchmaker, for
standardized machine production does not demand or develop creative craftsmanship in the work immediately in
hand. But, taking the working world as a whole, the
average worker is not a suppressed artist champing at the
bit in eager impatience to express an artistic creativeness.
There is a vast amount of mediocrity in the human breed.
And, to the credit of machine production, let it be said
that it has given mediocrity its first chance to make a good
living, a better living, in fact, than the artist-craftsmen
of the pre-machine era made. As a waggish friend of
mine, with a gift of effective exaggeration, put it, the machine has given the moron his first chance to live like a
gentleman. The mediocre workman, thanks to the machine economy, has a cottage and a car. In a handicraft
régime, he would be living in a hovel and walking.

And, under the machine economy, as technological progress is perfecting it, I doubt that the craftsman blessed
with the creative urge will finally find himself so badly off.
The further development of mass production and mass
distribution will provide him with the two inestimable
boons of leisure and means. The higher wages, shorter
hours, and lower prices that mass production and mass distribution make possible will mean freedom and funds for
the workman whose spirit is bigger than the set task he
does at the factory. There is no reason why, with short
hours and high wages, a creative minded workman may not,
in a machine age, become as all-round a man as his craftsman predecessor in the Middle Ages. If he does not utilize his new leisure to such ends, he will have only himself

to blame. G. K. Chesterton persistently presses the contrast between the variety of craft-outlets and the all-roundedness of development of the man of the handicraft age and the narrowing specialization of work and worker in the machine age. "The peasant almost always runs two or three sideshows and lives on a variety of crafts and expedients," he says in his *The Outline of Sanity*. "The village shopkeeper will shave travellers and stuff weasels and grow cabbages and do half a dozen such things, keeping a sort of balance in his life like the balance of sanity in the soul. The method is not perfect; but it is more intelligent than turning him into a machine in order to find out whether he has a soul above machinery." If the factory worker were doomed to long hours and low pay, he might look with justifiable envy upon the independence of peasant and the versatility of shopkeeper, which marked the pre-machine era, even if the independence was slender and the versatility employed in the commonplace ventures of beard-cutting, weasel-stuffing, and cabbage-growing. It may be questioned, however, whether he is not better off to stand the gaff of a short day spent in even the most uninspiring repetitive labor of a factory if leisure and means await him at the end of the day. Provided—and it is on this the issue stands or falls—the day is short enough, the leisure long enough, and the means large enough!

I am not here concurring in the faith of the uncritical idolater of modernism, who opens his creed with the affirmation that the machine can do no wrong. Even with an eight-hour day and the highest wage-scale to date, I can quite understand the nostalgia of a Chesterton for the un-mechanized work economy and the jack-of-all-trades improvising independence of mediævalism. It cannot be defensibly argued that the machine economy has brought to the man who must spend eight hours of the day in mech-anized factory labor a leisure long enough to compensate for the losses that mechanization admittedly brings to the spirit of the man in whom the potentialities of craftsman-

ship live. Nor can it be defensibly argued that the machine
economy has, in the provision of means, done anything of
a socially revolutionary character until it goes well beyond
a narrowly interpreted living wage to a richly interpreted
cultural wage. Despite the high levels to which wage-
scales were lifted in the post-war decade, the wages of
workmen have been or could have been wholly absorbed
in the maintenance of a still inadequate living standard for
their families. Technological advance is, happily, making
this unnecessary.

Technological advance is heading us straight for not
more than a four-hour day and a wage markedly above
existing scales. Politico-social reform cannot materially
shorten the worker's day or markedly increase the worker's
pay until technological advance makes such moves good
business. And this is what is happening before our eyes.
The fact that the morning edition of a metropolitan newspaper lies now on my table announcing a ten per cent
*reduction* in wages by a major American industry does not
shake the soundness of this assertion. I do not pretend to
predict what the managerial forces of the economic order
will do. I am only analyzing what the technological forces
of the machine order are making possible and profitable,
provided the managerial forces of the economic order will
bring the capacity and courage of statesmen to the exploitation of these potentialities. The machine may bring
Western man to the threshold of a social millennium, and
he may lack the wit to unlock the door. But events are
playing into the hands of social advance, despite the current economic dislocation which seems to contradict the
contention, for it is fast becoming so clear that he who runs
may read that, unless economic leadership fully exploits the
possibility of a radically shortened day and a radically
increased income for the working masses, we shall face
the prospect of a permanent stalling of the economic machine of the West. If and when economics plays the game
squarely with technology, we shall see a day short enough,

a leisure long enough, and an income big enough to compensate the craftsman for the spiritual disadvantages of a machine economy over a handicraft economy.

Let me forestall any possible misunderstanding of the position here taken. The happiest man in the world is the man whose work is at once a means of self-support and a medium of self-expression. The machine labor of the factory may not serve this dual function. For good or for ill, however, we are committed to machine production. We are not going to take out our telephones and beat a hasty retreat to the Middle Ages. Even the most creative craftsman must resign himself to the necessity of living in the machine age. I say simply that, faced with this necessity, it is gratifying to see technological advance making for shorter days, longer leisure, and bigger income, and that, when the machine economy has adequately and assuredly provided this leisure and means, it will remain for the worker to prove that he has it in him to make at least as intelligent use of his opportunity for a broad and free life as the peasant or the craftsman of pre-machine eras made of his opportunity.

If I may summarize my contentions respecting the effect of standardized work-processes upon the individual, I have suggested two judgments: (1) that the machine economy, even without a drastically short day or an extra-large cultural wage, has been an indisputable blessing to the mediocre workman, keeping him self-respectingly on his feet, where he would have dropped out of the march, an economic derelict, under the pre-machine economy, and (2) that, for the superior workman, with the creative instincts of the craftsman, who may have to serve in the ranks of the machine operators, technological advance in the machine order is making it possible for the economic order to make his day short enough, his income big enough, and his leisure long enough to give him time and means to satisfy the cry of his spirit outside the routines of his bread-winning.

So much for the impact of standardization upon the individual. What about the effect of standardization upon our civilization in general? I have broken my lance innumerable times in fights against the standardization of the American mind. There are lengths to which we dare not permit standardization to go, and chambers of our life into which we must be chary about letting it enter, but it is easy to overshoot reality in a revolt against standardization, which, after all, has a large and legitimate rôle in social evolution.

The great stabilizing traditions and folkways, that have given coherence and dependability in the midst of social experimentation, have been ventures in standardization. As George Santayana has put it, " . . . customs and ceremonies are the stay of the mind; in them it grows sober; without them its fine thoughts would go out like sparks, accruing to nothing and transmissible to nobody." The human spirit needs such scaffoldings.

The most intelligently organized life is routinized on the lower levels and released on the higher levels. To dredge up a confirmation from the commonplace, if we had not standardized the processes of shaving, dressing, and eating, and had to improvise techniques for these ventures each day, we should have to spend most of our time in the bath room and the dining room. Many men are able to do their most creative planning for the day while shaving and dressing. These processes have become so routinized that their minds are freed for more important things. Routine, in this limited sense, has meant emancipation rather than enslavement. Something of this sort can be true of a civilization. A rational race will so routinize and reduce the time spent upon the production of such basic necessities as food, clothing, and shelter that the major energies of the people are freed for ventures beyond bread-winning. And, in so far as the machine economy makes possible this routinization of technique and reduction of time, it is ministering to humanistic ends.

For another thing, the technological advance that has made possible the large-scale production, which has come to be thought of as the be-all and end-all of the machine economy, promises to make possible, paradoxically enough, a renaissance of small-scale production. It has been said, again and again, alike by the romantic and by the realistic rebels against the age of science and technology that the day of the small producer and of the small property holder is about over. If this were true, I should join the rebels in their regret. There is much to be said for Chesterton's "religion of small property" and for the social healthiness of small-scale production. The impersonal large-scaleness of the machine age needs the corrective of a concurrent small-scaleness of enterprise under intimately personal operation. It would be socially disastrous were the whole of life and its enterprise subjected to mass processes. Technological advance, rather than politico-social reform, is the force most likely to forestall any such fateful monopoly of life by the mass process. When transmissible motive power has been made everywhere cheaply available, we shall see, I think, the invention of more and more machines, manageable by one man or a dozen men, that will carry to completion the manufacture of many articles of food, clothing, and other of the simpler necessities. The machine age that started out to obliterate the small producer will give him back a place in the sun, not to supplant or seriously to compete with the large producer, but as a healthy supplement to him.

The small production plants these new machines will make possible will be smaller units than the "small factories" I suggested earlier as among the possibilities in an industrial system decentralized through transmissible motive power. They will be less ambitious and more nearly individual or very small group enterprises. These one-man or dozen-men plants taken together with the small factories will give us the small-scaleness of enterprise we need, alongside the dominant large-scaleness, as a corrective.

There is a valid division of field and function between the large-scale producer and the small-scale producer. And further research in production costs and related factors may uncover advantages in small-scale production, for certain fields, that we have uncritically assumed lay only in large-scale production. At least, mechanical invention and transmissible motive power promise, through these new small machines, to open up to the individual, if it is to his liking, the possibility of running two or three side-shows and living on a variety of crafts and expedients, like Chesterton's village shopkeeper, who shaved travellers, stuffed weasels, and grew cabbages.

It may be contended that, even if technological advance thus makes possible a renaissance of the small producer, his work, although potentially more varied, will be no less mechanized than the work of his fellows in the mass production factories, leaving the machine economy still confronted with the charge of its rebels that mechanized work means mechanized workers. I confess I cannot follow the thinking that sees something gloriously developmental to the human spirit in shaving travellers, stuffing weasels, and growing cabbages, and only a sinister deadening of the human spirit in working with and through machines. When the machine economy has existed long enough for us to sense its real rather than its seeming effect upon the working masses, we may discover that their experience with machines has sharpened rather than stultified their minds. Let me indicate why I think this may prove true.

In Charlotte Brontë's tale of *Shirley,* Joe Scott is made to say, "Them that's mechanics, like me, is forced to think. Ye know, what wi' looking after machinery and such like, I've getten into that way that when I see an effect, I look straight out for a cause." I was quoting this the other day to my colleague, C. K. Leith, who, as a consulting geologist, has spent much of his life in out-of-the-way places, where he has seen crude men in crude surroundings work, first, with their hands and hand-power tools, and, in later years, with power-driven machinery. I found him confirming, out of his experience, Miss Brontë's flash of insight. "It is always amazing to me," he said, "to watch the effect the use of machinery has upon men who have before used only their hands or very simple tools. I have seen men, accustomed to use only picks and shovels, begin to use a cheap automobile. At first it was intricate and baffling to them. But, when they had learned to run it, they began to adjust their minds to its mechanical precisions, and growled when it did not function flawlessly. They could be whimsical, variable, irresponsible with a shovel. They could not run a Ford without getting a new respect for precision of action." Here, I think, is something the rebels against the machine economy have left out of account. They have confused the effect of an abuse of machinery with the effect of the use of machines. A maladministration of the machine economy may, indeed, make the worker dull, but a wise use of machinery may remake him from a whimsical, variable, irresponsible man into a man with a mind that respects precision.

And I am not sure we must wait another generation to find verification of this contention. Something of the fruit of their experience with machines, in whose functioning or failure effects reflect discoverable and removable causes, is, I think, showing up in the attitude of the working masses in the phase of depression through which the West is passing.

As the executive head of a university which, despite the frownings of a Flexner, shamelessly concerns itself with the life of the state as well as the life of the mind, my professional duties give me contact with the workers on farms and in factories as well as with the savants of the library and the scientists of the laboratory. And, from the writing of a brief daily newspaper article on the issues that vex our time, there comes to my desk a sustained flow of correspondence from all sorts and conditions of men throughout the United States and two other nations. I find these contacts with the mind of my time an invaluable antidote to ingrown conceptions of the function of universities, but, in an even broader sense, they have enabled me to feel a subtle shift that is, I am sure, taking place in the mood of the Western masses.

Just as the capitalists are losing their dogmatic cocksureness, so the masses are losing their dazed credulity. The masses are not to-day standing tongue-tied in the presence of economic depression, as primitive men stood awe-struck in the presence of earthquake or famine, blindly trusting their leadership with traditional loyalty, and thinking some mysterious plague has fallen upon them from the sky. They are searching for a cause. Their search may be crude and their conclusions callow, but they have at least made the gain of suspecting that an economic effect that embraces the entire Western world is due to discoverable and removable causes. And it may well be that their experience with machines has given this new touch of realism to their mood. If so, here again the machine will, in the end, make for humanistic results, whatever may have been its sins at the outset.

The machine economy, as it matures, is effecting a self-correction of another of its pioneer shortcomings by escaping from its earlier enslavement to ugliness and becoming a producer of beauty. The man of the machine age, at the first onset of his drunkenness from the wine of modernity, exiled from his life several of the gracious things that gave salt and savor to the lives of his ancient and mediæval ancestors. Among these was beauty. With his new toy of mass production by machinery, he became absorbed in the game of making useful things quickly and cheaply. The imperative that drove him was, for the time, economic rather than æsthetic. The ugliness of his output did not seem to bother him if it were but useful and cheap. And, while the machine economy was finding itself, Western man was sentenced to a drab interlude between the old beauty that was exiled by the machine and a new beauty the machine was to evoke. But the machine economy grows, at last, sensitive to the claims of the beautiful.

Machine production emerges from its gawky age, and discovers that, far from being the enemy of utility, beauty is its best friend. A renaissance of good taste is under way among the many. We have grown consciously hungry for the beauty the old handicraftsman put into the things he made. We are not content to let beauty stay an exile in the antique shops. If we cannot do better, we shall assert our sensitiveness to the beautiful by buying antiques, but we should prefer not to have to sponge on the artistry of our ancestors. We should like to feel that we can create the beauty we crave, with its loveliness coming as a natural fruit of the purposes and processes of contemporary life. The machine economy is not only responding to this hunger for beauty, but is the most effective single force now stimulating it. The dual appeal of utility and economy is no longer adequate. Business begins to rest its case on the triple appeal of utility, economy, and beauty. It is no longer enough that an automobile shall run well. It must also look well. And the $600 car, no less than the $6,000 car, aspires to beauty of color and design.

Machine industry has committed high crimes against beauty, but one look at an exquisitely beautiful period cabinet that now houses the mystery of radio shows that something revolutionary has happened in machine production since the days of the first talking machine with its unutterably ugly horn jutting out into the room like a steamer funnel. And this revolutionary something is that business has succumbed to the lure of the beauty it once scorned. The most socially significant art movement of the time proceeds, in consequence, not from the studios of world-renouncing artists in monastic seclusion from the impacts of the machine age, but from factories where men are making automobiles, furniture, radio sets, bath room fixtures, kitchen cabinets, furnace room equipment, gas ranges, and the innumerable commoner tools of daily living. This movement is even more exhilaratingly evident, perhaps, in the dreaming and drafting rooms of architects with the modernist courage to create in terms of the machine age rather than to parody the designs of mediævalism.

This current quest of beauty by the directing forces of American manufacturing and selling has not been born of social legislation, the secular evangelism of artists, or a sudden conversion of big business men into Rembrandts and Raphaels. It has been sired by a more prosaic parentage. In it, machine production is simply following the same evolution from crudity to refinement that hand production followed. None of the implements, tools, or objects of the handicraftsman's art were beautiful in their beginning. The first potter was content to make a pot that would not leak. It was later that he made it lovely. With our memory of the perfected beauty of handicraft products still fresh, we have been impatient with the pioneer ugliness of machine products, but the machine begins to answer the pleas of our impatience by seeking to make things beautiful as well as useful. In addition to this normal evolution from the crude conception to the perfected product, economic interest comes in to support the case for beauty. Business is finding that beauty pays. And the economic argument may produce results where the æsthetic appeal might fail. I suspect that Henry Ford repented the graceless design of his Model T, not from a burst of artistic enthusiasm, but because Walter Chrysler built a more beautiful cheap car that outsold the long triumphant ugliness of the original Ford. Granted time and the combined impacts of demand from consumers and competition between manufacturers, the machine economy everywhere tends to bring beauty into its concept of utility. It is thus that Western man emerges from the drab interlude between the old beauty the machine exiled and a new beauty the machine evokes.

There is a type of mind that refuses to be convinced by the new beauty of the machine age, and lodges against it three indictments: (1) that this new beauty of the machine age is a consumable and, therefore, impermanent beauty unworthy to be compared with the enduring beauty older eras caught on canvas and in cathedrals; (2) that this new beauty of the machine age is expressed mainly in the common tools and equipment of daily living and, therefore, lacks the dignity of art that inheres in the masterpieces of painting, sculpture, and architecture in which the æsthetic genius of the ancients has been caught and carried on; and (3) that this new beauty of the machine age is but concubine to utility and can never, therefore, command the reverence we involuntarily accord to the virgin purity of pre-machine art, which was content to be beautiful just for the sake of being beautiful. There is, I think, a fallacy at the heart of each of these indictments that deserves to be burrowed into. Let me examine them in turn.

*First,* how valid is the contention that, because it is consumable and impermanent, the new beauty of the machine age is unworthy to be compared with the persisting beauty of canvas and cathedral? There is, in my judgment, little more than a chemical trace of validity in the contention. The evanescent loveliness of a summer sunset is beauty no less than the exaltation of spirit incarnate in a Sistine Madonna. The transient beauty of an orchid pinned for an evening to an exquisite gown belongs with the wind-swept loveliness of a Corot canvas. And, in like manner, beauty of color and design in the consumable products of the machine age belongs with the beauty corralled in galleries. There is no necessary connection between beauty and permanence.

A while ago I lumbered along for hours on a local train threading its way through a Virginia valley. In three hours I saw, from my car window, three phases of America's reaction to the problem of beauty: (1) I saw the crude but creative beauty of surviving log cabins that were beautiful because they fit naturally into the scene with an obvious kinship with soil and surroundings; (2) I saw the hideous ugliness of clap-board and barn-siding shacks that had succeeded the log cabin in spots where the adolescent machine age had been present in spirit if not in actual operation; and (3) I saw, in the graceful lines and gay colors of a relatively cheap automobile, racing along a concrete highway in an impudently triumphant competition with the train, the out-reachings of the machine age for a new beauty. In three hours I saw America achieve beauty, go apostate to its claims, and freshly attempt its reconquest. I saw America pass from the old beauty of her log cabins, through a colorless and characterless transition, to the new beauty of her modern motors. I turned from my car window and thumbed the advertising pages of the magazine that had lain neglected for the three hours I had spent watching this panoramic outline of the history of America's adventure in the renunciation and recovery of beauty. I counted forty-nine commonly used articles into the manufacture of which had gone a manifest concern for beauty. Fifty years ago these articles were essentially devoid of color and of character. This seemed to me significant. For, after all, industrial civilization has not been at the job as long as agricultural civilization had been functioning before it produced even the beauty of the thatched cottage of the peasant.

"I venture the guess," I said to the journalist accompanying me, a man who has never quite reconciled himself to life under a machine economy, "that the machine age, in the century ahead, will respond to the call of the beautiful in a more socially significant way than any of the cathedral-building centuries responded."

"I cannot join you in that," he said. "The machine age will, of course, progressively add to the attractiveness of its products, but it will be putting its beauty into short-lived articles, into clothes, into motor cars, into bath-room fixtures, and so on. It is, as yet, but a meretricious beauty the machine has made, but, even at its best, it will be a consumable beauty. The beauty of the cathedral-building centuries played for permanence. The great cathedrals were not used up, as even the most expensive motor car is used up. A Rolls Royce is beautiful, but it is hardly a Rheims. It plays its part and passes on. In a Rheims, mortal work puts on immortality. The beauty of the cathedrals was and is ageless. Great beauty is not created by the man who is working for an age, but by the man who is working for the ages. No, I am afraid the artists who serve the machine cannot hope to join the immortals you find in the Louvre and the Luxembourg. I am afraid the beauty of a car that passes in a season cannot be thought of in the same way you think of the beauty of a cathedral that endures through the centuries."

No one would, in saneness, suggest an equality of value between a masterfully designed motor car and a majestically built cathedral as single units of creation thrown into comparison, but, when one shifts the enterprise of valuation from a comparison of single units of creation to a comparison of the ways in which different ages differently express their genius for beauty, the problem of judgment is less simple. When one compares a pre-machine age, in which the *Zeitgeist* concentrates its genius for beauty in the creation of a few monumental enterprises that survive the rise and fall of peoples and polities, with a machine age, in which the *Zeitgeist* diffuses its genius for beauty in the manufacture of the myriad of things the people use and use up month by month and year by year, it becomes convincingly clear, to me at least, that the diffused, even if consumable, beauty of a machine age is socially more significant than the concentrated, even if enduring, beauty of a pre-machine age. The social significance of beauty lies, not in its immortality, but in its current impact upon the lives of common men and women. A less majestic beauty touching more lives is, in my judgment, preferable to a more majestic beauty touching less lives. And a beauty

expressed in the consumable articles of daily use touches
more lives, and with greater intimacy of effect, than the
beauty that breathes from the Elgin marbles, the Venus
de Milo, or the Fighting Gladiator.

I am jealously eager that the now diffused beauty of the
machine age shall here and there come to consummate expression in great painting, great sculpture, and great
architecture. I should like to feel that we of the machine
age will pay to posterity something of the æsthetic debt
we owe to ancestry, that, out of our mortal adventure in
beautifying the current life, we shall throw up at least a
few immortal legacies. But the creation of these immortal
legacies must not blind us to the fact that the ephemeral
is as valid a carrier of the beautiful as the eternal. It is
neither feasible nor desirable to make every suburban
cottage as permanent as a Chartres cathedral, nor to build
every skyscraper for the ages. There is sound justification
for transition construction in this age of ultra-rapid development in taste and technique of building.

*Second,* how valid is the contention that, because it is
expressed mainly in the common tools and equipment of
daily living, the new beauty of the machine age lacks the
dignity of the masterpieces of painting, sculpture, and
architecture willed to us by the ancients? Here, again, is
a contention in which I cannot concur. In discussing the
first contention, I have made clear why I cannot concur in
the second, but this further thing may be said. An art that
is to be more than copying must express the character of
a current life. We cannot ape the ancients or follow the
formulas of the mediævalists, if the culture of our common life is to have the ring of reality. We must, as the
shorthand of slang puts it, be ourselves. And, whether it
is a matter for regret or rejoicing, we are not in an age of
the special sort of faith that painted the Madonnas and
produced a Mont-Saint-Michel. The art of an age bears
an unavoidable kinship to the attitude of an age. The
major part of our æsthetic urge must perforce express it-

self in and through the things that are, as yet, absorbing the major energies of this machine age. And, all in all, I should prefer to belong to a generation, saturate with imagination and inventiveness, that made its motor cars, its furnaces, its bath-room fixtures, and its kitchen utensils beautiful than to belong to an unimaginative generation huddled about an ancient cathedral it would lack the creative genius to reconceive and to rebuild were it destroyed by earthquake. Some one—whether a modern Irish or an ancient Greek poet I do not recall—once said that a people can never know beauty until the pots and kettles of its kitchens are beautiful.

We are not shut up to such sharp alternatives, but, if I had to choose between the less dignified but more democratized art of the machine age and the more dignified but less democratized art of the pre-machine age, I should, for the time, forego dignity in the interest of democratization. I confess a bias. To me, the beautiful, like the good and the true, finds its supreme significance in its social significance. I never dip into the history of the Middle Ages, a period dear to the hearts of the rebels against the machine economy, without carrying away a vivid sense of the contrast between the majesty of the mediæval cathedrals and the misery of the mediæval communities. Men worshiped in splendor, while they worked in squalor. The matchless beauty of the cathedrals looked down upon the sordid serfdom of their communicants. This is not to say that the building of these ancient houses of prayer was a social blunder. Their very beauty served the serf! "How magically beautiful the parish church must have been beside the hovels of the serfs who brought it the pathos of their offerings!" exclaims James T. Shotwell, in his *The Religious Revolution of To-day.* "No other miracle, even of its saints, was more wonderful than this, which transformed the moments spent within its walls to a dream of unearthly peace and kindled the imagination of unimaginative men." Man lives by beauty as well as by bread. The men of the pre-machine age learned this lesson under the influence of religion. The men of the machine age are re-learning it under the influence of industry.

It is quite as important to build beautiful communities as to build beautiful cathedrals. And to build beautiful communities means, if repetition may be pardoned, to make our cottages, our motor cars, our furnaces, our bathroom fixtures, and our kitchen utensils beautiful. It is this that the machine economy is doing. And, in the doing of this, the men of the machine age may feel the comradely touch of the hands of the cathedral builders of older centuries.

*Third,* how valid is the contention that, because it is a by-product of the quest of utility and profit, the new beauty of the machine age does not deserve the reverence evoked by the disinterested art of the masters who ignored considerations of utility and computations of profit? Here is a contention that rests manifestly upon a romantic legendizing of the motives that moved the makers of ancient art. The motive of profit and the objective of utility both played decisive rôles in the lives of the older artists.

Botticelli, Titian, Michelangelo, Leonardo da Vinci, and the unutterably candid Cellini painted and produced, as artist or artificer, many of their masterpieces on order from the church or from rich patrons. They kept a weather eye on popes, prelates, and plutocrats as paying clients. They functioned no differently than a Rockwell Kent functions when he accepts and executes an order from an automobile manufacturer eager to grace his advertisements with distinction. That the classic masterpieces were created by men who scorned a paying job and went about lyrically apostrophizing art for art's sake is sheer legend.

And the assumption that to play for utility is to prostitute art will hardly stand up under examination. I stood the other day, with a singular stimulation of spirit, before the architectural modernism of a new skyscraper. It was modern to a marked degree in its prodigal use of glass. It was innocent of buttresses to give it the look of a Chartres of commerce. There were no massive columns to counterfeit a Grecian glory. It boasted no Gothic spires to suggest eyes lifted heavenward in quest of piety when they were really turned earthward in quest of profit. There were no narrow windows to mask its internal rush with the delusion of monastic calm. It displayed no arches to symbolize plutocracy at prayer. It was, without apology, a building of the machine age, by the machine age, and for the machine age. It was utility incarnate. To me, it was beautiful, because there was a royal reality about it. Form had taken its cue from function. Material and design had alike been dictated by purpose. It had set shamelessly out to be a useful building. If, to the traditionalist, it failed to achieve supreme beauty, it was not because its builders had played for utility. On that count, the builders of the immortally beautiful cathedrals and castles that arose in the long centuries of the pre-machine era would stand equally indicted. The men who dreamed, designed, and brought into being the great cathedrals and castles of ancient and mediæval days were not aloof æsthetes who scorned utility. The buttresses that give beauty to a Rheims or a Rouen, a Soissons or a Notre Dame, were to strengthen the walls. They had their origin in utility. The alluring arches were necessary to hold up the roof. They were not designed first for beauty's sake. The windows of the ancient castles were small that their walls might be strong and their defence easier.

To ape these features of an older architecture in a day when we may build vast and soaring structures around a steel skeleton, when we may have safety and strength with a thin wall of stone or brick or durably lovely tile, when we may substitute aluminum and light alloys for the bronze and cast iron of an earlier time, when we may make walls almost wholly of glass that gives us access to the health-inducing rays of the sun, is sheer pedantry and ancestor worship. If we want worthily to fill our place in the historic succession of the great builders, we must do it through an authentic modernism. We cannot do it through an artificial mediævalism. The makers of the great cathedrals were simply good and gifted workmen who used the materials they had and sought to serve the circumstances of their time to the best possible advantage for utility as well as for beauty. They did exactly what the best modern architects and builders are doing. And, if the architects and builders of the machine age are content to serve their age and none other, if they keep their eyes at once upon utility and beauty, and if they take full advantage of the latest knowledge of structural materials and design, they shall do for the machine age what the cathedral builders did for theirs. The machine economy is definitely in the process of doing penance for its having made Western man a prodigal in the far country of ugliness, and is building a new beauty out of its unique materials and processes.

I have said enough, I think, to indicate the grounds of my belief in the potential humanism of a machine economy. If I may summarize, I have done two things: (1) I have admitted that the sixteen counts in the indictment of the machine economy of the West, as drawn by the mystics and the muckrakers, are applicable to the adolescent phase from which the machine economy is emerging, but contended that they are inapplicable to the phase of maturity the machine economy is entering, and (2) I have argued that the machine economy is effecting a self-correction of its earlier evils as a by-product of technical advance and a scientific search for the soundest and most profitable ways of doing business, that technical progress, in short, is the ally rather than the antagonist of social progress.

In making this argument that the machine economy, in the normal course of its evolution, is effecting a self-correction of its earlier evils, I have submitted six illustrative exhibits: (1) I have indicated how, after the forces of politico-social reform have failed to cure the anti-social effects of industrial centralization, the forces of technical advance, in the field of transmissible motive power, promise to cure them by making industrial centralization unnecessary and industrial decentralization both possible and profitable; (2) I have indicated the potential social ministry of mass production and mass distribution in making possible high wages, short hours, low prices, and large total profits as a material base for social progress; (3) I have indicated how the forces of technical advance are making possible a functional correlation of industry and agriculture that may solidify the now disintegrating foundation of our rural life; (4) I have indicated the paradoxical possibility of a revival of a supplemental small-scale production in the midst of a large-scale industrialism; (5) I have indicated the compensations the machine economy offers for the losses that may be involved in the standardization it implies, tracing the incidence of standardization in the life of the mediocre workman, the superior workman, and our civilization in general; and (6) I have indicated a rapid evolution of the machine economy out of ugliness into beauty.

I have, in short, sought to write at least the preface to a defence of the machine economy as offering mankind, at last, potential freedom from drudgery, poverty, and insecurity, if he will but bring insight and foresight to its administration. I am aware that I have written this defence in the midst of a dislocation so profound and a depression so persistent that, to many, it may seem the machine economy has been weighed in the balance and found wanting. It is so easy to slip into this judgment that we may, with an undue continuance of depression, see marked accessions to the ranks of the rebels against the machine economy. But their rebellion will be reasonless, mistaking their savior for a satan. The machine order has not failed us. It is the economic order that has gone awry. The maniac may slash his throat with a razor without indicting the razor as a useful shaving tool for sane men.

The arguments I have advanced in defence of the machine economy have nothing in common with the ostrich optimism of the New Era school of economists, mainly lay, who, in the period of psychopathic speculation, lulled millions to sleep while the machine economy was being betrayed in its own household. My arguments say only that the machine economy is a tool of emancipation that Western man has not yet mustered the wit to use wisely.

# XII

## The Treason of Statesmanship

THE clear potentialities of the machine order stand in vivid contrast to the confused actualities of the economic order. The machine has not betrayed Western man; Western man has betrayed the machine. Statesmanship has gone traitor to its most significant tool. And by statesmanship I mean more than the here incisive and there irrelevant thinking of presidents and premiers. I mean economic and educational leadership as well.

Along the entire frontier of Western civilization the forces that have made for the collapse of markets, the retardation of economic enterprise, and the unsettlement of mass confidence in current leadership are challenging the worth and the workability of the Western economic order. The statesmanship of the West finds itself, in consequence, on a heavily shelled social battle-line. We do not yet know what the outcome of this challenge will be. The varied leaderships of the West may be beaten into panic retreat by the disintegrative forces of revolution or by the integrative forces of dictatorship. They may rest content with defensive tactics, dig themselves more deeply in, and do no more than hold their own for some time to come. Or they may evolve a fresh strategy of advance and move forward to new conquests of economic prosperity and social good. I am not foolhardy enough to venture a prophet's guess among these three conceivable ends. I am content to say that I think the third outcome is possible, and that it lies with politico-economic leadership to say whether or not it shall be realized.

As I swing into the writing of the closing pages of this

book, the United States is in the midst of the most serious economic crisis of its history. Between the early summer, when I began this book, and the early autumn, when I am concluding it, there has been a marked change in the mood of economic leadership. The hold-over of the ostrich optimism, which made men reluctant to admit the depression as more than a momentary dip in the economic curve, has been pretty generally dissipated. Even the average American, for all his credulity, has grown skeptical of the corner around which prosperity has been periodically announced as halting for a surprise entrance. But, for all this growing disillusionment with the glad-men, politico-economic leadership generally displays the same reluctance to face fundamental facts that it displayed in the now defunct New Era, which proved too old in character to be called new and too short in duration to be called an era. Even with markets tumbling about our ears and with salesmen reluctantly reporting their quotas unfilled, there is, save for the breadlines in our congested centers, a bright delusive air of well-being among our people that tends to hide the deeper significance of the depression through which we have been passing. We have known phases of slowing down in which the American people, as a whole, were on a far lower level of living than now, but, in certain fundamental aspects, the depression which fell with drastic impact in the latter months of 1929 has been unlike and more serious than any depression that has preceded it.

This assertion will not go unchallenged. It is quite possible to argue, with a battery of learned references, the thesis that this depression has been of a piece with the dozen depressions we have experienced during the past century. The phenomena that have marked other depressions have been manifest in this one. A four-fold formula has been constant through the recurrent economic cycles of the past century: (1) discovery, technological advance, and improved technique of organization and management,

sometimes singly and sometimes in combination, have produced a forward thrust in economic enterprise; (2) the
contagion of this forward thrust has stimulated the get-
rich-quick mood in men outside the ranks of the creative
industrialists, whose clear thinking and concentrated working have made this forward thrust possible, and a phase of
speculation, which quickly becomes a phase of over-speculation, is entered; (3) for a time the sound productiveness
of the new industrial expansion makes even unsound speculation seem sound, the normal hesitancy of the banker-
mind gives way to a naïve hopefulness, a Monte Carlo
spirit enters the money marts, and an over-extension of
credit takes place, further aggravating the disease of
over-speculation; and (4) when the house of cards, run
up by the speculators, begins to totter, the minds alike of
banker and of depositor suffer economic shell-shock, the
banker-mind induces an over-contraction of credit and
the depositor-mind indulges in an over-contraction of confidence, the bankers hesitate and the depositors hoard,
consumption shrinks, production slows down, and economic paralysis, creeping if not complete, ensues.

That these four marks of other depressions have been
manifest in this depression does not mean that still other
factors may not set it quite apart from preceding slumps
in character and seriousness. This, I am convinced, is the
case. The triple phenomenon of over-extension of credit,
over-speculation, and over-contraction of credit has, indeed, marked this depression as it has marked preceding
depressions, but the fact that a man has run a temperature
in a dozen successive illnesses does not necessarily mean
that his last illness is the same as the first. The first may
have been a plain cold and the last poliomyelitis. The
analogy here is, I think, accurate.

Any realistic analysis of the 1929 depression must begin
with the fact that it is the first general economic crisis that
has befallen the West since our machine economy has
come to measurable maturity. It is not a matter of

momentary maladjustment in any one section of the world. It is not a matter of momentary speculative mania having disrupted an otherwise statesmanlike and stable economic program. Momentary maladjustments, here and there and yonder throughout the West, are in the picture. A mad-house speculation has done its deadly work. Many political and purely monetary factors are involved in the prevailing sickness of Western society. Beneath and beyond all this, however, is the fact that we have been so busy perfecting our technical processes for producing goods that we have neglected to perfect our economic policies for distributing wealth widely enough to create an adequate and assured outlet for the output of our machine economy with its ever-increasing rapidity and volume of production.

Tentative and insecure phases of recovery may be brought about by various devices of political stimulation and monetary sleight-of-hand, but, until this basic problem of the relation of popular buying power to the rapidity and volume of production under a machine economy is seen and solved by politico-economic leadership generally, the West must resign itself to an increasingly serious economic insecurity, unless it wants to take the only alternative road to a balanced economy in a machine age and deliberately reduce the scale of its industrial enterprise. There is nothing to be gained by beating about the bush. The entire economic order of the Western world has reached an impasse from which only the most clear-headed, creative, and courageous politico-economic leadership can extricate it. That this is not the facile generalization of a frightened academician is clear, I think, if looked at in the light of four obvious aspects of the depression through which we have been passing.

*First,* the depression has not been simply American; it has been world-wide. I call a partial roll of the areas that are feeling, in varying degrees, the impact of economic dislocation. The United States. Great Britain. Canada.

Australia. India. Germany. Poland. Czechoslovakia. Sweden. Norway. Denmark. Switzerland. Italy. The East Indies. The Netherlands. Mexico. Chile. Peru. Brazil. The Argentine. And so on. We are plainly in the presence of a world phenomenon. The Americas, Europe, Asia, Africa, and the Antipodes, all stand as if some subtle spell of economic witchcraft had been put upon them.

*Second,* the depression has not been simply financial; it has been industrial as well. We should to-day be wrestling with forces of economic retardation even if there had been no Black October in the 1929 operations of the Stock Exchange. The market debacle was but an eddy in a major current of economic tendency. In the United States, significant sections of industry, such as the automobile industry, had been reaping the easy harvest of a first-sale market, but were beginning to reach the point at which, by and large, the market was settling down to a matter of replacements and of meeting the new demands created by normal growth of population or by radically new departures in design, quality, or price. American business and American industry had been catching up on the postponed building and buying that had kept the air electric with enterprise in the immediate post-war decade, but as the catching-up process proceeded a slowing down ensued. Our export trade had been abnormal during the war years and for a time after, but retardation of exports had set in some time before the market crash. Various artificial stimulii to business, such as installment buying and the mania for annual models, were rounding out their pioneer push and settling down to a normal pace of development. And throughout the West the potential energies of the machine economy were beginning to feel the irrational restrictions of tariffs and trade policies that stood and still stand in utter violation of the clear conclusions of common sense and of all the canons of constructive statesmanship.

I need not here attempt a comprehensive listing of the

many factors, other than speculation, that were setting the
stage for economic retardation before 1929. That ground
has been burned over in nearly every rational analysis of
the depression that has appeared in recent months. I want
only, by calling attention to these typical factors in American economic life, to illustrate and intensify the contention
that the depression through which we have been passing
is more than a *faux pas* of the financiers. It is a kind of
judgment day for politico-economic leadership! We might
effect every desirable reform of the Stock Exchange and
still the organic disease of depression would not down, for
it sinks its roots in all the policies and processes of our industrial order.

*Third,* the depression has not been simply financial and
industrial in nature; it has been agricultural as well. The
agricultural aspect of the depression has struck, with utter
impartiality, exporting and importing countries alike.
Exporting countries like the United States, Canada, and
Australia and importing countries like Great Britain and
Germany have felt its impact. That alongside a world-
wide industrial depression there should exist a world-wide
agricultural depression again emphasizes the fact that the
phenomenon we have been facing goes to the very foundation of the economic order of the United States, in particular, and of the West, in general. There is nothing save a
failure of leadership the world around to account for this
agricultural debacle. For every existing agricultural surplus anywhere in the world there are somewhere in other
parts of the world under-nourished bodies enough to absorb it, but we seem not to be able to muster a statesmanship that can lift the peoples of these areas of under-
consumption to the level of paying customers and bring
the supply into contact with the need. And so we must
admit a bankruptcy of leadership and shame ourselves by
confessing a world-wide agricultural depression which, in
the light of the manifest and unmet needs, would be un-
thinkable to a really intelligent race.

*Fourth,* the depression has not been marked by an over-production of manufactured goods alone; it has been marked by an over-production of antecedent materials as well. In the last decade or two, there has been a staggering increase in the production of raw materials and food-stuffs. World production figures for the twenty years before the onset of depression in 1929 are illuminating.

From 1909 to 1914, the average world production of sugar was 19,363,000 short tons. By 1929, it has jumped to 29,970,000 short tons, or, roughly, a fifty per cent increase. In less than two decades, the United States increased its wheat acreage from 47,000,000 to 61,000,000 acres, while Australia and Canada more than doubled theirs. The world had a full year's supply of coffee on hand when the 1930 crop was ready for harvest. The world output of tea jumped, in four years, from 856,000,000 to 945,000,000 pounds. From 1926 to 1929, the world output of tin jumped from 145,000 to 195,000 metric tons, lead from 1,606,000 to 1,775,000 metric tons, zinc from 1,245,000 to 1,908,000 metric tons. From 1910 to 1914, Australia's average wheat production was 90,479,000 bushels. Twelve years later, it had jumped to 160,762,000 bushels. In 1913, Australia's wool production was 711,500,000 pounds. By 1927, it had jumped to 883,304,000 pounds. And, even in the face of the rapid development of synthetic nitrates in the United States, Great Britain, and Germany, the output of Chilean nitrates jumped from 2,772,000 metric tons in 1913 to 3,163,000 metric tons in 1928.

But I need not go on. There are many readily accessible sources to which one may turn for a comprehensive statistical summary of world production totals. I have taken these figures, more or less at random, and with no attempt to paint a complete picture, in order to emphasize the fact that wherever we turn on the map we find the same sweeping rise in the production of raw materials and foodstuffs. At the root of the depression, that took so many Westerners unawares, lay not only a glut of manufactured goods but a glut of raw materials and foodstuffs as well. All of which points, I think, to the fact that the depression has dramatized more than a momentary matter of over-supply. If it were but a matter of momentary over-supply, we should hardly find the phenomenon operative in virtually all fields and the world around. The depression has revealed a disturbing lack of balance between the arrangements the West has made for producing and the arrangements the West has made for consuming and using.

We are face to face, then, with a phase of economic depression that is world-wide in scope, financial, industrial, and agricultural in character, and marked by a sluggish surplus alike of manufactured goods and of raw materials. And, although it was at the outset an economic depression alone, it has swept every aspect of Western life within the orbit of its influence. Political life is rent by its implications. Cabinets come and go in terms of what they do or fail to do in the face of its onsweep. The press, education, religion, and the innumerable social enterprises of local, state, and national government find its pinch affecting their policies.

The implications of these wider impacts of economic dislocation I shall consider at length in the epilogue to follow. I want here to narrow the canvas and to suggest what I think the current juncture in Western affairs implies respecting the dereliction of economic statesmanship in the past and the opportunity open to economic statesmanship for the future. And I shall speak in terms of the depression as we have seen it and suffered it in the United States.

As the United States swung into the closing months of 1929, our machine order was never more efficient from the point of view of potential productive capacity, but our economic order found itself swamped rather than served by this efficiency. I use the term "machine order" to indicate the whole array of processes by which we make goods and produce wealth. I use the term "economic order" to indicate the whole array of policies by which we use goods and distribute wealth. Never was there less defensible excuse for economic depression than in the closing months of 1929. Let me recall the stage-setting of the collapse.

There was no shortage of money. There was no shortage of basic resources. There was no lack of willing hands to work. There was no lack of productive efficiency. There was no plague-like adversity of wind or weather. There was no insect pest, either nation-wide in its ravages or seriously out of hand. There was no invader hammering at our gates to terrify our spirits and to disrupt the normal processes of our enterprise. On the contrary! There was an ample money supply. There was a surplus of nearly all basic resources. There were millions of workers ready to work. The productive efficiency of the nation was such that the needs of its people and much besides could have been easily supplied with shorter working days and a shorter working week. At no moment in human history had a people found itself in possession of so nearly all of the material essentials for a great and glowing civilization.

When the market collapse and economic retardation befell it, the United States was basically at the point towards which the dreams of prophets and seers have pointed through the centuries. As we re-read the literature of Utopian thought and list the things that the social seers have, with striking unanimity, set down as elementary requirements of an ideal society, we find that the United States was in position to provide them all in the closing months of 1929. Its technical genius had invented machines enough to free its people from drudgery. Its organizational genius had achieved a manufacturing efficiency that made possible the production of everything its people needed without their slaving from dawn to dusk. Leisure in which its people might laugh and love and adventure among things of the mind and spirit was within the nation's grasp. It was at such a moment that the United States found the shadow of a serious economic depression falling athwart its life.

If some sinister spirit had been seeking to brew an exquisite irony, this turn of fortune could not have been timed with more devilish aptness. Just when we had reached the point at which emancipation from drudgery, the capacity to produce all the essentials of material well-being without the slavery of inhuman hours, and the potential achievement of prosperity and leisure for all were at hand, we found ourselves victimized by a financial debacle, an economic recession, and a social unsettlement at once sweeping and severe. What must the gods have thought as they watched this tragi-comedy!

I do not want to join the over-simplifiers, and bring a false clarity to a situation that is admittedly complex. The cause of the depression that has swept the Western world cannot be captured in a phrase or its cure distilled in an epigram. It is not a simple sickness that has fallen upon us, and it will not yield to any simple and single remedy. A lush variety of causes lies at the root of the economic crisis of the United States, in particular, and of the West, in general. Political unrest the world around! Mounting armaments! Speculative mania! Abortive governmental attempts to stabilize certain commodity prices! The fall in the price of silver! Provincialism of policy in the fields of foreign trade, tariffs, and the exploitation of the world supply of natural resources! The direct impact of war debt payments upon Europe and the indirect impact upon the United States! The gravitation of an undue amount of the world supply of gold into French and American hands! And so on to the end of a list I need not rehearse. Even a casual diagnosis of the confusion and arrest that have fallen upon Western affairs compels us to consider all of these factors in addition to the obvious issues of wages, hours, prices, technology, and management, as well as the deeper issues of security, leisure, and self-respect for the toiling millions.

To all these issues—and more—we must bring a clear-headed and courageous statesmanship before we can expect the Banquo's ghost of depression to absent itself permanently from the economic table or even to schedule its appearances at more decently long intervals. I do not, let me repeat, want to join the over-simplifiers. There is no pink pill for pale business that can be confidently hawked in the market place with the guaranty that it will cure all our economic ills in thirty days or money refunded. But, in any situation, however complex, there may be one factor more fundamental than the rest, so fundamental, indeed, that the presence of all other factors cannot compensate for its absence. Is there any single factor thus fundamental to the economic recovery of the West? I think there is. And we shall find it, I think, by finding the major cause of the economic relapse of the West. A long series of causes lay back of this relapse, but one thing seems to me sun-clear: The leadership that has determined our policies for using goods and distributing wealth has proved inferior to the leadership that has developed our processes for making goods and producing wealth. The production of goods has halted because the distribution of goods has halted. And the halt in the distribution of goods is due to a fault in the distribution of wealth.

We cannot, of course, tear the machine order and the economic order thus cleanly apart in action as we can in analysis. They are intimately interlocked in operation. But, in the deepest sense, I think it is accurate to say that the depression through which the United States, at least, has been passing is, in essence, an indictment, not of the machine order, but of the economic order. The machine order is ready to produce goods. The economic order is not ready to produce customers.

An old tale comes to mind. A rich young man, concerned with the issue of eternal life, sought an interview with

Jesus of Nazareth, prophet extraordinary, who was cutting under the surface of the life of his time and calling men back to reality. "What shall I do that I may inherit eternal life?" asked the rich young man. "Keep the commandments!" was the laconic reply. "Which?" asked the young man, a little puzzled by this advice. And when Jesus jogged the young man's memory by recalling a half dozen of the more important directions of the decalogue, he was still more puzzled. "All these I have observed from my youth," he said. "What lack I yet?" Here was a young man who had, on the face of it, a flawless record. He seemed animated by a sincere desire to push his life towards perfection. Seemingly some crucial thing, which he had not yet fully understood, blocked the road to this perfection. "One thing thou lackest; go thy way, sell whatsoever thou hast, and give to the poor, and thou shalt have treasure in heaven. . . ." Jesus further advised him.

This tale applies, I think, with trenchant aptness to the problem now confronting the economic order of the West. I do not mean that the plight of the West can be cured by philanthropy. I do not mean that, if the rich should scatter their possessions among the poor and themselves turn mendicant, as a kind of ritual atonement for whatever sins of policy may have produced the depressions of the past, the economic life of the West would achieve stability. There is a profounder parallel between the rich young man of this ancient tale and the economic order of the modern West. Western man, through his machine economy, has kept all the commandments of science, technology, and organization, as the rich young man had kept all the commandments of the Mosaic decalogue, but economic security still eludes him, as the assurance of eternal life eluded the rich young man. Statesmanship must, without indulging in shallow simplification, find the "one thing" the West lacks to bring its innumerable efficiencies into harmonious functioning for human ends.

It is by now a threadbare platitude, even if a young

platitude, to say that our machine economy is in trouble because our capacity to purchase has not kept pace with our capacity to produce. Following the war, some of the more far-sighted leaders of American business and industry saw that a point had been reached in the evolution of our machine economy at which they must concern themselves with the purchasing capacity of the masses as well as with the producing capacity of their manufacturing plants. They adopted, in consequence, a new credo in which they asserted that stable prosperity and healthy industrial development require high wages, short hours, and low prices. This ran contrary to the naïve business thinking of earlier days when business leadership generally thought that low wages, long hours, and high prices made for maximum profit. But outstanding industries throughout the United States proved by their balance sheets that high wages, short hours, and low prices were not only good for the masses but good for the manufacturers as well. And we fell victim to depression, I am convinced, not because we followed this new credo of business, but because we did not follow it generally enough or apply it far enough.

The simple fact is that a machine economy must, along with the making of commodities, see to it that the consuming millions have money with which to buy and leisure in which to enjoy the products the machine economy creates. And this means higher wages than we have yet paid, shorter hours than we have yet set, and lower prices than we have yet fixed. That is to say, it means all this on those sectors of the industrial front where mass production and mass distribution are logically applicable and socially desirable.

Our machine economy is to-day sinking us in a sea of surplus production, or surplus productive capacity, that could, were we but statesmanlike enough, be used to our advantage and to the good of the world at large. I speak of surplus production with some reluctance, for it is, in my judgment, a false surplus that is to-day choking the economic West. It would mark a definite gain in economic realism if we should reserve the term surplus production for goods not really needed instead of using it, as we do, for goods that are simply difficult to sell at the moment. In the light of the social function of industry, business leadership has no right to regard as a surplus goods for which an authentic human need obviously exists. Unmovable goods, unless they are at the same time unneeded goods, are not a sign that business leadership has been too zealous in producing goods, but a sign that it has not been zealous enough in building buying power among the masses.

I cannot concur with the observers who contend that we have been producing too much. There are 123,000,000 of us in the United States. As late as 1928, a year of prosperity, 8,000,000 Americans were living below the poverty line, and some 12,000,000 Americans living at a bare subsistence level. And to-day millions of our population have far from satisfied the legitimate demands of a healthy and civilized folk. There is a whole world outside our frontiers in which millions upon millions of men and women and children, outside the ranks of the dire poor, are living far below the consumption level we have known and that health and civilized values dictate. If we are at all sensitive to the physical and spiritual needs of mankind, to say that we are now or shall be for a long stretch of decades to come at the point where humanity is surfeited with goods and services it does not need for better living is, to me, too incredible to consider seriously.

But that we are producing, or are equipped to produce, more goods than the consuming millions have, at the moment, either the mood or the means to buy is obvious. Industry after industry is geared to a productive capacity markedly in excess of current demand, although alongside this unused and, at the moment, seemingly unusable productive capacity there lies, in ironic juxtaposition, a vast world of unsatisfied need. Production and consumption are seriously out of balance. Setting aside, for the time, other less fundamental factors in the rise and fall of prosperity, there are two obvious ways to deal with this disturbed balance between production and consumption: (1) we can slow down production by deliberate policy, or (2) we can speed up consumption by deliberate policy. I shall not attempt to disguise my conviction that to throw the brakes on our productive capacity as a policy for the future, before we have fully explored the possibility of building a buying power adequate to absorb, to sound social advantage, our potential output of consumer goods, is a coward's policy and a social retreat.

I am not at all interested in a shallow and sinister doctrine of consumptionism that would make it possible for the millions of earth to buy prodigally only that business may grow bigger and the nation be swept into a kind of St. Vitus dance of industrial activity. An intelligent people will never trump up business just for the sake of doing business. I am concerned, however, that we shall not, in panic fear, take counsel of our timidity, and, under the magic of the new gospel of social planning, rush pell-mell into a restriction of production, thus allowing to lie even partially unused this matchless instrument of social emancipation our genius has forged. Restriction of production is the line of least resistance. It has its appeal in a phase of sluggish inventories. It is implicit in much of the current agitation for national planning. It occupies the councils of most of our great trade associations. But, until legitimate human need is served and saturated, a wholesale restriction of production is a confession that our capacity for economic statesmanship has gone bankrupt. What will be the judgment of future generations upon our genius if, after succeeding in elaborating a machine economy capable of putting an end to drudgery and poverty and insecurity, we say, "Now that we have sharpened this tool, we must dull its edge;

now that we have perfected this swift efficiency, we must throw on the brakes!"

The fact is, as I suggested earlier, that the machine economy has brought us to the threshold of a social millennium, but we have lacked the wit to unlock the door. And my contention here is that, instead of planning to adjust ourselves to the half-hearted and insecure existence that marks the current economic order which swings like a pendulum between panic and plenty, we should be searching for the key that will unlock the door into this social millennium of prosperity, leisure, and security which science and the machine have made possible. I think we know what the key is. The only question is whether we shall have the courage and statesmanship to use it. The key is a wider distribution of the national income.

The machine economy can, if we will but follow the policies its processes foreshadow, emancipate the race from drudgery, lift the standard of physical well-being throughout the world, and give mankind at last leisure in which to cultivate values that lie beyond the creature comforts of food, clothing, and shelter. But the machine economy will never perform this socio-spiritual ministry unless and until the leadership of business and industry sees to it that a larger share of the national income is shifted into the pockets of the consuming millions and until the margin of leisure for the millions is markedly increased.

I am quite aware that this smells suspiciously of the soap box. A wider distribution of wealth has long been a favorite topic to be talked from the soap box. From his soap box rostrum the proletarian agitator has contended that an undue concentration of a nation's wealth in the hands of a few is unjust, and he has pleaded, in the name of justice, for a wider distribution of wealth. In the past such preachment has been looked upon as a peril to capitalistic industrialism. Men who talked too freely about a wider distribution of wealth were jeered at and sometimes

jailed. To-day, however, events are proving that a wider
distribution of wealth is essential to the solvency and
success of capitalistic industrialism itself, on the simple
grounds that it is obviously self-defeating for Western
industrialism to get itself in position to produce vast
quantities of goods unless, at the same time, it sees to it
that there are vast masses of potential consumers ready
with money with which to buy and leisure in which to enjoy
the goods that the high-powered industrial machine produces. Unless we can bring millions upon millions of men
and women into position to buy the lavish output of Western industrialism, even our existing investment in its mar-
velous productive facilities will become a permanently
frozen asset. A too great concentration of wealth means
money in the hands of those who will invest it in producer
goods. A wide distribution of wealth means money in the
hands of those who will invest it in consumer goods. And
it is the absence of an adequate and dependable market for
consumer goods that is stalling the economic machine of
the West.

It has thus come about that the plutocrat has an even
greater stake than the proletarian in the widest feasible
distribution of the nation's income, not in the superficial
and sophomoric sense of dividing up by decree wealth
already in existence, but in the statesmanlike sense of so
balancing the factors of wages, hours, prices, profits, and
so on, that, in the very process of producing wealth, industry will be making its market while it is making its
goods. In an era of laggard industrialism and limited production, the leadership of business and industry could
afford to leave the soap box on the street-corner to be
occupied by the proletarian agitator, pleading for a wider
distribution of wealth in the interest of social justice, but,
in this era of swiftly efficient industrialism and almost
limitless productive capacity, sound economic statesmanship suggests that the soap box be taken indoors, that it
be set up in the directors' room, and that it be henceforth

occupied by the industrial administrator, pleading for a wider distribution of wealth in the interest of industrial stability. We shall, in short, achieve a popular and permanent prosperity to the degree that the administrator takes the place of the agitator in handling this crucial issue of the distribution of the national income.

Even a few short years ago this statement would have been set down as the envious and irresponsible raving of a disinherited radical. But experience—the experience of the current economic dislocation—has taught many men many things. Shortly following the sharp impact of depression in the closing months of 1929, I argued this thesis of a wider distribution of the national income as the *sine qua non* to economic stabilization in a machine age before three significant assemblies of business, industrial, and financial leaders. A veritable flood of letters has come to my desk from these business men, industrialists, and bankers, and there is a touch of the sensational about the virtually unanimous concurrence of these conservative leaders in the contention that the solvency and success of our business and industrial system, to say nothing of the welfare of the consuming millions, depend upon our shifting a larger share of the national income into the pockets of the majority.

What has happened that a contention, considered a radical attack upon the *status quo* but a little while ago, is to-day hailed as the soundest of sound business policy? It is surely not that the big business man has turned bolshevik! No! It is simply that it has become so plain that he who runs may read that the capitalistic industrialism of the West will inevitably collapse unless, along with its prolific production of goods and services, it deliberately provides the consuming millions with money with which to buy and leisure in which to enjoy the products it is geared up to produce.

It has been dinned into our ears, by both the advertising and the editorial pages of the press, that, following the market collapse in 1929, American business and American industry found themselves the victims of frozen buying power, and that, if every American who could buy would buy, economic recovery would be assured. There is something in this contention. But the frozen buying power that then congealed American enterprise was due to something deeper that the scared masses hoarding their slender savings in socks or hiding them behind loose bricks in the chimneys. There has been, beyond doubt, a good deal of this sort of hoarding. And much of it has been a useless and costly economy that has resulted in an unnecessary reduction of the living standard of many American families. But the frozen buying power that has threatened our whole industrial system with a kind of creeping paralysis is something quite apart from this hesitant buying of frightened customers.

In the fall of 1929, when American business and industry slowed down and found themselves with excess products and excess productive capacity on their hands, it was not because there was a lack of *buying power* in the country, but only because there was a lack of *buying*. In the fall of 1929, there was ample *buying power* in the United States to absorb every existing excess of products and to call for still greater production. I am speaking here of the total national production and the total national buying power. That here and there individual industrial plants indulged in an unintelligent orgy of over-expansion does not invalidate my contention. In terms of national totals, the buying power of the nation was adequate for the productive capacity of the nation. But much of this buying power, as far as its use in the purchase of consumer goods was concerned, was frozen. Why was not this inactive buying power brought into play? Why did it not flood the country with a consumer-demand that would have stopped the oncoming depression in its tracks? At least part of the answer to this question seems obvious.

When American economic enterprise slowed down in

the fall of 1929, an undue proportion of the nation's buying power was in the hands of a minority who, for personal or family consumption, neither needed nor desired to buy more, while the vast majority of American consumers who, for personal or family consumption, both needed and desired to buy more, had little surplus buying power. The minority, not needing to spend its surplus buying power for personal or family consumption, was investing too much in means of production. The majority, not having surplus buying power to spend for personal or family consumption, was investing too little in products. The result was inevitable. Our business and industrial system back-fired, and we found ourselves in the unhappy position of producing too much and purchasing too little.

I am quite aware that the regularization of production and the stabilization of prosperity require the concurrent elaboration of varied policies to deal with the varied aspects of the socio-economic life of the West. I am convinced, however, that the major key to the economic health of Western industrialism is the release of a larger amount of the social surplus of buying power for the purchase of consumer goods. If economic leadership will devise ways and means of routing a larger share of this social surplus into the pockets of the consuming millions who, for personal or family consumption both need and desire to buy more, the wheels of industry and the marts of trade will hum with new activity, economic depression will become a memory, and, paradoxically enough, the minority now owning this surplus buying power will actually be better off as far as total wealth is concerned.

But how shall America, for instance, effect this shifting of a larger share of the national income into the pockets of the consuming millions? How shall America markedly increase the margin of leisure for the millions? How shall we go about this difficult undertaking of a wise and businesslike distribution of social buying power? All sorts of governmental devices will suggest themselves to the political mind. Large-scale charity does a little of this redistributing. Unemployment insurance does a little more. A gigantic program of public works, financed by government bonds, bought by those who now control a large part of the nation's inactive buying power, with the interest and retirement of such bonds financed by taxation of the inactive surplus of buying power, would go still further in effecting a wider distribution of buying power. And the radical political mind dreams of more drastic steps towards the socialization of the nation's wealth. But I do not believe that the United States either wants or needs a revolutionary politics to achieve this end. The imperative redistribution of social buying power can be effected through far-sighted business, industrial, and financial leadership, without resorting to political devices. I am convinced that a statesmanlike administration of the triple problem of wages, hours, and prices can go far towards resolving the economic dilemmas that confront business and industrial America. If the leadership of American business, industry, and finance becomes really convinced that only prosperous consumers make profitable customers, we can create on this continent a contented and prosperous people immune to the allurement of reckless radicalisms.

Two convictions must come to ascendancy in the mind of business and industrial leadership: (1) that wages are not exclusively a production-cost, but represent an investment in market-development as well, and (2) that the conquest of poverty is to the selfish advantage of the manufacturers as well as to the social advantage of the masses. Let me play a moment with these two contentions.

Business and industrial America is, as I write, in a phase of wage-cutting. I do not suggest that wages should not at any time be readjusted in the light of other factors in the industrial scene. The merely formal maintenance of a wage-scale may be meaningless. A wage-scale may be rigidly maintained while other factors in the economic process shrink or swell the purchasing power of the worker's dollar. Over-time or part-time may double or halve the worker's actual income. I do not suggest that a reduction of a formal wage-scale is always and inevitably a social backsliding. To say that would be the economics of infantilism. But we must not, in the rush of readjustment, fall into the easy error of assuming that wages are simply a charge on industry, and that every dollar subtracted from wages means a dollar added to profits. The contrary may be true. The highest practicable wage means not only a reward to the man who receives it but a return to the man who pays it. This is true because the working millions are not only industry's servants but also industry's customers. Unless other factors exist as an offset, if industry put twenty-five per cent less into the pockets of labor through reduced wages, industry must expect at least twenty-five per cent less to come out of the pockets of labor in the form of purchases of the goods industry produces. We cannot eat our cake and have it! I am not arguing here against an intelligent balancing of all the factors in the industrial process. I am arguing only against the ancient fallacy that industry can grind labor and gain by it. What industry pays in wages is an investment in industry's market, just as definitely as what industry pays for advertising is an investment in industry's market. And, as a corollary to this contention respecting wages, the conquest of poverty is one of industry's greatest opportunities for extending its market. The age-old social agitation for the conquest of poverty becomes, in this machine age, good business policy. I cannot but believe that the political and economic genius of the Western nations, acting in concert, could, by a constructive administration of credit and a statesmanlike direction of industrial policy, go far towards ridding the world of all preventible poverty. The under-consumption to-day represented by poverty is more than enough to absorb the danger of over-production.

The logic of events is at last proving that the basic

policies that are best for labor are the policies that are best for capital and *vice versa*. In the entire history of economic America, every general reduction of hours and every general rise in wages, however bitterly fought by short-sighted leadership at the time, has been followed by a fresh accession of business activity and general prosperity. It is one of the ironies of history that the very things for which labor and liberalism have pleaded through the generations, on the ground of simple justice, such as high wages, short hours, and low prices, are now seen to be the only things that can, in the interest of the solvency of capitalism, keep our industrial system a going concern. Despite its complexity, a simple and single challenge lies coiled at the heart of the depression through which we have been passing: Will the leadership of business and industry prove as capable in producing civilized consumers as it has proved itself capable in producing consumable commodities? Unless it does, we must resign ourselves to the certainty that our economic order will slump into chronic depression and court ultimate collapse. But if and when the leadership of industry assumes as one of its major duties increasing the income and leisure of the millions, it will discover that, as a by-product of this social ministry, it has made greater total profits than ever before.

Three possible roads of economic destiny stretch before us, each having as its goal a wider distribution of wealth: (1) the road along which economic leadership may seek to effect a wider distribution of wealth by the way it administers wages, hours, prices, profits, and the other factors of business and industry; (2) the road along which political leadership, in the event economic leadership goes renegade to its responsibility, may seek to effect a wider distribution of wealth by taxing incomes and inheritances more and more drastically; and (3) the road along which social leadership, in the event that both economic and political leadership fail or refuse to effect a wider dis-

tribution of wealth, will seek to effect a revolutionary over-
turn. I hope America may travel the first road promptly,
and that we shall never have to take the third road. And
it lies with politico-economic leadership to say whether
or not the road of revolution shall be taken. The multitude of men will not permanently submit to life under a
machine economy that periodically plays havoc with their
lives. Before our captains of business and industry can
lay claim to supreme success they must help us make our
economic order as socially efficient in its policies for using
goods and distributing wealth as they have made our
machine order technologically efficient in its processes for
making goods and producing wealth.

If we content ourselves with hastily improvised policies
to jack up morale or hastily improvised protests to provide
stump-speech copy for a next campaign, we shall find ourselves citizens of a fear-ridden future in which we shall
be dragged at the heels of forces and fears over which we
shall be able to exert no more control than we exerted over
the forces that brought a bloated market to explosion in
the fall of 1929. This fear-ridden and uncontrolled future
need not be. There is genius enough in America to evolve
and to execute political and economic policies that will
give us, in point of material well-being and social enrichment, a future that will far outstrip our feverishly and
fleetingly prosperous past. If America does not realize
this finer and more fruitful future, and begin her realization of it with decent promptness, it will be either because
at the top we suffer a breakdown of political and industrial
leadership or because at the bottom the people, in some
moment of leaderless confusion, fanatically follow some
false prophet from either the ultra-reactionary or the
ultra-radical camp. It will not be because the cards of
destiny are stacked against us. They are not. Every card
in the deck is in our hands. It is a matter of playing them
expertly.

# Index

## A

Ability, ascent of, 97–99

Action, education for creative, 224; closely akin to artistic creation, 238

Adaptability, lost in commodities of machine age, 306–307

Adjudication, machinery of, alone no insurance against war, 275

Advances, formula underlying creative, in common life, 159–61

Advertising, in U. S., 72

Agriculture, functional correlation of, with industry, 322–23, 342–44, 364; in current depression, 371

Aloofness, as a church policy toward war, 271–72

Americanizations, of the world, 278–91

Americans, "hatred" of, 283

Antagonism, bred between classes by machine economy, 308–309

Anthropologists, on race character, 257–58

Anti-democrats, cult of, 101–104

Application, social, goal of all scientific discovery, 145

Art, of machine age, 360

Artisans, *vs.* machines, 284, 285; as artists in a pre-machine age, 305–306

Authoritarianism, not for to-day, 152

Automobile, its effect on conduct, 118

## B

Ballot-box magic, 102

Bankers, in New Industrial Revolution, 13

Bankruptcy, road to biological, 47, 55; of leadership, 371

Beauty, recovery of, 12; natural, destroyed by a machine economy, 301–302, 309, 326; of a premachine age, 302, 303, 305; waste of, 310; machine economy as a producer of, 353–56, 364; worthiness of, 356–59; *vs.* dignity in machine age, 359–61; as by-product of quest for utility and profit, 361–63

Bergson, Henri, his influence on conduct, 121–22

Bigness, two kinds of, 107–108; mania for, 108; resentment of, 108–109; reaction against, 110; worship of, 287

Biologists, and trend in quality of Western peoples, 46–49; and rate of increase of world population, 46, 49–53; and tension between white and colored races, 46, 53–55; and furtherance of realistic pacifism, 199–201; on race character, 257–58; goal of, 263–64

Biology, the new, and ethical unsettlement, 113, 120–21, 125; politics of, 248; a different mission suggested for, 263

Birth control, as seen by biological prophets of doom, 47–52

Body, education of the, 223

Books, imperfect guides, 6, 7; on future of civilization, 17

Bourbons, present-day, 67, 68; danger from, 99

Brutality, growth in, 33; towards weakling, 112–13

Burden of civilization, 191–93

Business, *vs.* government, 14; prewar passion of, 21; efficiency in, *vs.* size and complexity, 106–108

Business men, in New Industrial Revolution, 13; his part in realistic pacifism, 197

Buying power, increase of, basic problem in depression, 369, 378; frozen, 384–85; distribution of, 385–86

## C

Candor, *vs.* concealment, 112, 123
Capacity, individual, community bearing of, 106–107; intellectual, now stationary, 151
Capek, Karel, his indictment of American civilization, 285–91
Capitalism, fear as to future of, 105, 106, 178; record of, 177; challenged by Communism, 178–79; need of changing emphasis in its philosophy, 179–84
Capitalists, and planning, 41
Careers, in U. S. and in Europe, 289
Centralization, 117; self-correction by machine economy of excessive, 333–39
Challenges, to democracy, 69–99
Character, education of, 223; researches in race, 257–58
Charity, 386
Chauvinism, 166, 170
Checks and balances, constitutional, 42
Chesterton, G. K., his nostalgia for handicraft age, 346; his "religion of small property," 350
Christianity, trans-racial from the beginning, 250–51; its contribution to constructive race relations, 252–57; enfeebled by organizing, 267
Churches, hampered by institutionalism, 140; scholar-prophets and, 188; and beauty, 189; and war, 266–77
Citizen, myth of omnicompetent, 176
Citizenship, need of revised method of determining, 83; bad, a product of machine economy, 311
Civilization, Western: decay of, 7–8; renewal, stabilization, and enrichment of, 11; its need of a workable philosophy, 14–15; initiation of renewal of, 16; before the war, 21–25; disunity of, 33–34; speculation on downfall of, 42; threat of crowd-mind to, 61–62; change of, from agricultural, 74–80; leadership in, 93–97; resources of social health in, 133, 134, 137; education and social insecurity of, 212–17; education for effective participation in, 223, 224; renewal of, must be deeply religious, 227;

resurgence of jungle ethics in, 243; mechanizing of, 278–91; realistic criticism of, 295–315; divergent hypotheses as to future of, 317–18; major philosophies battling to control, 320–24
Class-consciousness, a product of machine economy, 309
Classicism, debilitated *vs.* dynamic, 11
Clergymen, and the crowd-mind, 57; and war, 269
Commodities, loss in adaptation of, in machine age, 306–307
Communication, effect of increase of means of, 62–64, 66, 73–74; knowledge as, 144–45
Communism, answer to its challenge, 163; its challenge to Western industrial system, 177, 178, 182, 184
Complacency, racial, creeping paralysis of, 265
Compromise, as a church policy toward war, 271, 272–73, 274; by state, school, or church, 276–77
Concealment, *vs.* candor, 112
Concentration, of wealth, weakness of too great, 382
Conduct, effect of machines on, 118; effect of idea of evolutionary change on, 120–21; effect of new philosophy on, 121–23; influence of new psychology on, 123; influence of new physics on, 125; changing standards of, 126
Conflict, bred between classes, by machine economy, 308–309
Congestion, in cities, caused by machine economy, 325
Congress, now tri-cameral, 77–79
Constitution, idolatrous reverence for, 79, 80
Consumers, production of civilized, 388
Consumption, level of, too low, 379–80
Control, agencies of international, called for, 169–70, 171
Controversy, under majority rule, 85–86
Coöperation, loss of faith in, to achieve common ends, 28, 31–35, 39
Corruption, in government, 74; the worst, 202

# Index

Coudenhove-Kalergi, on true champions of masses, 326–29

Courage, need of, 202–204; education to develop, 224; creative, 239–40

Craftsmanship, in pre-machine culture, 295, 310; spirit of, destroyed by a machine economy, 305–306, 326; prospect for, in a machine economy, 345, 348

Creativeness, social, 61; release of latent, 84, 140; cultivation of, 224; secret springs of social, 236, 237; in a pre-machine age, 305

Credulity, in age of science, 136–37

Crisis, of Western spirit, four phases of, 20; economic, variety of causes of, 375

Criticism, political, essential, 67

Cross-breeding, of races, caution advised in, 260

Crowd, domination by the, 56–66, 94; and the new physics, 125; leadership and the mind of, 153

Culture, social renewal of, 11, 12; the highest, 148–49

Curriculum, revolution in, involved in integration of education, 219

Cynicism, post-war, 8, 20, 27–39; escape from, 42; weakness of, 236, 239; incentives, 240

## D

Dark age, escape from a new, 16, 128, 130, 138

Darwinism, twisting of, 120–21

Death, biology of, and economic internationalism, 168–69

Debunker, use of the, 202–203

Decentralization, goal of Western industry, 322–23, 334–39, 342, 364

Dedication, to high purpose, loss of, 28, 37–38; to great ends needed for New Renaissance, 227

Defense, militarisms an outgrowth of idea of national, 165; organization for, 274, 275

Degeneration, race, 191

Degrees, as academic labor union cards, 218

Delocalization, of interests, 81–83

Demands, four basic, of industrial nations, 172–73

Democracy, skepticism of, 32; correlation of, with dictatorship a

necessity, 34–35; and reproduction control, 48; challenges to, 68–99; peril of revolution to a, 97, 98–99, 100; disbelievers in, 101–104; friends of, 104–105; and the new politics, 114; consummation of, 145

Departmentalism, necessary smashing of excessive, 219

Depression, current, due to deeplying sickness of Western world, 19; and social planning, 40; current, a proof of West's economic unity, 170–71; and the future of capitalistic system, 178, 180–81; and men's receptiveness to new ideas, 244; its effect on captains of industry, 330–32; current, unlike and more serious than any previous, 367–75; current, an indictment of the economic order, 376–77

De-secularization, of religion, 186–89

Despair, literature of, 42, 43–126

Destruction, spiritual, always brought by war, 271

Development, national requisites for unhampered, 173

Dewey, John, his influence on conduct, 122; on consummation of democracy, 144–45; on presentation of knowledge, 148

Dictatorship, 13, 32; correlation of, with democracy, 34–35; a reaction to democracy run wild, 68; types of, 101

Discipline, revolt against, 33

Discontent, with government, 67–68; among machine-workers, 308

Discrimination, against colored peoples, 54; elimination of racial, 249

Discussion, under majority rule, 86; under party system, 88, 90

Disillusionment, after war, 30–32, 34, 36, 38; levels of, 43–45; of student of statecraft, 70; of politico-social reformers, 334

Disruption, of Western life, 1

Distance, its challenge to democracy, 69, 71–74

Distribution, planned, 41; mass, 107; mass, potential social ministry of, 340–42, 364; faulty, of wealth fundamental factor in current depression, 376–77

Disunity, of Western civilization, 33–34, 39
Drudgery, emancipation from, 12, 324–27, 381
Dynamic, spiritual, needed by a social diagram, 226–47

E

Economic order, its lack of a workable philosophy, 14; profit the prewar goal of, 21; way to stabilization of, 173; foundation of, threatened by current depression, 371; swamped by efficiency of machine order, 373–75; current depression an indictment of, 376–77
Economics, the new, a source of ethical unsettlement, 113, 114–19, 125
Economy, as an appeal in machine economy, 353, 354
Education, of the majority, 87; for leadership, 138; developing scientific spirit, needed, 146; for social mastery, 205–25; revitalizing of civilization unlikely through, 232–35
Educational system, effectiveness of, 4; and the crowd-mind, 64–66
Educator, objective of, 222; tardy in adjustment to new knowledge, 233–34
Efficiency, vs. size and complexity, 106–108; pre-machine age untroubled by, 295; price of, in a machine economy, 299
Elective system, origin and character of, 212
Emancipation, of woman, 116; from orthodoxy, 119–20; vs. enslavement by technological economy, 288, 324–27; from drudgery, 381
Emotions, in education, 223
Employment, insecurity of, 12
Encyclopedists, need of a new group of, 140–47; marching orders for, 148–49; field for, 151–52; and single great leader, 155–56
Engineer, his philosophy, 320–24; true champion of the masses, 326–28; need of dominance by, development and control of power, 342
England, evils of party system in, 91–92
Enslavement, vs. emancipation by technological economy, 288; to a system, 305

Enterprise, mobility of, 82–84; fear as to size and complexity of, 106–10
Environment, influence of, 21–22; religion and the social, 185–86, 187; elaboration of social, 191
Envy, democracy as government by, 103, 104
Equality, vs. excellence, 103; and the incompetent, 104; vs. a high standard of living, 327–28
Escapists, influence of, 38
Ethics, and the new theology, 119–20
Ethnology, of extreme racialists, its weakness, 258–59
Eugenics, 47–49; and survival of Western social order, 191–94
Europe, its reluctance to embrace technological economy, 279–82; "Americanization" of, 283, 285; compared with U. S. in cultural and political leadership and condition of the masses, 289–90
Evangelism, against mechanizations, 285–88
Every-man-for-himself, 179
Evolution, consciously controlled, the means of realizing New Industrial Revolution, 13
Exaltation, of war period, 27
Excellence, vs. equality, 103
Expediency, social, 119
Experimentalism, in life, 126
Experts, disagreement of, 7; democracy and the, 70
Exploitation, of backward territories, dynamite in, 173; for private gain, and the Gospel, 267

F

Factories, and farms, functional correlation of, 322–23, 342–44, 364; beauty from, 354
Faith, in planned progress, 20, 39–42; ultra-rational, the basis of love, 240
Family, under modern industrialism, 115–19
Fanaticism, racial, 250, 261
Farming, functional correlation of, with industry, 322–23, 342–44, 364
Fascism, less sound than régime of free capitalism and political liberty, 182
Fear, uses of, 135; education against, 224

Feeling, progress initiated by, 238
Fighting, philosophy of getting by, 33
Flunkey-mindedness, 290
Food, production of, *vs.* population growth, 53
Ford, Henry, and Gandhi, antitheses and agreements of, 320–24
Freedom, of the press, 57; of thought, 59–60, 61, 66; education for, 65–66; outlook for, 104; advocates of new, 112; origin of new, 113; relativity and new, 125; in transportation decreased by machine economy, 304–305
Freeman, R. Austin, his indictment of machine economy, 297, 315
Freud, Sigmund, his influence on conduct, 123
Fundamentalists, biological, 261
Futility, of romantic rebellion against machine age, 291

### G

Gandhi, Mahatma, as leader, 154–55; his attitude toward machine economy, 292–94; antitheses and agreements of, with Henry Ford, 320–24
Genius, of Western man, 16; in a democracy, 97, 98–99; in a stratified society, 97–98
Geologist, his part in furtherance of realistic pacifism, 197–99
Germany, neo-paganism in, 24–25
Gods, five war-time, 28
Gospel, the, militarism, and exploitation for private gain, 267
Government, *vs.* business, 14; postwar problems of, 66–105; lack of interest in, as result of machine economy, 311
Graduate schools, distressingly undergraduate, 218
Greeks, dynamic classicism of ancient, 11
Guyau, parable from, 134–35

### H

Hatred, of Americans, 283
Hedonism, perverted, 21, 38
Heredity, and race improvement, 264–65
Hope, literature and leadership of, 127–57; uses of, 135

Hoarding, in current depression, 384
House of Technologists, need of a, 78–80
Humanism, in New Renaissance, 12; in New Industrial Revolution, 15; scientific, the viewpoint of this book, 17; materials at hand for scientific, 232, 239; of Jesus, 250–51; scientific, 261, 262; through technology, 319–65
Humanity, the nation and, 164–65

### I

Ibsen, on the majority, 86
Idealism, of war, 20, 25–27, 28–29, 32, 36, 37
Ideas, three, that condition every man's future, 9; socially significant, buried in jargon, 141; rallying power of, 156, 161–64, 201, 206, 244
Illiteracy, political, 66
Imagination, synthesis of, with investigation the way to a great civilization, 240–41
Imperialism, perverted, 21; Darwinism as a mandate for, 121
Impossible, demanding the, 240
Incapacity, hidden in a crowd, 58; of the specialist, 214
Income, national, larger share of, for masses essential, 381–85; taxation of, 388
Inconsistencies, war-time, of the church, 270
Independence, loss of, in crowd, 57–60
Individual, the crowd-mind and the, 4, 56–66; capacity of, limited, 106–107; democratic emphasis upon, 114; debased by industrialism, 115; effect of machines on, 118; integration of his life and personality, aim of education, 222, 224; both love and knowledge essential to complete, 230–32; privacy of the, 263; development of, in pre-machine culture, 295–96, 303
Individualism, a vigorous, imperative, 85
Industrial Revolution, not simply on economic adventure, 9, 10, 11; anti-social results of, 12

Industrial Revolution, New: idea of, 9, 11, 12–13
Industrial system, its effect on religion, 10
Industrialism, perverted, 21; chronic discontent with, 59; its effects on individual and family, 115–19; mass-conscious, 162, 177–84; evils of, 296; threatened collapse of capitalistic, 383
Industrialization, comparative, in Europe and the United States, 279–82; European rebellion against, 283–91
Industry, trans-national interests of, 281–82; integration of, 313; decentralization the goal of, 322–23, 334–39, 342, 364; in current depression, 370–71
Inflexibility, of political system, 83–84
Inheritances, taxation of, 388
Inge, W. R., disillusionment of, 43, 44, 45; qualifies his prophecy of doom, 127; on the churches and war, 267
Initiative, 95, 96; vs. routine, 311
Injustice, danger from social, in a democracy, 99
Insecurity, economic, 12, 14; rescue from, through planned progress, 20; post-war, 37; of our civilization, 65; danger from, in a democracy, 99, 105; under capitalism, 180–81, 182; call for courage to face and conquer, 203–204; impotence of education to prevent social, 212–17; in machine economy, 314
Institutionalism, religious, 12, 140; in school and state, 140; in education, 234, 241; in Christianity, 256, 267, 268; a society of, 276
Insurance, unemployment, 386
Integration, of educational process, imperative, 212, 215, 219, 222; of industry, 313
Intellectualism, confusion brought by, in religion and morals, 115
Interdependence, growth of national, 58, 166–67, 168, 169, 171–72; of sciences, 209–10
Intermarriage, racial, 252, 253, 259–60
Internationalism, economic, 162, 167–74

Intolerance, danger from, 86–87
Inventor, animated by itch to invent, 298–99; true champion of the masses, 326–28
Investment, opportunity for, vital to industrial nations, 172–73
Irresponsibility, social, in an age of interdependence, 81–82; problem of, in public service, 96; social, following World War, 243; in racial attitudes, 252
Isolation, end of, 63–64
Issues, under party system, 88, 89–91; moral, and the church, 273

J

James, William, his outburst against bigness, 108; his progmatism, influence of, 122–23
Japan, distrust of, 55
Jews, copied by Ku Klux Klan, 250
Journalism, marriage of science to, essential, 148–50
Judgment, exercise of independent, 120; suspended, the essence of scholarship, 143
Judgment day, social, 192
Jung, C. G., his influence on conduct, 123
Justice, education in a realistic sense of, 224

K

Keyserling, Count H., on journalistic gift, 149
Knowledge, true purity of, 144–45; the presentation of, 148–50; need of distillation of, 153; artificial synthesis of, not the great need, 214–15; love and, in the good life, 230–32, 235; pedagogy and theology tardy in adjustment to new, 233–34
Ku Klux Klan, party differences on, 91; symbol of psychology of racialism, 249–51
Ku Kluxism, 32, 33, 249, 251

L

Labor, hard, "for machines, not for men," 324–25
Laissez-faire, no longer possible, 40
Laws, making and breaking, 102–103; physical, no longer thought universal or immutable, 124

Leadership, palsy of, 1, 5, 8, 9; creative, courageous, 11; in New Industrial Revolution, 12–14; perilous, 18; to a sterile peace, 31; its challenge to democracy, 69, 93–97, 100; difficulties of political, 72–73, 74, 76, 80, 81, 83, 84; under majority rule, 85–87; of political parties, 88–93; impotence of, before economic relapse, 106; in renewal of civilization, 137, 138, 139, 140; in science, 148; in new renaissance, 150–57; new, and the masses, 159–60, 161; true political, 176–77; breakdown of, 207; abdication of educational, 210–12; lack of, for scientific humanism, 239; lost opportunities of socio-spiritual, 241–43; need of a spiritual, in science and industry, 244–45; religions, in reducing race tensions, 265; American, in machine civilization, 282–91; business and industrial, 328, 329; reluctance of, to face facts of depression, 367; economic, political, and social to a wider distribution of wealth, 388–89

League of Nations, party differences on, 91

Leisure, for the many, 13; machine civilization attacked for its threat to, 285; 286–87; in pre-machine culture, 295; possibilities of, in machine economy, 324–25, 345, 348

Lenin, as leader, 154–55

Levity, apostles of new, 111, 112

Liberals, American, partly to blame for shoddy peace, 31; strength and weakness of, 330, 331–32

Libertinism, release of, 32

Liberty, apostles of new, 111–12

Life, unity of man's, 10; as a going experimentation, 122; creative advances in the common, 159–61; love and knowledge in the good, 230–32, 235, 236

"Lion hunting," 290

Literature, of social analysis, 8; of social reconstruction, 36; of national planning, 41; of despair, 42, 43–126; of hope, 127–57

Lobbies, secret, progress through, 78–80

Localism, resurgence of, 110

Looseness, the new, 111, 112–13

Love, and knowledge in the good life, 230–32; lack of, 235, 236; a social dynamic, 238; source of, 240

Loyalties, traditional, and politics, 72

M

Machiavellism, pre-war, 24

Machine, its promise, 4; vs. artisan, 284, 285; tyranny of, 298–99; uselessness of running away from, 320; in agriculture, 343; a mind sharpener, 351–52, 353

Machine economy, assets and liabilities of, 105–106; ethical implications of its machines, 118; relative development of, in Europe and the United States, 279–82; values lost in, 283; views on, of social mystics, 292–94; portrayal of, by realistic rebels, 294–315, 319, 363; revolutionary transformation by, of Western social milieu, 315–16; its major evils inevitable by-products of large-scale production, 316; its extinction unlikely, 319–20; humanity's most effective instrument of emancipation, 324; welfare of the masses its price of survival, 331–32; self-correction of its evils by, 332–64

Majority, its challenge to democracy, 69, 84–87, 100

Maladies of social order: biologist's diagnosis of, 46–56; psychologist's diagnosis of, 46, 56–66; as seen by student of statecraft, 46, 66–105; economic diagnosis of, 46, 105; as seen by student of administration, 46, 106–10; moralist's diagnosis of, 46, 110–26

Maladjustment, between fluid social and fixed political order, 82–84; danger of political, in a democracy, 99; correction of 133; in society, not incurable, 139; between old policies and new problems, 159, 161; correction of, in machine order, 329; in current depression, 369

Maladministration, under majority rule, 87; of large-scale enterprises, 109

Malthus theory of population, origin and development of, 50–51; doubts of, 52; present acceptance of, 53

Man power, no longer decisive in war, 197

Management, slow growth of statesmanship of, 107; responsibilities of, no attraction to masses, 181; breakdown in social, 207

Masses, idealism of, in war, 25–27, 28–29; response of, to leadership, 155, 159–60, 161, 176, 245; verdicts by, on men and measures, 176; strength of Communist appeal to, 179, 181; welfare of, and capitalism, 179–84; few in, concerned with issues raised by science, 236; better off in U. S. than in Europe, 289; hope for, in great engineers, inventors, and industrial statesmen, 326–32; attitude of, in current depression, 352; buying power of, 378; profits from increasing income and leisure of, 388

Materialism, new, 20–25, 38

Mathematics, absorption of modern philosophers in, 122–23

Mazzini, on moral factor as true instrument of progress, 227–28

Mechanization, romantic rebels' case against, 283–91; relentless drive toward complete, 300

Mediocrity, human, under a machine economy, 345

Mentality, racial differences in, 257–58

Mergers, shortcomings of many, 109; attacks on tendency toward, 110

Migration, opportunity for, vital to industrial nations, 172–73

Militarism, an outgrowth of national defense, 165; the Gospel and, 267

Millennium, threshold of the social, 381

Mind, free, character of a, 59, 61; subconscious, education concerned with, 223

Minerals, need of international control of, 171–72

Minority, its function under majority rule, 85–87

Mob-mindedness, taught by war, 4, 56–57; instruments of communication and, 74; as inevitable product of machine age, 296

Modernism, Gandhi's renunciations of, 293

Monotony, of work, 12; as inevitable product of machine age, 296, 303, 326

Montague, C. E., on a lost opportunity of socio-spiritual leadership, 242–43

Morality, the higher, as seen by biologists, 48–49; effect of machines on, 118–19; and the new theology, 119–20; effect of idea of evolutionary change on, 121; influence of new physics on, 125

Muddling through, 6

Multi-millionaire, menace of, 313

Mystics, social, their indictment of machine economy, 292–94, 319, 320–24; recruits to, 334

N

Nakedness, the new, 63

Nationalism, religion of, 24; resurgent, 29, 30, 163; cultural, 162, 164–67; industrialization of Europe retarded by, 281–82

Newspapers, and the crowd-mind, 57–64; and the individual, 64; and struggle for national-mindedness, 73

Nomadism, its challenge to democracy, 69, 80–84

Non-resistance, doctrine of, 269, 274

Nordics, claims for, reviewed, 260–61

Normalcy, 36

O

Obscurantism, revivals of, 150

Occident, its predisposition to objective life, 21–22

Opportunity, in a democracy, 97, 98–99

Optimism, contrasted with hope, 133–36, 202

Organization, limits of its efficacy, 107

Originality, stifling of, 58

Orthodoxy, emancipation from, 119–20

Over-centralization, correction of, 12

# Index

399

Over-population, fear of, 49–53, 55
Over-production, inevitable in a machine economy, 314; ending of agricultural, 344; in current depression, 372–73
Over-specialization, the cause of inadequacy of education, 207

## P

Pacifism, realistic, 162, 194–201
Parable, of heart of Western man, 134–35
Pacific Ocean, mastery of, 55
Paganism, ancient and modern, 20–21; pre-war, 22–25, 26, 29, 30, 38
Paradox, of a crowd-civilization, 58
Parties, failure of, 88, 89–93
Party, its challenge to democracy, 69, 87–93, 100
Peace, drabness of, 33; need of a science of, 195; little offered by organized religion to lovers of, 267
Pedagogy, tardy in adjustment to new knowledge, 233–34
Peffer, Nathaniel, exemplifies spirit of realistic rebellion against machine economy, 295–96
Permanence, evil of, in parties, 89–93; no necessary connection between beauty and, 356
Pessimism, post-war, 39
Philosophy, a workable, needed by machine civilization, 14–15; slump of Western, 34; social, of science and of democracy, 70; the new, a source of ethical unsettlement, 113, 121–23, 125; and creative advances in common life, 159, 160–61; patchwork, behind Western policies, 256; of social mystic vs. that of engineer, 320–24
Physicians, family, vs. specialists, 284
Physics, the new, and ethical unsettlement, 113, 123–25
Planning, business, 5; importance of motivation in political, social, and economic, 226
Platforms, party, formation of, 90, 91
Pleasure, pre-war passion for, 21
Plutocrat, his interest in widest feasible distribution of national income, 382

Politics, of God, the subject of this book, 17; pre-war passion of, 21; goal of post-war, 36; demagogic, and race improvement, 99; regionalism and, 71–72; patterns of American, 74–77; leadership in Western, 94–97; the new, a source of "unmoralism," 113, 114, 125; rationalized, 162, 174–77; conversion of world, into competition in excellence, 167; world, increasingly politics of biology, 248; of race, 252–55; its bankruptcy in war prevention, 275
Population, problem of, 49–53; dynamite in surplus, 173; improving quality of, 192, 193
Poverty, in a time of prosperity, 379; conquest of, 387
Power, pre-war passion for, 21; from the crowd, 58; of words, 158–59; moral, of the church, 273; interrelation of machines and, 299; concentration of, 313, 323; transmissible, its transformation of industry, 334–39, 342, 364
Progmatism, its influence on conduct, 121–22
Prayers, war-time, for victory, 271
Prejudice, racial, 249
Prestige, importance of, to single great leader, 155
Production, planned, 41; mass, pointless without mass consumption, 183; mass, potential social ministry of, 339–42, 364; revival of small-scale, 350–51, 364; surplus, 378–81
Profit, pre-war passion for, 21; private, its weakness as major incentive of industrial system, 177–84; beauty as by-product of quest for, 361–63; from increasing income and leisure of masses, 388
Progress, loss of faith in, 28, 38–39, 43–45; birth of, 86–87; blocking of, by parties, 88–89; the scholar and social, 142–45; of science and society, 216; moral factor true instrument of, 227–28; the way to, 239; social vs. technical, 326, 327, 342; paradox of, in machine age, 330; social, a realistic foundation for, 339–40
Prohibition, party differences on, 91

Propaganda, and the crowd-mind, 62, 66; effectiveness of, 162
Prophecy, failure of, 5; social, 43
Prophets, of doom, 9, 43–126, 174
Prosperity, stabilized, 12; under capitalism, 180; material, of the church, 273; Americans as press agents of, 282; poverty in a time of, 379
Psychologists, their fear of a crowd-civilization, 56–66
Psychology, the new, a source of ethical unsettlement, 113, 123, 125
Public utilities, social control of, 337

**Q**

Quality, degradation of, in machine age, 306–307
Quantity, passion for, 287, 326

**R**

Race, idea of a well-bred, 162, 190–94
Races, collaboration of, 248, 252, 255, 265
Racialism, and Christianity, 248–65
Radicalism, prevention of, 331
Radio, and the crowd-mind, 62; and struggle for national-mindedness, 73
Rathenau, Walter, his philosophy of the social dynamic, 237–39; his "Shepherds of Arcady," 320
Reactionaries, and the schools, 65
Reason, revolt against, 121–23; ineffective without support of ultra-rational impulses, 236–37, 238, 240; in its most exalted mood, 240
Rebellion, romantic, against machine economy, 283–91, 320; realistic, against machine economy, 294–315, 319
Recall, 95, 96
Reconstruction, 40–41
Recovery, single factor fundamental to economic, 376
Referendum, 95, 96
Reform, educational, 214; politico-social, of factory system, 333–34
Reformation, not simply a religious adventure, 9, 10, 11
Reformation, New: idea of, 9, 11, 12; needed as a spiritual dynamic, 226, 245–47

Reformer, professional, 37; social, in war of human liberation, 327, 328, 329–30
Regeneration, by war, 270
Regionalism, in the U. S., 71–72, 100
Relativity, its effect on conduct, 125
Religion, its effect on life, 10; in New Reformation, 12, 16; of nationalism, 24; hungered for by West, 34; traditional, and race improvement, 48–49; socialized, 162, 184–90; social dynamism of, 226–47; an untapped resource of policy in race relations, 261; organized, little offered to peace lovers by, 267
Renaissance, not simply a cultural adventure, 9–11
Renaissance, New: idea of, 9, 11–12; road to, 128, 130, 139, 140, 142; leadership in, 150–57; seven rallying cries for, 162–202
Renunciation, as a church policy toward war, 271, 273–77
Reorientation, of education, necessary to stop decline of West, 206
Representation, occupational, needed under Constitution, 78–80; problem of political, 94–99
Repression, under majority rule, 85, 86
Reproduction, as seen by biological prophets of doom, 47–52
Research, functions of scientific, 128; its contributions to literature of hope, 129–33; how to save its results from demagogue, 141; progress through practical, 143–44; periodic formulation of tentative dogmatisms from, advised, 145–46; need of an inventory of socially usable ideas from, 146; specialization in, 208–10; in social values and relationships, 221–22; in race character, 257–58; in biological results of race mixture, 259–60; European leadership in fundamental, 280
Research institutes, for promotion of scholarship and training of professional scholars, 217–19
Resources, war increasing a contest in material, 197–99; depletion of, in a machine economy, 300–301
Responsibility, stimulation of sense of social, 220

Revival, of religion, 246
Revolt, social often heralded by cultural, 10
Revolution, menace of social, 54; its challenge to democracy, 69, 97–99, 100; incitement to, by a majority, 85; greatest in next half-century, 326
Ross, Edward A., his indictment of the crowd, 60–61
Routine, vs. initiative, 311; emancipation in, 349
Russell, Bertrand, on regeneration of society, 229; on love and knowledge in the good life, 230–32; his belief in education, 232; on lack of love, 235

## S

Salesmanship, high-pressure, 310, 341
Sameness, sickening, of machine-age construction, 303
Santayana, George, disillusionment of, 43, 44, 45
Scholar, and social progress, 142–45; sins of the, 149–50
Scholar-prophets, of religion in a workaday world, 188–89
Scholars, professional: training of, a distinct enterprise, 215–16; separate institutes for training and research of, advised, 217–19
Scholarship, need of its marriage to journalism, 148–50; difference between education and, 215–17; promotion of, 217–19
Schools, as nurseries of individualism, 64–66; their failure to train for machine era, 109; afflicted with institutionalism, 140; as seedbeds for social statesmanship, 220
Schweitzer, Albert, on greatest task of spirit, 255–56
Science, its effect on religion, 10; in New Renaissance, 12; its challenge to democracy, 69–71; and superstition, 136–37; need of an evangelism of, 141–47, 150; two obligations of, 144–45, 147; its internationalizing effect, 167, 170; and politics, need of an alliance between, 174–75; specialization in, 208–10; progress of, 216; every, as

a social science, 220; few in masses concerned with issues it raises, 236–37; its need of a spiritual leadership, 243–44; its suggestion as to racial improvement, 263
Selection, natural vs. rational, 263
Self-defense, wars of, 270
Self-determination, its interference with unification, 170
Self-expression, vs. self-control, 123; in work, 308–309, 322, 348
Self-interest, enlightened vs. unenlightened, 13; intelligent, plus intensive scientific investigation insufficient for New Renaissance, 226–27; argument of intelligent, 329
Self-sufficiency, destroyed by machine economy, 311–13
Sentimentality, in discussion of race problem, 252
Sex, rescue of, from sentimentality and sniggering, 224
Shepherds of Arcady, 320
Shoddiness, in a machine economy, 306, 309; avoided in authentic mass production, 341
Shop-keepers, degradation of, in machine age, 307
Size, disadvantages of, 109; passion for, 285, 287
Skepticism, in New Reformation, 12; post-war, 28, 32, 39; of reform of schools, 65; joined with gullibility, 136–37
Smith, Adam, his theory of way to public good still accepted, 179–80, 182
Snobbery, cultural, 290, 291
Social analysis, literature of, 8; the prophet and, 45; products of, 136
Social control, of machine civilization, 12, 42; sounder, 64; vs. social suicide, 139–202; muddling in, 214; education in, 219–25
Social order, maladies of, 42, 43–126; may have a rebirth, 127–28, 137; price of survival for, 166–67; scholar-prophets and, 188; eugenics and survival of, 191–94; realistic pacifism necessary for survival of, 194–95; education for creation, comprehension, and control of, 215, 216–17, 219–25; an urbane and useful, 227; both love and knowledge essential to a cre-

ative, 230–32; stabilization and enrichment of, 239, 244; the church in the battles of, 266–77

Social planning, loss of faith in, 28, 35–37, 39; new interest in, 40–41; difficulties in way of, 42

Social renewal, raw materials of, 9, 16, 130, 132, 136, 138, 139, 140, 141, 150; secular movement of, 11; leadership in, 151–57

Socialization, of wealth, 386

Society, pre-war passion of, 21; effect of its size on democracy, 71–74; progress of, 216; religion and regeneration of, 229

Specialists, generation of, as partialists, 214; vs. family physicians, 284

Specialization, danger in, 152; in education, rise and implications of, 207–17

Speed, passion for, 285, 286–87, 305, 306; drudgery of, 325, 326

Spenglerian school, 5, 8, 9

Sportsmanship, under majority rule, 85–86, 87

Stabilization, way to economic, 173

Stagnation, economic, 41

Standard of living, equality vs. a high, 327–28

Standardization, fear of, 56–66; of thought, 73–74, 86; of politics, 90–92; by nationalism, 165; European revolt against industrial, 283; compensation for losses involved in, 344–49, 364

State Socialism, anticipation of its advocates, 105–106

States, artificial boundaries of, 82–83; modern, unmanageable, 109

Statesmanship, field of, 11; industrial, 12, 13, 14; collapse of, 31–32, 34; prospect for a new, 39; in the technologic era, 77; failure in, of political parties, 89–91; opportunity of social, 146; importance of rallying cries to, 159, 160, 161; economic, 173–74; schools as seedbeds of social, 220; sterile before racial relations, 249; patchwork, behind Western procedures, 256

Sterilization, of education, 210–12

Students of statecraft, and governmental readjustments, 66; his belief in revision of democracy, 66–68

Subserviency, as a political asset, 97

Success, passion for, 285, 287

Superficiality, of romantic rebellion against machine age, 291

Superiority, theory of racial, 55, 253–54, 257–59, 262, 264; jealousy of, 86

Surplus, agricultural, vs. starvation, 371

Survival, of the fittest, 47; price of, for Western social order, 166–67; religion and the struggle for, 186, 188; chance of, for Western social order, 225

Sympathy, education stimulating and disciplining, 224

Synthesis, final justification of all, 145

T

Taste, degradation of, by machine economy, 309

Taxation, of incomes and inheritances, 388

Teachers, vs. intelligence and psychological tests, 284

Teaching, revolution in method of; involved in integration of education, 219

Technology, its challenge to democracy, 69, 74–80, 83; internationalizing effect of, 167, 170; as main source of trouble in machine economy, 317; humanism through, 319–65

Television, symbol of new nakedness, 62, 63; and struggle for national-mindedness, 73

Tension, race, 53–55; between old political and new social order, 77–80; race, 248–49, 251, 265

Tests, intelligence and psychological, vs. teachers, 284; of success machine economy, 288

Theology, in New Reformation, 12; the new, a source of ethical unsettlement, 113, 119–20, 125

Trade, opportunity for, vital to industrial nations, 172–73; development of business ethics in, 197

Traditions, need of stabilizing, 113; arresting power of, 296

Transit, vital of industrial nations, 172–73

Transportation, effects of facile, 80, 82–83; loss in, in a machine economy, 304–305

Tyranny, of crowd-mind, 58, 60, 61, 65; and majority rule, 85–86, 87; of the machine, 298–99; old-time, of distance, 303

## U

Ugliness, as a product of machine age, 302, 309, 326; evolution from, to beauty of machine economy, 353–56, 364

Under-consumption, 371, 387

Unemployment, fear of, 181; problem of, created by machine economy, 307–308; insurance against, 386

Unfit, restriction of, 192–93

Unification, difficulties in, 170; psychological vs. physical, 248

Uniformity, sterile, of a machine economy, 303, 306, 326

United States, incidence of interdependence upon, 166–67, 169; its easy adoption of technological economy, 279–81

Unity, economic, collapse threatened by West's failure to function as, 170–71

Universe, theory of, greatest task, 255–56

Universities, criticism of mushrooming, 109, 110; tradition-bound, 233–34

Unmoralism, causative sources of, 113–26

Utility, associated with ugliness, 309, 326; beauty as a by-product of, 361–63

Utopianism, 17; eclipse of, 37, 38

## V

Values, spiritual, and the church, 273; lost in a machine economy, 283; insensitiveness to delicate and daring, 287; transvaluation of, by a matured machine economy, 290

Variety, lacking in a machine economy, 302–304, 306, 326

Versailles, Treaty of, a betrayal, 30

Vitality, physical, education for preservation of, 224

Voting machines, representatives as, 95–96

Vox populi, vox Dei, 86

Vulgarity, as inevitable product of machine age, 296, 309

## W

Wages, in a pre-machine age, 305; in a machine economy, 306; living vs. cultural, 345–48; an investment in market-development, 386, 387

War, mob-mindedness taught by, 4, 56–57; and the crisis of the Western spirit, 20; disillusionment with, as an instrument of national policy, 28–31, 39; race, fear of, 54–55; exalted by preparation for national defense, 165; way to security from, 173; as an instrument of national policy, 194; to end war, 195, 196, 201; causes of, 195–96; increasingly a conflict in resources, 197–99; horror of, no guarantee against its outbreak, 199; research in biology of, 199–201; color, 252, 262, 265; and the church, 266–77; class, 309; presures toward, intensified by a machine economy, 314

Wastefulness, encouraged by machine economy, 310; in mass selling, 341

Weaklings, under the new freedom, 112–13

Wealth, piling up of, 313; universal, as a goal, 328; faulty distribution of, fundamental factor in current depression, 376–77; wider distribution of, essential to recovery, 381–85; socialization of, 386; three roads to wider distribution of, 388

Wells, H. G., on death of democracy, 71; on political necessities of this century, 84; on intellectual conflict of to-day, 132

Weltanschauung, a definite and distinctive, Christianity's contribution in race relations, 254–57, 261, 263

Women, under modern industrialism, 116–17

Words, power of, 158–59

Work, confusion of, with play, 295; humanistic objectives of a sound economy of, 321–22

Workers, growing discontent of, in machine economy, 308–309; leisure, dignity, and independence of, 321–22; mechanized, 351–52, 353

World-view. *See* Weltanschauung

World War, the fruit of the new materialism, 22–25; idealism of masses in, 25–27, 28; faith in progress killed by, 38; its effect on conduct, 113; transient optimisms of, 133; and nationalism, 166; mineral resources in, 198; failure to seize spiritual opportunity presented by, 241–43; the church in the, 269, 270–71

Worship, ancestor *vs.* descendant, 190–94

## Y

"Yellow peril," 53–55